P9-DCU-879

Science Notebook

Glencoe Science

Biology
The Dynamics of Life
Teacher Edition

Consultant
Douglas Fisher, Ph.D.

McGraw Hill **Glencoe**

New York, New York   Columbus, Ohio   Chicago, Illinois   Peoria, Illinois   Woodland Hills, California

About the Consultant

Douglas Fisher, Ph.D., is a Professor in the Department of Teacher Education at San Diego State University. He is the recipient of an International Reading Association Celebrate Literacy Award as well as a Christa McAuliffe award for Excellence in Teacher Education. He has published numerous articles on reading and literacy, differentiated instruction, and curriculum design as well as books, such as *Improving Adolescent Literacy: Strategies at Work and Responsive Curriculum Design in Secondary Schools: Meeting the Diverse Needs of Students.* He has taught a variety of courses in SDSU's teacher credentialing program as well as graduate-level courses on English language development and literacy. He also has taught classes in English, writing, and literacy development to secondary school students.

Glencoe

The McGraw-Hill Companies

Send all inquiries to:
Glencoe/McGraw-Hill
8787 Orion Place
Columbus, Ohio 43240-4027

ISBN 0-07-873043-0

Printed in the United States of America

1 2 3 4 5 6 7 8 9   047   08 07 06

Table of Contents

John Gerard

Table of Contents

Dear Science Teacher,

As you begin a new school year, one of the biggest challenges you will probably encounter is getting students to read their textbooks. Informational text can overwhelm students, leaving them less likely to read and more likely to become apathetic about learning. I believe that this Science Notebook *will help students use their textbooks more effectively as they learn about Biology.*

Note-Taking and Student Success

There is considerable research evidence that addresses how students understand difficult concepts and content in school. Glencoe/McGraw-Hill has developed the *Science Notebook* for science students based upon that research. Evidence indicates that students need to know how to take notes, use graphic organizers, learn vocabulary, and develop their thinking skills by writing in order to achieve academic success.

The ability to take and organize notes predicts how well students will do in school. Peverly, Brobst, Graham, and Shaw (2003) showed that when students use background knowledge and take notes, they are likely to perform well on tests. Pauk (1974) observed that note-taking was a critical skill for college success. Notes serve as an external storage function (meaning on the paper) that builds comprehension and content understanding (Ganske, 1981). This *Science Notebook* is a tool that students can use to achieve this goal. I would like to share some of the features of this *Science Notebook* with you before you begin teaching.

The Cornell Note-Taking System

First, you will notice that the pages in the *Science Notebook* are arranged in two columns, which will help students organize their thinking. This two-column design is based on the **Cornell Note-Taking System**, developed at Cornell University. Faber, Morris, and Lieberman (2000) found that the Cornell Note-Taking System improves comprehension and increases test scores.

The column on the left side of the page highlights the main ideas and vocabulary of the lesson. This column will help students find information and locate the references in their textbooks quickly. Students can also use this column to sketch drawings that help them visually remember the lesson's information. In the column on the right side of the page, students will write detailed notes about the main ideas and vocabulary. The notes they take in this column will help them focus on the important information in the lesson. As students become more comfortable using the Cornell Note-Taking System, they will see that it is an important tool that helps them organize information.

The Importance of Graphic Organizers

Second, there are many graphic organizers in this *Science Notebook*. Graphic organizers allow students to see the lesson's important information in a visual format. In addition, graphic organizers help students summarize information and remember the content. I hope that you will encourage students to use the graphic organizers because they will help them understand what they are reading.

Research-Based Vocabulary Development

Third, you will notice that vocabulary is introduced and practiced throughout the *Science Notebook*. When students know the meaning of the words used to discuss information, they are able to understand that information better. Also, students are more likely to be successful in school when they have vocabulary knowledge. When researchers study successful students, they find that as students acquire vocabulary knowledge, their ability to learn improves (Martino and Hoffman, 2002). The *Science Notebook* focuses on learning words that are very specific to understanding the content of the textbook. The *Science Notebook* also highlights general academic words that students need to know so that they can understand any textbook. These vocabulary words are based on the Academic Word List (AWL) developed by Averil Coxhead. The AWL includes the most common 570 words found in academic texts, excluding the 2,000 general English words such as *the*, *in*, and *that*. Research indicates that students who master the words on Coxhead's list score significantly higher on standardized tests.

Writing Prompts and Note-Taking

Finally, there are a number of writing exercises included in this *Science Notebook*. Writing is a useful tool that helps students understand the information that is being presented. Writing helps them to assess what they have learned. You will see that many of the writing exercises require students to practice the skills of good readers. Good readers *make connections* between their lives and the text and *predict* what will happen next in the reading. They *question* the information and the author of the text, *clarify* information and ideas, and *visualize* what the text is saying. Good readers also *summarize* the information that is presented and *make inferences* or *draw conclusions* about the facts and ideas.

I wish you well as you begin another school year. This *Science Notebook* is designed to help students understand the information in your Biology class. The guide will be a valuable tool that will also provide students with skills that they can use throughout their lives.

I hope you have a successful school year.

Sincerely,

Douglas Fisher

References

Faber, J. E., Morris, J. D., and Lieberman, M. G. (2000). The effect of note taking on ninth grade students' comprehension. *Reading Psychology*, 21, 257–270.

Ganske, L. (1981). Note-taking: A significant and integral part of learning environments. *Educational Communication and Technology: A Journal of Theory, Research, and Development*, 29, 155–175.

Martino, N. L., and Hoffman, P. R. (2002). An investigation of reading and language abilities of college freshmen. *Journal of Research in Reading*, 25, 310–318.

Pauk, W. (1974). How to Study in College. Boston: Houghton Mifflin.

Peverly, S. T., Brobst, K. E., Graham, M., Shaw, R. (2003). College adults are not good at self-regulation: A study on the relationship of self-regulation, note taking, and test taking. *Journal of Educational Psychology*, 95, 335–346.

Van Leeuwe, J., and Aarnoutse, C. (1998). Relation between reading comprehension, vocabulary, reading pleasure, and reading frequency. *Educational Research and Evaluation*, 4, 143–166.

Note-Taking Tips

Your notes are a reminder of what you learned in class. Taking good notes can help you succeed in science. The following tips will help you take better classroom notes.

- Before class, ask what your teacher will be discussing in class. Review mentally what you already know about the concept.
- Be an active listener. Focus on what your teacher is saying. Listen for important concepts. Pay attention to words, examples, and/or diagrams you teacher emphasizes.
- Write your notes as clear and concise as possible. The following symbols and abbreviations may be helpful in your note-taking.

Word or Phrase	Symbol or Abbreviation	Word or Phrase	Symbol or Abbreviation
for example	e.g.	and	+
such as	i.e.	approximately	≈
with	w/	therefore	∴
without	w/o	versus	vs

- Use a symbol such as a star (★) or an asterisk (*) to emphasis important concepts. Place a question mark (?) next to anything that you do not understand.
- Ask questions and participate in class discussion.
- Draw and label pictures or diagrams to help clarify a concept.
- When working out an example, write what you are doing to solve the problem next to each step. Be sure to use your own words.
- Review you notes as soon as possible after class. During this time, organize and summarize new concepts and clarify misunderstandings.

Note-Taking Don'ts

- **Don't** write every word. Concentrate on the main ideas and concepts.
- **Don't** use someone else's notes as they may not make sense.
- **Don't** doodle. It distracts you from listening actively.
- **Don't** lose focus or you will become lost in your note-taking.

Biology: The Study of Life

Before You Read

Use the "What I Know" column to list three things you know about biology. Then list three questions you have about biology in the "What I Want to Find Out" column.

K What I Know	W What I Want to Find Out
1. Accept all reasonable entries. _____ _____	1. _____ _____
2. _____ _____	2. _____ _____
3. _____ _____	3. _____ _____

Science Journal

Animals, plants, and even bacteria and viruses are considered living things. But what do we mean when we say that an organism is a living thing? In the space below, describe two characteristics that are common to all living things.

Accept all reasonable responses. _____

_____

_____

_____

_____

_____

_____

_____

Biology: The Study of Life

Section 1.1 What is biology?

Main Idea —— **Details** ——————————————————————

Skim *Section 1 of your book. Write three questions that come to mind from reading the headings and the illustration captions.*

1. Accept all reasonable responses._____

2. _____

3. _____

New Vocabulary

adaptation

biology

development

energy

environment

evolution

growth

homeostasis

organism

organization

reproduction

response

species

stimulus

Use your book to help you write the correct vocabulary term in each blank.

The study of life that seeks to provide an understanding of the natural world is called __biology__ . A(n) __organism__ is anything that possesses all the characteristics of life. A(n) __species__ is a group of organisms capable of interbreeding and producing fertile offspring in nature.

The gradual change in a species through adaptations over time is called __evolution__ . The __environment__ is the surroundings to which an organism must adjust; it includes air, water, weather, temperature, organisms, and many other factors. A __stimulus__ is anything in the environment that causes an organism to react. An organism's reaction to a change in its environment is called a __response__ . A(n) __adaptation__ is the evolution of a structure, behavior, or internal process that enables an organism to respond to environmental factors and survive to produce offspring.

There are several characteristics of living things. __Organization__ is the orderly structure of cells in an organism. __Growth__ refers to changes in an organism resulting in an increase in the amount of living material and the formation of new structures, and __development__ refers to the changes that take place during an organism's life. __Reproduction__ is the production of offspring by an organism. Organisms have __homeostasis__ , or the ability to control their internal environment to maintain conditions suitable for survival. Organisms use __energy__ , or the ability to cause change, to perform biological functions.

Section 1.1 What is biology? (continued)

Main Idea	Details

The Science of Biology

I found this information on page _____.

SE, pp. 3–4
RE, p. 1

List *four kinds of information you learn about living things when you study biology.*

1. where they live

2. what they are like

3. how they depend on each other

4. how they behave

Describe *one way that human beings depend on plants and one way that humans depend on animals.* Accept all reasonable responses.

Humans depend on plants to produce oxygen. Humans depend on

animals to provide food.

Biologists Study the Diversity of Life

I found this information on page _____.

SE, p. 5; RE, p. 1

Explain *why it is impossible to study one living thing without studying other living things.* Accept all reasonable responses.

Every living thing requires other living things to survive, and every

living thing affects other living things in some way.

Characteristics of Living Things

I found this information on page _____.

SE, pp. 6–10
RE, pp. 2–3

Complete *the graphic organizer about living and nonliving things by writing the correct term in each blank.*

Living and Nonliving Things

Nonliving things can have one or more characteristics of life, but it is necessary to have all of the characteristics of life to be considered living.

Things that have all the characteristics of life are known as organisms.

All organisms are made of one or more cells.

Each cell contains the DNA that has the information needed to control the life processes of the organism.

Section 1.1 What is biology? (continued)

Main Idea	Details

Characteristics of Living Things

I found this information on page _____.

SE, pp. 6–10
RE, pp. 2–3

Consider *the picture in your book of the students studying organisms. Considering the environment the students are searching in, list four organisms that they might find.* **Accept all reasonable responses.**

1. dragonflies _____

2. mosquitoes _____

3. green algae _____

4. mussels _____

Create *Read the information in your book about reproduction and species. Then construct two review questions that can be answered from the given information.* **Accept all reasonable responses.**

Question: _____

_____

Answer: _____

_____

Question: _____

_____

Answer: _____

_____

Describe *two examples of adaptation using the graphic organizers below.*

```
                          ┌─────────────────────────┐
                          │ 1. The leaves of many   │
                          │ desert plants have a    │
                          │ thick, waxy coating     │
         ┌────────────┐   │ that helps preserve them.│
         │ Adaptation │───┤                          │
         └────────────┘   └─────────────────────────┘
                          ┌─────────────────────────┐
                          │ 2. Owls have large eyes,│
                          │ which allow them to see │
                          │ well at night.          │
                          └─────────────────────────┘
```

Section 1.1 What is biology? (continued)

⸻Main Idea⸻ ⸻⸻ **⸻Details⸻** ⸻⸻⸻⸻⸻⸻⸻⸻⸻⸻⸻

Characteristics of Living Things

I found this information on page _____.
SE, pp. 6–10
RE, pp. 2–3

Summarize *Complete the outline of the characteristics of living things.* **Accept all reasonable responses.**

I. **Structure or Organization**
   A. Organisms can be made up of one cell or billions of cells.
   B. All parts of an organism work together in an orderly system.

II. **Reproduction**
   A. Reproduction is the ability of an organism to make more of the same organism.
   B. A species is a group of organisms that can mate and produce offspring that can reproduce.

III. **Growth and Development**
   A. Growth leads to the formation of new structures and a larger amount of living material.
   B. Development is the changes that occur during an organism's lifetime.

IV. **Environmental Adjustments**
   A. Anything that makes an organism react is called a stimulus.
   B. The reaction to a stimulus is called a response.
   C. An organism's ability to make internal changes is called homeostasis.

COMPARE How is biology similar to and different from other sciences you have studied, such as Earth science? **Accept all reasonable responses.**

Biology is similar to other sciences because it uses scientific methods and procedures. It is different because it involves studying living things, not the physical world.

Biology: The Study of Life
Section 1.2 The Methods of Biology

Main Idea	Details
	Scan *the titles, boldfaced words, pictures, figures, and captions in Section 2. Write two facts you discovered about the methods of biology as you scanned the section.*
	1. Accept all reasonable responses. _____
	2. _____

New Vocabulary   *Use your book to define each term.*

control	in an experiment, the standard against which results are compared
data	information gathered from an experiment
dependent variable	the condition in an experiment that results from the changes made to the independent variable
experiment	procedure that tests a hypothesis by collecting information under controlled conditions
hypothesis	an explanation for a question or problem that can be tested
independent variable	in an experiment, the condition that is tested because it affects the outcome of the experiment
scientific methods	procedures that scientists use to gather information and answer questions
theory	an explanation of a natural phenomenon supported by a large body of scientific evidence obtained form many different investigations and observations

Section 1.2 The Methods of Biology (continued)

Main Idea ———— **Details** ——————————————————————

Observing and Hypothesizing

I found this information on page _____.

SE, pp. 11–12
RE, p. 5

Summarize *the relationship between observations and hypotheses by completing the graphic organizer. Write each of the following in the correct locations:*

- an explanation for a question or problem that can be tested
- helps scientists decide what questions to ask
- hypothesis
- observation

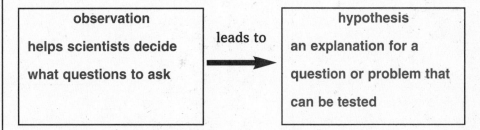

observation

helps scientists decide

what questions to ask

leads to

hypothesis

an explanation for a

question or problem that

can be tested

Experimenting

I found this information on page _____.

SE, pp. 12–18
RE, pp. 5–6

Contrast *Define control group and experimental group. Then give an example of each from your book.*

Control Group: The control group is the part of an experiment that represents the standard condition. An example is plants that receive no fertilizer.

Experimental Group: The experimental group is the test group that receives experimental treatment. An example is plants that receive fertilizer.

Classify *each of the following as a dependent variable or an independent variable. Write* dependent *or* independent *next to each description.*

the plant produces more seeds	dependent
giving a plant extra water	independent
the plant grows taller	dependent
limiting the sunlight a plant receives	independent
planting seeds in sand	independent
the plant dies	dependent
planting seeds in clay	independent

Section 1.2 The Methods of Biology (continued)

⎛**Main Idea**⎞ —— ⎛**Details**⎞ ——————————————————

Experimenting

I found this information on page _____.
SE, pp. 12–18
RE, pp. 5–6

Complete *the pyramid diagram to help you review scientific methods. Arrange the steps used in scientific research in the order that they usually take place. Place the letter next to each step in the correct order in the pyramid.*

a. conduct experiments
b. form a hypothesis
c. observe and identify a problem to solve
d. study results data to see if hypothesis is supported

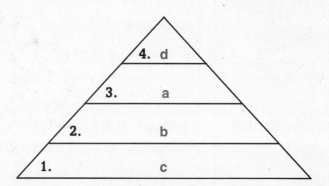

Summarize *why it is important for information about experiments to be published in scientific journals and computer databases.*

Accept all reasonable responses.

It allows scientists to compare the results of their experiments with

the results of other studies and it lets other scientists test the results

by repeating the experiment.

Explain *the difference between a hypothesis and a theory.*

A hypothesis is an explanation for a problem or a question. A theory

is a hypothesis that is supported by many different experiments.

┌─ **SYNTHESIZE** ──
│ Suppose you conduct an experiment in which one group of
plants receives extra fertilizer and another group receives extra water. Is your
experiment controlled or uncontrolled? Explain.

Your experiment is uncontrolled, because all the plants receive an experimental treatment.

There is no control because none of the plants receives a standard treatment.
└──

Biology: The Study of Life

Section 1.3 The Nature of Biology

(Main Idea) —————— **(Details)** ————————————————————

Skim *Section 3 of your book. Write three questions that come to mind from reading the headings and the illustration captions.*

1. Accept all reasonable responses._____

2. _____

3. _____

4. _____

Review Vocabulary *Use your book to define the following term.*

experiment   procedure that tests a hypothesis through collection of information

New Vocabulary *Use your book to define each term.*

ethics   moral principals and values held by humans

technology   application of scientific research to society's needs and problems

Write a paragraph that tells how ethics influence the ways that people use technology. Give an example. Accept all reasonable responses.

Ethics may influence how health care is distributed. For example,

there could be a shortage of flu vaccinations, and society would

have to decide who receives the available medicine.

Academic Vocabulary *Define the following terms.*

principle   a comprehensive and fundamental law, doctrine, or assumption

qualitative   relating to or based on the quality or character of something, often

as opposed to its size or quantity

Section 1.3 The Nature of Biology (continued)

⟨Main Idea⟩ —————— **⟨Details⟩** ————————————————————

Kinds of Information

I found this information on page _____.
SE, pp. 19–21
RE, p. 8

Classify *each of the following examples as quantitative data, qualitative data, or neither. Write the letter for each example in the correct column. Then write your own example of each type of data on the lines below the table.*

a. how birds build nests

b. how long it takes a student to finish his/her homework

c. how wasps gather mud

d. if a movie is good

e. the number of ants that live in an ant colony

f. whether kittens are cute

Quantitative	Qualitative	Neither
b, e	a, c	d, f

Quantitative data: Accept all reasonable responses.

_____

Qualitative data: _____

_____

Science and Society

I found this information on page _____.
SE, pp. 21–23
RE, pp. 8–9

Compare and contrast *pure science and technology. Write a brief description in each area of the Venn diagram.*

Pure Science **Both** **Technology**

studied and practiced to learn new things, not for a specific need

types of scientific study

purpose is to meet society's needs or solve its problems

REAL-WORLD CONNECTION Suppose you were on a committee to decide whether to spend research money on pure science or on new technology. Which choice would you support? Explain.

Accept all reasonable responses.

_____

Tie-It-All-Together

Formulate *Suppose your friend tells you that a car can be characterized as a living thing because it possesses organization—all of its parts work together in an orderly system. Construct a response using the four characteristics of living things to disprove your friend's statement.* Accept all reasonable responses.

A car does seem to possess one of the characteristics of living things—organization. However,

all four of the characteristics for life must be met before something can be considered a living

thing. A car does not possess the other three characteristics, which are reproduction, growth,

and development.

_____

_____

_____

Research *a case where an introduced species has caused damage to a native species and/or the environment. Find a case that is not discussed in your book.* Accept all reasonable responses.

North American gray squirrels are driving native red squirrels to extinction in Great Britain and

Italy. The gray squirrels are foraging for nuts more efficiently than the native species. This

could eventually result in the loss of the native species of squirrels in these two countries.

_____

_____

_____

Create *your own sketch of an example of a stimulus and response that an organism might experience. Use your book for ideas, but create your own unique sketches.*
Student sketches will vary. Accept all reasonable work.

causes →

Biology: The Study of Life Chapter Wrap-Up

In the "What I Wanted to Find Out" column, copy the questions you listed in the Chapter Preview. In the "What I Learned" column, write down the answers you discovered as you worked through the chapter.

W What I Wanted to Find Out	L What I Learned
1. Accept all reasonable entries. _____ _____	1. _____ _____
2. _____ _____	2. _____ _____
3. _____ _____	3. _____ _____

Use this checklist to help you study.

☐ Study your Science Notebook for this chapter.

☐ Study the definitions of vocabulary words.

☐ Review daily homework assignments.

☐ Reread the chapter and review the tables, graphs, and illustrations.

☐ Review the Section Assessment questions at the end of each section.

☐ Look over the Study Guide at the end of the chapter.

SUMMARIZE

After reading this chapter, list three things you have learned about biology.

Accept all reasonable responses.

_____

_____

Principles of Ecology

Before You Read

Use the "What I Know" column to list three things you know about ecology. Then list three questions you have about ecology in the "What I Want to Find Out" column.

K What I Know	W What I Want to Find Out
1. Accept all reasonable entries. _____	1. _____ _____
2. _____ _____	2. _____ _____
3. _____ _____	3. _____ _____

Science Journal

Organisms such as birds get what they need to survive from their environment. Hypothesize why is it important for birds to be able to fly long distances.

By flying a huge range or distance, the bird is more likely to find the food on which it

survives. Food is the matter that provides energy for the bird. Without adequate food, the

bird could not reproduce.

_____

_____

_____

_____

_____

Principles of Ecology
Section 2.1 Organisms and Their Environment

Main Idea —— **Details** ——————————————

Skim *Section 1 of your book. Write two questions that come to mind from the headings and illlustration captions.*

Accept all reasonable responses.
_____

_____

New Vocabulary

Use the vocabulary words in the left margin to complete the graphic organizer below. List the biological levels from largest to smallest.

abiotic

biological community

biosphere

biotic

Levels of Organization
biosphere
ecosystem
biological community
population

commensalism

ecology

Compare the terms in the tables by defining them side-by-side.

ecosystem

habitat

mutualism

niche

parasitism

habitat place where the organism lives out its life	**niche** all strategies and adaptation a species uses in its environment; includes all biotic and abiotic interactions as an animal meets its needs for survival and reproduction
abiotic the nonliving parts of an organism's environment such as soil, wind, moisture, light, and temperature	**biotic** includes all the living organisms that inhabit an environment

population

symbiosis

symbiosis permanent, close association between two or more organisms of different species		
commensalism one species benefits and the other species is neither harmed nor benefits	**mutualism** both species benefit	**parasitism** one species benefits and one is harmed

Define the prefix eco- *and the suffix* -logy *using your book.*

eco- means "environment" and -logy means "study of"

Section 2.1 Organisms and Their Environment (continued)

| Main Idea | Details |

Sharing the World

I found this information on page _____.

SE, p. 36
RE, p. 11

Identify *the abiotic and biotic factors in this sequence. Write abiotic or biotic in each square.*

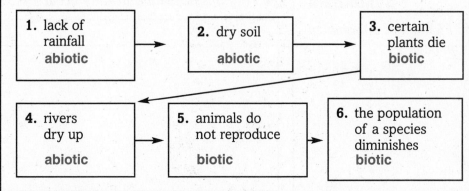

1. lack of rainfall
   abiotic

2. dry soil
   abiotic

3. certain plants die
   biotic

4. rivers dry up
   abiotic

5. animals do not reproduce
   biotic

6. the population of a species diminishes
   biotic

Describe *the environment in a journal entry. Imagine that you are an ecologist. Choose one plant or animal in nature and write four observations of that organism.*

Journal Entry   Date _____

Organism _____

1. Encourage students to demonstrate thoughtfulness and list
   aspects such as what the animal might eat, where it sleeps,
   appearance, play behavior, adaptations, etc.

Biosphere

I found this information on page _____.

SE, pp. 36–38
RE, p. 11

2. _____
   _____

3. _____
   _____

4. _____
   _____

Levels of Organization

I found this information on page _____.

SE, pp. 38–41
RE, pp. 11–13

Classify *each level of organization that is described.*

____population____ a group of organisms all the same species

____communities____ interacting populations

____organism____ an individual living thing made of cells

____ecosystem____ all the different populations in a community

Section 2.1 Organisms and Their Environment (continued)

Main Idea	Details

Organisms in Ecosystems, Symbiosis

I found this information on page _____.
SE, pp. 42–45
RE, pp. 13–14

Model *a community with several organisms. Show two organisms occupying the same niche. Below your sketch, explain why those two organisms cannot usually occupy the same niche for very long.*

Two organisms cannot occupy the same niche for very long because

they compete for the same resources. Eventually one species will out-

compete the other.

Write *your own example of mutualism, commensalism, and parasitism.*

1. mutualism: Certain types of bacteria in our intestines help digest our food.

2. commensalism: Lichen grows on tree branches.

3. parasitism: A lamprey eel feeds on the blood of another fish.

CONNECT Bacteria live inside our bodies. Discuss good, neutral, and harmful things that bacteria do while living in our bodies. Incorporate the terms parasitism, mutualism, habitat, and niche in you discussion.

Accept all reasonable responses. While good bacteria use our body as their habitat, they occupy

the niche and keep harmful bacteria out. The good bacteria may benefit us by keeping invaders at

bay or by eating harmful substances, which is a mutualistic relationship. Bad bacteria may act as

parasites by eating food we need, causing infections, or harming our bodily structures.

Principles of Ecology

Section 2.2 Nutrition and Energy Flow

Main Idea — **Details** —

Organize *As you read this section, make a list of the ways in which organisms obtain energy.*

Accept all reasonable responses, such as using light energy, eating

food, and breaking down dead organisms.

Review Vocabulary

Use your book to define the following term. Then name the ultimate source of energy for Earth.

energy — the ability to cause change; the Sun

New Vocabulary

Use your book to fill in vocabulary terms in this paragraph about food chains. Then make a sketch to illustrate at least five of the terms.

autotroph

biomass

decomposers

food chain

food web

heterotrophs

trophic level

In a __food chain__, matter and energy move from __autotrophs__ to __heterotrophs__ to __decomposers__. A food chain is made of many steps; each organism in the food chain represents a step called a __trophic level__. A model that shows all the possible feeding relationships at each trophic level is called a __food web__. If you were a scientist and you wanted to determine the weight of living matter at a certain trophic level, you would measure the __biomass__.
Accept all reasonable sketches. One possibility is a sketch of a food chain that shows an autotroph, a heterotroph, and a decomposer with the trophic levels labeled.

Academic Vocabulary

Define the following terms.

annual — yearly, occuring or returning once a year

community — a social group of any size whose members reside in a specific locality, share a government, and often share cultural and historical heritage

Section 2.2 Nutrition and Energy Flow (continued)

Main Idea ——— **Details** ———————————————————————————

How Organisms Obtain Energy/Flow of Matter and Energy in Ecosystems

I found this information on page _____.

SE, pp. 46–52
RE, pp. 17–20

Summarize *three ways that organisms get energy by completing the table.*

Type of Organism	Autotrophs	Heterotrophs	Decomposers
Other name(s) for this type	producers	consumers, herbivores, carnivores, scavengers, omnivores	no other name
Food comes from	soil and the Sun	1. eating plants or 2. eating animals or 3. eating plants and animals	dead organisms
Chemical reactions that occur	light energy and carbon dioxide are stored in energy-rich compounds	the organisms that are eaten are turned into energy and molecules for the consumer's body	complex - compounds of dead organisms are turned into simpler compounds for use by producers
Examples	algae, plants	bears, lions, deer	fungi, bacteria

Describe *your own example of cycling.*

Energy is trapped in grass by the process of photosynthesis.

When a cow eats the grass, it uses the energy for its own

processes and the matter for its own body.

Contrast *a food chain with a food web.*

Food chains show how matter and energy move through an

ecosystem. Food webs show all feeding relationships at each trophic

level in a community.

State *two things that an ecological pyramid shows that food webs and food chains do not show.*

An ecological pyramid shows that energy decreases as you go up

the trophic levels. There are more organisms in the lower trophic

levels.

Section 2.2 Nutrition and Energy Flow (continued)

Main Idea ——— **Details** ————————————————

Cycles in Nature

I found this information on page _____.

SE, pp. 52–57
RE, pp. 20–21

Create *mini-models for each cycle of matter in nature. Use words or pictures to sketch a simple cycle or two for each type to show the movement of matter.* Accept all reasonable models.

A. The Water Cycle Models should show water falling from clouds as precipitation, moving through the earth and water table back into lakes and oceans, and evaporating again. Models may include tree transpiration.	**B. The Carbon Cycle** Models should show plants using carbon dioxide to make sugars, animals eating the sugars, respiration, and combustion putting carbon into the air.
C. The Nitrogen Cycle Models should show bacteria fixing nitrogen from the air into the soil, plants using it, animals eating plants and making the nitrogen into proteins. Animals make urine that goes into soil. Die and decay back into soil. They may show bacteria putting nitrogen from soil back into air.	**D. The Phosphorus Cycle** (short-term and long-term) Short-term models should show soil to plants to animals to decay back to soil. Long-term models should show rocks dissolving into the water table and precipitating back onto the rocks.

CONNECT Describe current farming practices that are designed to make the best use of energy flow in ecosystems and cycles of matter.

Accept all reasonable responses. Fertilizers are used to replace nitrogen, phosphorus, and

other minerals that are lost from the soil when vegetable matter is harvested and removed.

Pesticides and herbicides try to stop consumers from eating crops, and other plants from

stealing the nutrients in the soil from the crop. Greenhouses are used to make the most of the

Sun's energy.

Principles of Ecology Chapter Wrap-Up

In the "What I Wanted to Find Out" column, copy the questions you listed in the Chapter Preview. In the "What I Learned" column, write down the answers you discovered as you worked through the chapter.

W What I Wanted to Find Out	L What I Learned
1. Accept all reasonable entries.	1.
2.	2.
3.	3.

Use this checklist to help you study.

☐ Study your Science Notebook for this chapter.

☐ Study the definitions of vocabulary words.

☐ Review daily homework assignments.

☐ Reread the chapter and review the tables, graphs, and illustrations.

☐ Review the Section Assessment questions at the end of each section.

☐ Look over the Study Guide at the end of the chapter.

SUMMARIZE

After reading this chapter, list three things you have learned about ecology.

Accept all reasonable responses. _____

_____

_____

Name_____ Date _____

Communities and Biomes

Before You Read

Use the "What I Know" column to list three things you know about communities and biomes. Then list three questions you have about communities and biomes in the "What I Want to Find Out" column.

K What I Know	W What I Want to Find Out
1. Accept all reasonable entries.	1.
2.	2.
3.	3.

Science Journal

"Organisms in a community reflect the resources and climate of that community." Give some examples to illustrate this statement.

Accept all reasonable responses.

Communities and Biomes
Section 3.1 Communities

(Main Idea) ——— **(Details)** ————————————————————

Observe and Infer *List changes that occur in your neighborhood in a year. Include changes that you have observed in plants, temperatures, or rainfall. Explain how your neighborhood is an ecological community.*

Accept all reasonable responses. Students should describe seasonal

changes that they have experienced and include factors that have

contributed to these changes (i.e. normal changes in temperature,

daylight, or unanticipated factors such as excessive humidity).

Students can also include changes to buildings, the street itself, or in

the number of people living there. Your neighborhood is a community

because there is more than one species in the area.

(New Vocabulary) *Use the new vocabulary terms to complete the following sentences.*

climax community

limiting factor

primary succession

secondary succession

succession

tolerance

_____Succession_____ is the orderly and natural change that takes place in communities over time.

The colonization of barren land by pioneer organisms is

_____primary succession_____.

The sequence of changes that take place after a community is disrupted by natural disasters or human actions is called

_____secondary succession_____.

A stable community that undergoes little or no change is a

_____climax community_____.

Any factor that restricts the existence, numbers, reproduction, or distribution of an organism is a _____limiting factor_____.

If an organism is able to survive and thrive in a changing environment it is showing _____tolerance_____.

Section 3.1 Communities (continued)

Main Idea	Details

Life in a Community

I found this information on page _____.

SE, pp. 65–66
RE, pp. 24–25

Describe *the community you can see outside a window of your classroom. List three abiotic and three biotic factors that contribute to that community.*

Biotic Factors	Abiotic Factors
green grass	air
worms	soil
birds	sunshine

Describe *four limiting factors that cause trees not to grow above the timberline.*

1. elevation is too high
3. too windy

2. too cold
4. soil is too thin

Analyze *the effect of drought as a limiting factor on producers, herbivores, and carnivores in a community. Use a specific example.*

Accept all reasonable responses. Drought may result in fewer

producers (for example, the grass dies). Rabbits (herbivores) will

also die, and the foxes (carnivores) that eat those rabbits will have

less to eat and will die off or move.

Sketch *a standard bell curve similar to the one in the Limits of Tolerance figure in you book; include the Optimum range label. Below your figure, place the following in the correct location on the standard bell curve.*

- right amount of sunlight
- not enough water
- too much water
- right amount of water
- too much sunlight
- not enough sunlight

The bell curve should resemble the figure in the book. Not Enough Water and Not Enough Sunlight should be placed near the lower limit. Right Amount of Sunlight and Right Amont of Water should be placed in the middle of the curve. Too Much Water and Too Much Sunlight should be placed near the upper limit of the curve.

Section 3.1 Communities (continued)

⟨Main Idea⟩	⟨Details⟩

Succession: Changes Over Time

I found this information on page _____.

SE, pp. 67–69
RE, pp. 25–26

Explain *the difference between primary succession and secondary succession. Give an example of each.*

Accept all reasonable responses. Primary succession takes place on land where there is no living organism. An example is a place where a volcano has left cooled lava. Secondary succession takes place on land where the existing community has been seriously disrupted. An example is a forest fire.

Create *a concept map or diagram about succession with the words below.*

climax community	grass	lichens	soil
fire	lava	pioneer species	trees

Accept all reasonable responses. Students may make a landscape-type diagram or a concept diagram.

CONNECT Sequence changes that might occur over one hundred years in a meadow. Accept all reasonable responses.

1. Grass grows freely.

2. Grasses become taller, thicker, wildflowers appear.

3. Scrub bushes and perennials appear.

4. Small animals and birds begin to live there.

5. Larger animals such as deer begin to live there.

6. Larger bushes and small trees enter the area.

7. Larger trees grow.

8. Grasses disappear.

9. More trees grow.

10. The meadow is now a forest.

Communities and Biomes

Section 3.2 Biomes

Main Idea	Details

Skim *Section 2 of your book. Write two questions that come to mind from reading the headings and the illustration captions.*

1. <u>Accept all reasonable responses.</u>

2. _____

New Vocabulary — *Use your book to define each term.*

biome	<u>a group of organisms with the same climax communities</u>
desert	<u>the driest biome; an arid region with sparse or nonexistent plant life</u>
estuary	<u>a coastal body of water, partially surrounded by land, in which fresh water and saltwater mix</u>
grassland	<u>biome covered with rich soil, grasses, and similar plants</u>
intertidal zone	<u>portion of the shoreline that lies between high and low tides</u>
photic zone	<u>portion of the marine biome that is shallow enough for sunlight to penetrate</u>
plankton	<u>heterotrophs and autotrophs that drift and float in the photic zone</u>
taiga	<u>biome south of the tundra, boreal or coniferous forest with mineral-poor topsoils</u>
temperature/deciduous forest	<u>biome composed of forests of broad-leaved hardwood trees</u>
tropical rain forest	<u>warm, wet biome located near the equator with lush plant growth and more species than any other biome</u>
tundra	<u>treeless biome that circles the poles and has permafrost</u>

Section 3.2 Biomes (continued)

Main Idea —— **Details** ——————————

Aquatic Biomes

I found this information on page _____.

SE, pp. 70–74
RE, pp. 28–30

Describe *the adaptations an animal in an intertidal zone needs to survive.*

Accept all reasonable responses. Animals must cling to rocks or sand during the incoming and outgoing tide. Such adaptations include suction cup claws, glue, and an ability to bury themselves in sand.

List *three examples of plankton and explain why they live in the photic zone.*

Examples include diatoms, eggs, and very young marine animals.

They live in the photic zone because that is where sunlight can penetrate (for photosynthesis).

Compare *a marine biome, a freshwater biome, and an estuary. Identify the following in the rows of the table. Some boxes have been done for you.*

1. an example of each type of body of water
2. characteristics of the water
3. where most of the organisms are located
4. examples of types of organisms
5. how nutrients are passed along and/or decay occurs
   Accept all reasonable responses.

	Marine Biome	Freshwater Biome	Estuary
1.	open ocean	pond, lake	where stream meets sea
2.	saltwater	no salt in the water cold in deeper waters	fresh and salt water
3.	photic zone	most in shallow, fewer in deep waters	in thick grasses
4.	plankton, animals that eat plankton (fish, whales, sharks)	insects, fish	thick grasses, snails, crabs, shrimp
5.	plankton begin the process, all animals eat plankton or another animal that eats plankton	bacteria break down organisms in cold deep waters and recycle nutrients	stems and roots trap food material for small organisms, other organisms eat these little ones

Name _____ Date _____

Section 3.2 Biomes (continued)

⟨**Main Idea**⟩ ——— ⟨**Details**⟩ ——————————————————————

Terrestrial Biomes

I found this information on page _____ .

SE, pp. 74–83
RE, pp. 30–32

Compare *examples of vegetation and animals in each terrestrial biome by completing the table below.*

Biome	Animal	Vegetation
tundra	weasels, arctic foxes	a few grasses and small plants, dwarf shrubs
taiga	elk, deer, moose	fir and spruce
desert	hawks	cacti, plants that conserve water
grassland	ferrets	grasses, wildflowers, grains
rain forest	monkeys	lush plant growth
temperate forest	mice, rabbits, bears	deciduous trees

Describe *the biome in which you live.*

Accept all reasonable responses. Look for descriptive words about

organisms, climate, and communities.

_____

_____

_____

_____

CONNECT Describe adaptations that allow three particular organisms of your choice to survive in their biome.

Accept all reasonable responses. The snowy owl survives in the tundra because it is

camouflaged to avoid predators. Since the climate is cold with lots of snow it is a good place

for a white owl. Cacti and kangaroo rats survive in the dry climate of the desert. The rat is

adapted to use water resulting from the chemical breakdown of their food. Rats conserve

moisture by coming out of their burrows at night when the humidity is highest. Cacti are adapted

to conserve their water.

Communities and Biomes Chapter Wrap-Up

In the "What I Wanted to Find Out" column, copy the questions you listed the Chapter Preview. In the "What I Learned" column, write down the answers you discovered as you worked through the chapter.

W What I Wanted to Find Out	L What I Learned
1. Accept all reasonable entries.	1.
2.	2.
3.	3.

Use this checklist to help you study.

☐ Study your Science Notebook for this chapter.

☐ Study the definitions of vocabulary words.

☐ Review daily homework assignments.

☐ Reread the chapter and review the tables, graphs, and illustrations.

☐ Review the Section Assessment questions at the end of each section.

☐ Look over the Study Guide at the end of the chapter.

SUMMARIZE After reading this chapter, list three things you have learned about communities and biomes.

Accept all reasonable responses. _____

_____

_____

Population Biology

Before You Read

Use the "What I Know" column to list three things you know about population biology. Then list three questions you have about population biology in the "What I Want to Find Out" column.

K What I Know	W What I Want to Find Out
1. Accept all reasonable entries. _____ _____	1. _____ _____
2. _____ _____	2. _____ _____
3. _____ _____	3. _____ _____

Science Journal

How could scientists use knowledge about animal populations to help species from becoming extinct?

Accept all reasonable responses. Influences on population decline include crowding,

reproduction, feeding patterns, competition with other populations, and competition within

populations.

_____

_____

_____

_____

_____

Name_____   Date_____

Population Biology
Section 4.1 Population Dynamics

Main Idea ——————   **Details** ——————————————————

Skim *Section 1 of your book. Write three questions that come to mind from reading the headings and the illustration captions.*

1. Accept all reasonable responses._____

2. _____

3. _____

Review Vocabulary) *Use your book to define the following term.*

population | a group of organisms of the same species which interbreed and live

in a specific area at the same time

New Vocabulary) *Use your book to define each term.*

carrying capacity | the number of organisms of one species that an environment can

support indefinitely

exponential growth | a growth pattern where a population grows faster as it increases

in size

life-history pattern | an organism's pattern of reproduction

Compare density-dependent factors and density-independent factors by defining them side-by-side.

Density-Dependent Factors	**Density-Independent Factors**
limiting factors such as disease, parasites, and food availability that affect the growth of a population	factors such as temperature, storms, floods, drought, or habitat disruption that affect all populations regardless of their density

density-dependent factors

density-independent factors

Section 4.1 Population Dynamics (continued)

Main Idea	Details

Principles of Population Growth

I found this information on page _____.
SE, pp. 91–93
RE, pp. 34–35

Draw *and label J-shaped and S-shaped population graphs. Compare and contrast the meanings of the shapes of the graphs.* Students should draw curves similar to the ones on RE, p. 34, 35, SE, p. 92, 93. The J-shaped curve shows that populations grow exponentially, while the S-shaped graph shows what happen to populations as the carrying capacity is reached.

_____

_____

_____

Analyze *carrying capacity by filling in the blanks.*

If a population grows larger than its carrying capacity, there will be

more ___deaths___ than ___births___ .

Until the carrying capacity is reached, there are usually more

___births___ than ___deaths___ .

Reproduction Patterns

I found this information on page _____.
SE, pp. 93–97
RE, pp. 35–36

Identify *five examples each of density-dependent factors and density-independent factors.*

Density-Dependent Factors	Density-Independent Factors
disease	volcanic eruptions
competition	temperature
predators	storms
parasites	drought
food	habitat disruption

Section 4.1 Population Dynamics (continued)

Main Idea ——— **Details** ———————————————————————

Organism Interactions Limit Population Size

I found this information on page _____.

SE, pp. 97–99
RE, pp. 37–38

Create *a population cycle starting with mice as the primary food source for wolves.*

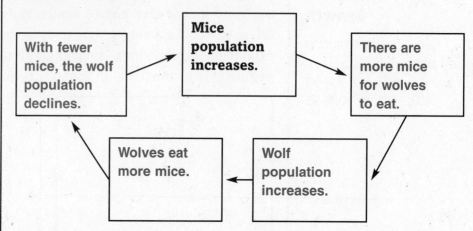

Describe *ways that individual behavior may change due to the stress of overpopulation.*

Organisms show signs of stress. Individuals may become aggressive,

stop caring for their young, and even lose their ability to bear young.

Stress also makes animals more at risk for disease.

CONNECT | Write a brief paragraph describing one population in your environment. Predict three changes for the population.

Accept all reasonable responses.

A population of sparrows that frequents the student's backyard birdfeeder, with descriptions

of the different kinds of sparrows, what they eat, and how they roost. Changes might include

feeding capacity, reproduction patterns, space, disease, or predators.

Population Biology

Section 4.2 Human Population

Main Idea	Details

Find the Main Idea *As you read this section, make a list of the ways in which human populations change.*

Accept all reasonable responses.

Review Vocabulary

Use your book to define the following term.

limiting factor

any biotic or abiotic factor that restricts the existence, numbers,

reproduction, or distribution of organisms

New Vocabulary

Use your book to define each term.

age structure

portions of a population that are at different age levels

birthrate

number of live births per 1000 population in a given year

death rate

number of deaths per 1000 population in a given year

demography

study of population characteristics such as growth rate, age

structure, and geographic distribution

doubling time

time needed for a population to double in size

Academic Vocabulary

Define the following term.

eventual

the eventual growth in a population leads to a change in the available

natural resources of an area

Section 4.2 Human Population (continued)

Main Idea	Details

World Population

I found this information on page _____.

SE, pp. 100–103
RE, pp. 40–42

Analyze *the growth of the human population by making a list of factors that have changed over the past 100 years.*

1. Many illnesses can be treated with medicine.

2. Humans can grow their own resources.

3. People live longer and are able to produce more children.

Identify *the factors that scientists use to determine the growth of a population. Fill in the chart below.*

Factors That Increase Population	Factors That Decrease Population
births people moving into a population	deaths people moving out of a population

Write *the PGR formula.*

Birthrate − Death Rate = Population Growth Rate

Describe *the possible effects on the environment in an area with a fast human doubling time.*

Accept all reasonable responses.

Exhaustion of food resources, increased amount of waste, diminishing

fuel resources, decreased amount of space for everyone. If a society

becomes too crowded, the amount of waste may be too much and

disease may spread.

Section 4.2 Human Population (continued)

Main Idea ——— **Details** ————————————————————————————

World Population

I found this information on page _____.

SE, pp. 100–103
RE, pp. 40–42

Create *an age structure graph based on data that you collect from your school, family, or community.*

Graphs should resemble the bar graph on RE, p. 42, SE, p. 103. Accept reasonable variations but encourage students to pay attention to the details of the correct format.

Describe *how the human population has affected the environment where you live.*

Accept all reasonable responses. Societies pollute the water and air

and change ecosystems.

_____

_____

CONNECT How does human population growth affect the availability of resources? Describe methods that are already in use, and resource protection strategies that humans might use in the future, to accommodate population growth.

Accept all reasonable responses. The farmers of the Midwest could change crops to increase

food production to ensure that human populations will have enough to eat and reproduce.

People could try to reduce resource use such as fossil fuels, forests.

Population Biology Chapter Wrap-Up

In the "What I Wanted to Find Out" column, copy the questions you listed in the Chapter Preview. In the "What I Learned" column, write down the answers you discovered as you worked through the chapter.

W What I Wanted to Find Out	L What I Learned
1. Accept all reasonable entries. _____ 2. _____ _____ 3. _____ _____	1. _____ _____ 2. _____ _____ 3. _____ _____

Use this checklist to help you study.

☐ Study your Science Notebook for this chapter.

☐ Study the definitions of vocabulary words.

☐ Review daily homework assignments.

☐ Reread the chapter and review the tables, graphs, and illustrations.

☐ Review the Section Assessment questions at the end of each section.

☐ Look over the Study Guide at the end of the chapter.

SUMMARIZE After reading this chapter, list three things you have learned about population biology.

Accept all reasonable responses.

_____

_____

_____

Biological Diversity and Conservation

Before You Read

Use the "What I Know" column to list three things you know about conservation and diversity among plants and animals. Then list three questions you have about conservation and diversity in the "What I Want to Find Out" column.

K What I Know	W What I Want to Find Out
1. Accept all reasonable entries.	1.
2.	2.
3.	3.

Science Journal

For many years the bald eagle was close to extinction but now lives and reproduces in the wild. Hypothesize how scientists used their knowledge of diversity to save the bald eagle.

Accept all reasonable responses. Scientists studied the effects of the chemical DDT on the

eagle; they understood its nesting habits; they cleaned up its feeding sites.

Biological Diversity and Conservation

Section 5.1 Vanishing Species

Main Idea	Details
	Skim *Section 1 of your book. Read the headings and the illustration captions. Write two questions that come to mind.*
	1. Accept all reasonable responses._____
	2. _____
Review Vocabulary	*Use your book to define the following term.*
habitat	the place where on organism lives out its life
New Vocabulary	*Use your book to define each term.*
acid precipitation	rain, snow, sleet, or fog with a pH below 5.6 which causes damage to the environment
biodiversity	the variety of species in a particular area
edge effects	different environmental conditions that occur along the boundaries of an ecosystem
endangered species	a species in which the number of individuals becomes so low that extinction is possible
exotic species	species that are not native to an area
extinction	the complete disappearance of a species when its last member dies
habitat degradation	damage to a habitat by air, water, or land pollution
habitat fragmentation	the separation of wilderness areas from other wilderness areas
ozone layer	a layer of the atmosphere that helps to protect living organisms on Earth's surface from damaging doses of ultraviolet radiation
threatened species	a species that is likely to become endangered

Section 5.1 Vanishing Species (continued)

(Main Idea)———— (Details)————————————————————————

Biological Diversity

I found this information on page _____.
SE, pp. 111–113
RE, pp. 44–45

Compare and contrast *the biodiversity of different areas.*
Accept all reasonable responses.

	Rain Forest	Corn Field	Vegetable Garden	Tundra
Plants	hundreds of species of plants	one type of plant	carrots, broccoli, corn, tomatoes, weeds, sunflowers	wild grasses, flowers
Animals	hundreds of species of birds, thousands of species of insects	hundreds of insects, several birds or animals	insects, moles, toads	polar bears, seals, birds

Importance of Biodiversity

I found this information on page _____.
SE, pp. 113–114
RE, pp. 45–46

Analyze *the effect of an attack by pests on a corn field compared to a similar attack by pests on a rain forest.* Accept all reasonable responses.

If the corn field is attacked, the whole field might die because there

is just one species. The ecosystem might not remain stable if there

is a change in species. If one species dies out in the rain forest, it is

not such a large problem because there are many other species. The

ecosystem could remain stable if there is a change in species.

Discuss *how humans are dependent on plants and animals by describing two ways that you use products of each.* Accept all reasonable responses.

Products of Animals	Products of Plants
eating meat	breathing oxygen
wearing wool clothing	eating a salad, wearing cotton

Section 5.1 Vanishing Species (continued)

⟨Main Idea⟩ ————— ⟨Details⟩ —————————————————————————

Loss of Biodiversity

I found this information on page _____.
SE, pp. 115–116
RE, p. 46

Compare *the meanings of extinct, endangered, and threatened species.*

An extinct species has already disappeared. An endangered species

exists in such low numbers that it might become extinct. A threatened

species is on its way to becoming endangered.

Threats to Biodiversity

I found this information on page _____.
SE, pp. 116–120
RE, pp. 46–48

Describe *the effects of each change in habitat on species of animals.*
Accept all reasonable responses.

edge effects	different organisms live at the edge of a habitat than in a middle of a habitat due to different conditions
exotic species	exotic species often destroy native species as they feed on them or disturb them
habitat degradation	air, water and land pollution can destroy soil and vegetation and make animals get sick and/or die
habitat fragmentation	species diversity can drop as some species leave an unsuitable area, and other species may die out; as populations are divided, genetic isolation occurs
habitat loss	species may become extinct

CONNECT Choose an area near you. Make a list of the biodiversity in that specific area. Hypothesize what would happen to the ecosystem if one species died out.

Accept all reasonable responses. Students should describe several species of plants and

animals and understand that as one species dies out, other species will be affected.

_____

Biological Diversity and Conservation

Section 5.2 Conservation of Biodiversity

Main Idea ————   **Details** ————————————————

Research an animal that has been brought back from near extinction. Describe steps taken by conservationists. What are the strengths and weaknesses of such programs?

Students may check *bdol.glencoe.com* for links to sites with lists of

threatened or endangered species, such as the American bald eagle,

the American alligator, the brown pelican, or the gray wolf.

Review Vocabulary   *Use your book to define the following term.*

biodiversity | the variety and abundance of organisms in a specific area

New Vocabulary   *Use your book to define each term.*

captivity | when people keep members of a species in zoos or conservation

facilities

conservation biology | field of biology that studies methods and implements plans to

protect biodiversity

habitat corridors | natural strips of land that allow the migration of organisms from one

wilderness area to another

natural resources | those things in the environment that are useful or needed for living

organisms

reintroduction programs | when endangered species are bred in captivity and released

sustainable use | philosophy that lets people use natural resources in a way that will

benefit them and maintain the ecosystem

Academic Vocabulary   *Define the following term.*

benefit | to be useful or profitable

Section 5.2 Conservation of Biodiversity (continued)

Main Idea	Details

Conservation Biology

I found this information on page _____.

SE, pp. 121–125
RE, pp. 50–51

Create *a job description for conservation biologist. Include at least three important roles of conservation biology in society.*

Accept all reasonable responses. Conservation biologists develop

ways to conserve and protect species and natural resources.

Because of conservation biologists and their research, laws are

made to protect species, parks are created, and habitat corridors

are designed.

List *three national parks created to preserve threatened and endangered species.*

1. Yellowstone National Park

2. Crater Lake National Park

3. Big Bend National Park

Choose *the diagram that best represents a habitat corridor.*

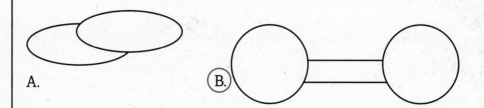

A.   B.

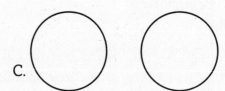

C.

Explain *the purpose of a habitat corridor.*

to help both plant and animal species stay strong and be able to

reproduce

Section 5.2 Conservation of Biodiversity (continued)

Main Idea ——— **Details** ————————————————————————

Conservation Biology

I found this information on page _____.
SE, pp. 121–125
RE, pp. 50–51

Identify *one example of a sustainable use.*

Accept all reasonable responses. One example of a sustainable use

is the harvesting of Brazil nuts in the rainforest.

Sequence *the stages of species protection. Put the sentences below in the correct order in the flow-chart boxes.*

Elephants are reintroduced to the wild.
Elephants are killed by poachers; the number of elephants is greatly diminished.
Elephants run free in abundance in the wild.
Elephants are caught and put in captivity for breeding.

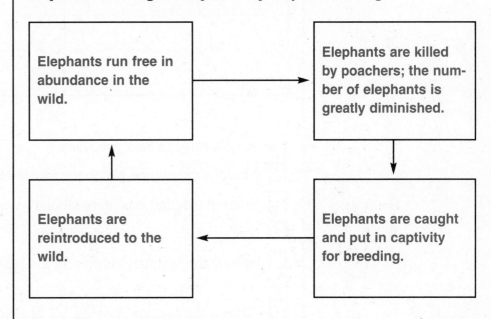

CONNECT Hypothesize why it is easier to reintroduce plants into the wild than animals. Think of specific examples.

Accept all reasonable responses. Animal species may lose behaviors that are needed for

survival in the wild. Wild cats or wolves might forget how to hunt, or herbivores might forget

how to avoid predators.

Biological Diversity and Conservation Chapter Wrap-Up

In the "What I Wanted to Find Out" column, copy the questions you listed in the Chapter Preview. In the "What I Learned" column, write down the answers you discovered as you worked through the chapter.

W What I Wanted to Find Out	L What I Learned
1. Accept all reasonable entries._____ _____	1. _____ _____
2. _____ _____	2. _____ _____
3. _____ _____	3. _____ _____

Use this checklist to help you study.

☐ Study your Science Notebook for this chapter.

☐ Study the definitions of vocabulary words.

☐ Review daily homework assignments.

☐ Reread the chapter and review the tables, graphs, and illustrations.

☐ Review the Section Assessment questions at the end of each section.

☐ Look over the Study Guide at the end of the chapter.

SUMMARIZE
After reading this chapter, list three things you have learned about diversity and conservation.

Accept all reasonable responses.

_____

_____

_____

The Chemistry of Life

Before You Read

Use the "What I Know" column to list three things you know about chemistry in biology. Then list three questions you have about chemistry in biology in the "What I Want to Find Out" column.

| K
What I Know | W
What I Want to Find Out |
|---|---|
| 1. Accept all reasonable entries.
_____ | 1. _____
_____ |
| 2. _____
_____ | 2. _____
_____ |
| 3. _____
_____ | 3. _____
_____ |

Science Journal

Consider the characteristics of a living and a nonliving thing. Describe a few ways that the two are alike and a few ways that the two are different.

Accept all reasonable responses.
_____
_____
_____
_____
_____
_____
_____
_____

The Chemistry of Life

Section 6.1 Atoms and Their Interactions

Main Idea — **Details** _____

Compare and Contrast *What makes a living thing different from a nonliving thing? How are the particles that make up a rock similar to those of a coral?*

Living things and nonliving things are all made of atoms. It is the way

the atoms combine into different elements that affects their physical

and chemical properties and whether they are living or nonliving. The

particles that form a rock and the hard outer covering of a coral are

made of similar substances that are combined differently.

New Vocabulary *Use the five terms to the left to complete the following paragraph.*

atom

element

isotope

metabolism

nucleus

An ___element___ is a substance that can't be broken down into

simpler chemical substances. The smallest particle of an element

that has the characteristics of that element is called an ___atom___.

The ___nucleus___ is the positively charged center of an atom

composed of neutrons and positively charged protons, and

surrounded by negatively charged electrons. ___Isotopes___ are

atoms of the same element that have different numbers of neutrons

in the nucleus. ___Metabolism___ refers to all of the chemical reactions

that occur within an organism.

Categorize the ten terms to the left as relating to compounds and bonding or mixtures and solutions.

acid
base
compound
covalent bond
ion
ionic bond
mixture
molecule
pH
solution

Compounds and Bonding (5 terms)	compound	covalent bond	molecule	ion	ionic bond
Mixtures and Solutions (5 terms)	mixture	solution	pH	acid	base

Name_____ Date _____

Section 6.1 Atoms and Their Interactions (continued)

Main Idea ——— **Details** ——————————————————————

Elements

I found this information on page _____.
SE, pp. 141–142
RE, p. 53

Summarize *information about elements by completing the paragraph.*

About __25__ elements on Earth are needed by living organisms. Four

of these elements—____carbon, hydrogen, oxygen, and nitrogen____

—together make up more than ____96____ percent of the mass of

the human body. ____Trace____ elements are needed by organisms,

but only in very small amounts. ____Plants____ get trace elements by

taking them in through their roots. ____Animals____ get trace elements

from the foods they eat.

Identify *the elements represented by each of the symbols.*

C: ____carbon____ H: ____hydrogen____ O: ____oxygen____ N: ____nitrogen____

Carbon: The Building Blocks of Elements

I found this information on page _____.
SE, pp. 142–143
RE, p. 54

Apply *The nucleus of a carbon atom contains six protons. Sketch a model of a carbon atom similar to the examples in your book. Be sure to label the following.*

• electrons   • energy level 2   • nucleus
• energy level 1   • neutrons   • protons

Models should resemble those found in the book. Six protons and
neutrons should be shown in the nucleus. Energy level 1 should
contain two electrons, and energy level 2 should contain four
electrons.

Isotopes of an Element

I found this information on page _____.
SE, p. 144
RE, p. 54

Describe *how your model of the carbon atom above would be different if you were to draw an isotope of the atom.*

The number of neutrons would be different. The number of protons,

energy levels, and electrons would stay the same.

Compounds and Bonding

I found this information on page _____.
SE, pp. 145–147
RE, pp. 55–56

Identify *the elements that combine to form table salt.*

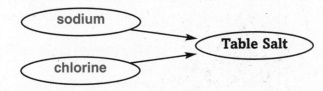

Section 6.1 Atoms and Their Interactions (continued)

Main Idea ————   **Details** ————————————————————

Compounds and Bonding

I found this information on page _____.
SE, pp. 145–147
RE, pp. 55–56

Explain *why atoms form bonds.*

Accept all reasonable responses. Atoms combine chemically with

other atoms to form compounds only when the result is more stable

than the individual atoms. This happens when the outer energy level is

filled with the maximum number of electrons it can hold (usually eight).

Examine *the figure of the water molecule below. Label the two hydrogen atoms and the oxygen atom. Then circle the shared electrons.*

Students should correctly label the two hydrogen atoms and the oxygen atom. Students should then circle the two pairs of electrons that are closest to the hydrogen atoms.

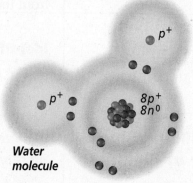

Water molecule

Draw *a sodium atom and a chlorine atom. Include the electrons in each atom's energy levels. Then show how the atoms become stable.*

Drawings should show that the sodium atom loses an electron to the chlorine atom. As a result, the sodium and chlorine atoms are both stable with outer energy levels of eight electrons.

State *why the sodium and chlorine atoms form an ionic bond.*

As a result of the ionic bond, the sodium atom becomes a positively

charged ion, and the chlorine atom becomes a negatively charged

ion. The opposite charges of the ions attract, forming an ionic bond.

Section 6.1 Atoms and Their Interactions (continued)

Main Idea	Details

Chemical Reactions

I found this information on page _____.
SE, pp. 147–148
RE, pp. 57–58

Label *the chemical reaction with the following terms.*

- compound
- element
- molecule
- product
- reactants
- reaction arrow

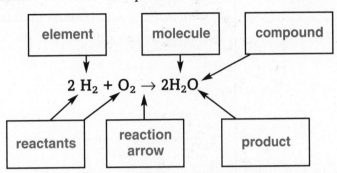

Accept all reasonable responses. Note that students may label the water molecule as the molecule, but the elements in this case are also molecules.

Mixtures and Solutions

I found this information on page _____.
SE, pp. 148–151
RE, pp. 58–59

Summarize *information about mixtures, solutions, and acids and bases. Give the definition of each and an example.*

Solutions: solute dissolves in solvent; example: drink mix

Acids and Bases: pH 0-7 is acid, forms H^+ in water; example: vinegar; pH above 7 is base, forms OH^- in water; example: ammonia

Mixtures: combination of substances in which each substance keeps its own properties and do not combine chemically; example: sand and sugar

---

CONNECT Describe two examples of chemical reactions that you see around you in your everyday life. Give examples that were not discussed in the section.

Accept all reasonable responses. Aquarium fish need water to have the right concentrations of nutrients and oxygen. Ocean fish can't usually move to fresh water. Milk is almost neutral and it soothes an upset stomach. Mammals use iodine to produce hormones. Plants use magnesium to make chlorophyll. Plants make sugar.

The Chemistry of Life

Section 6.2 Water and Diffusion

Main Idea ———— **Details** ————————————————————

Organize Information *As you read this section, make a list of the properties of water. Next to each property, write how it is important in maintaining homeostasis in living organisms.*

Properties of Water	Importance of Homeostasis
1. polar	1. allows tops of plants to get water from soil
2. resists temperature change	2. helps prevent large temperature changes in organisms
3. expands when it freezes	3. bottoms of lakes and ponds won't freeze

Review Vocabulary *Use your book to define the following term.*

homeostasis | regulation of the internal environment of a cell or organism to maintain conditions suitable for survival

New Vocabulary *Use your book to define each term.*

diffusion | net, random movement of particles from an area of higher concentration to an area of lower concentration, eventually resulting in even distribution

dynamic equilibrium | result of diffusion where there is continuous movement of particles but no overall change in concentration

hydrogen bond | weak chemical bond formed by the attraction of positively charged hydrogen atoms to other negatively charged atoms

polar molecule | molecule with an unequal distribution of charge, resulting in the molecule having a positive end and a negative end

Section 6.2 Water and Diffusion (continued)

Main Idea ——

Details ———————————————————

Water and Its Importance

I found this information on page _____.
SE, pp. 152–153
RE, pp. 61–62

Explain *what makes water a polar molecule. In addition, describe the positive and negative ends.*

Accept all reasonable responses. A water molecule does not share

electrons equally. Electrons in the water molecule spend more time

near the oxygen nucleus than they do near the hydrogen nuclei. As a

result, the oxygen end of a water molecule is slightly negative and

the hydrogen end is slightly positive.

Locate *Refer to the figure below. Circle the electrons that are closest to the oxygen nucleus.*

Students should circle the electrons that are located below and to the left of the oxygen nucleus.

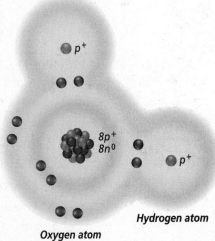

Hydrogen atom

p^+

$8p^+$
$8n^0$

p^+

Hydrogen atom

Oxygen atom

Describe *two special characteristics of water by completing the organizer.*

Special Characteristics of Water

Water resists temperature change. It takes more heat to raise the temperature of water than it does to raise the temperature of most other liquids.

Water expands when it freezes. As a result, ice is less dense than liquid water. This is why ice floats when it forms in water.

Section 6.2 Water and Diffusion (continued)

⟨**Main Idea**⟩ —————   ⟨**Details**⟩ ———————————————————

Diffusion

I found this information on page _____.
SE, pp. 154–156
RE, pp. 62–63

Model *the diffusion of concentrated orange juice in water. Label the following in your sketch: area of higher concentration of particles, area of lower concentration of particles, and direction of diffusion.* Accept all reasonable responses. Students should label the concentrated juice as the area of higher concentration and the water as the area of lower concentration. Arrows should indicate that the concentrated particles are moving toward the water.

Summarize *three factors that affect diffusion by describing each one in the organizers below.* Accept all reasonable responses.

Concentration
The more concentrated a substance, the more quickly it diffuses.

Temperature
Increased temperatures speed up particle motion, speeding up diffusion.

Pressure
Increased pressure speeds up particle motion, speeding up diffusion.

The example that has not reached equilibrium should have more particles outside the cell than inside. The example that has reached equilibrium should have about the same number of particles inside and outside the cell.

Sketch *an example of diffusion that has not reached dynamic equilibrium and an example of dynamic equilibrium.*

Cell

Cell

┌─────────────┐
│ **A**NALYZE │ Describe the effect of the oceans on Earth's climate.
└─────────────┘

Accept all reasonable responses. The oceans carry heat from the equatorial regions to more

northern coastal regions. Water also can carry cold temperatures from the northern polar

regions south. This explains the mild Pacific climates. Students also may mention local

climates around rivers or lakes and the temperature differences related to fog.

The Chemistry of Life

Section 6.3 Life Substances

Main Idea	Details

Scan *the titles, boldfaced words, pictures, figures, and captions in Section 3. Write three facts you discovered about life substances as you scanned the section.*

1. Accept all reasonable responses._____

2. _____

3. _____

New Vocabulary *Use your book to define each term.*

carbohydrates   organic compounds used by cells to store and release energy;

composed of carbon, hydrogen, and oxygen

enzyme   type of protein found in all living things that changes the rate of

chemical reactions

lipids   large organic compounds made mostly of carbon and hydrogen with

a small amount of oxygen; examples are fats, oils, waxes, and

steroids; are insoluble in water and used by cells for energy storage,

insulation, and protective coatings, such as in membranes

nucleic acid   complex biomolecules such as RNA and DNA, that store cellular

information in cells in the form of a code

nucleotides   subunits of nucleic acid formed from a simple sugar, a phosphate

group, and a nitrogenous base

proteins   large, complex polymers essential to all life composed of carbon,

hydrogen, oxygen, nitrogen, and sometimes sulfur; provide structure

for tissues and organs and help carry out cell metabolism

Section 6.3 Life Substances (continued)

Main Idea	**Details**

The Role of Carbon in Organisms

I found this information on page _____.

SE, pp. 157–163
RE, pp. 65–66

Identify *the bonding abilities of carbon by completing the paragraph below.*

Carbon is one of the substances found in ____living organisms____.

Carbon atoms can form ____covalent____ bonds with other carbon

atoms and with many other ____elements____.

Carbon atoms can form a ____single____ bond, ____double____ bond, or

____triple____ bond with other carbon atoms to make ____straight____

chains, ____branched____ chains, or ____rings____. The chains and rings

are called ____carbon compounds____. Carbon compounds

may contain only one or two carbon atoms. But some carbon

compounds contain ____tens, hundreds, or thousands____ of

carbon atoms. These large compounds are called ____biomolecules____.

Describe *how a single, double, and triple bond is represented in the figures in your book.*

Single bond: ____a single bar between carbon atoms____

Double bond: ____two bars between carbon atoms____

Triple bond: ____three bars between carbon atoms____

Sketch *an example of a single, double, and triple bond in the space below. Be sure to label each bond.*

Sketches should be properly labeled and resemble those in the book.

Section 6.3 Life Substances (continued)

Main Idea —— **Details** ————————————————

The Role of Carbon in Organisms

I found this information on page _____ .
SE, pp. 157–163
RE, pp. 65–66

Distinguish *the types of biomolecules by completing the table below.*

Type	Composition	Functions
Carbohydrates	carbon, hydrogen, oxygen	used to store and release energy
Lipids	carbon, hydrogen, small amount of oxygen	used for energy storage, insulation, protective coatings
Proteins	carbon, hydrogen, oxygen, nitrogen, sometimes sulfur	provide structure for tissues and organs, and carry out cell metabolism
Enzymes	type of protein (carbon, hydrogen, oxygen, nitrogen, sometimes sulfur)	change the speed of chemical reactions within the body
Nucleic Acid	made of smaller units called nucleotides	stores coded cellular information
Nucleotides	carbon, hydrogen, oxygen, nitrogen, phosphorus	store coded cellular information

CONNECT   Write one example of food sources from each of the following biomolecules: proteins, carbohydrates, and lipids.

Accept all reasonable responses. Proteins are found in meat and beans. Carbohydrates are

found in pasta, potato, fruit and candy. Lipids are found in animal fat and vegatable oil.

_____

_____

_____

The Chemistry of Life Chapter Wrap-Up

In the "What I Wanted to Find Out" column, copy the questions you listed in the Chapter Preview. In the "What I Learned" column, write down the answers you discovered as you worked through the chapter.

W What I Wanted to Find Out	L What I Learned
1. Accept all reasonable entries.	1.
2.	2.
3.	3.

Use this checklist to help you study.

☐ Study your Science Notebook for this chapter.

☐ Study the definitions of vocabulary words.

☐ Review daily homework assignments.

☐ Reread the chapter and review the tables, graphs, and illustrations.

☐ Review the Section Assessment questions at the end of each section.

☐ Look over the Study Guide at the end of the chapter.

SUMMARIZE
After reading this chapter, list three things you have learned about chemistry in biology.

Accept all reasonable responses._____

_____

_____

A View of the Cell

Before You Read

Use the "What I Know" column to list three things you know about cells. Then list three questions you have about cells in the "What I Want to Find Out" column.

K What I Know	W What I Want to Find Out
1. Accept all reasonable entries. _____	1. _____ _____
2. _____ _____	2. _____ _____
3. _____ _____	3. _____ _____

Science Journal

Imagine that you were small enough to fit inside a cell. Describe what you think you might observe while you are there.

Accept all reasonable responses._____

_____

_____

_____

_____

_____

_____

_____

A View of the Cell

Section 7.1 The Discovery of Cells

Main Idea —— **Details** ———————————————————

Skim *Section 1 of your book. Write three questions that come to mind from reading the headings and the illustration captions.*

1. Accept all reasonable responses. _____

2. _____

3. _____

Review Vocabulary) *Use your book to define the following term.*

organization | the orderly structure of cells in an organism

New Vocabulary) *Use your book to define each term.*

cell | the basic unit of all living things

cell theory | theory that all organisms are made of one or more cells, which

are the basic unit of all life, and that all cells come from other cells

compound light microscope | microscope that uses light and a series of lenses to magnify objects

electron microscope | microscope that uses a beam of electrons instead of light to magnify objects

eukaryote | unicellular or multicellular organisms whose cells contain a nucleus

and membrane-bound organelles

nucleus | the cell organelle that controls the cell's activities and contains DNA

organelle | membrane-bound structures with special functions within eukaryotic

cells

prokaryote | unicellular organisms that lack membrane-bound organelles

Academic Vocabulary) *Define the following term.*

function | the purpose for which something is designed or exists; role

Name_____ Date_____

Section 7.1 The Discovery of Cells (continued)

Main Idea ——— **Details** ——————————————————

The History of the Cell Theory

I found this information on page _____.
SE, pp. 171–173
RE, pp. 68–69

Create *a timeline or flow chart to identify six scientists and summarize their contributions to the cell theory using microscopes. Include details, such as types of microscopes, subjects studied, nationalities of scientists, and dates.*

Accept all formats. Encourage students to focus on the logical progression of science and the way that collective knowledge increases as each scientist builds on the work of scientists before them. Responses should include the following information:

1600s Anton van Leeuwenhoek used a single lens microscope to view bacteria.

Robert Hooke looked at thin slices of cork under a compound light microscope. He thought the cork shapes looked like rooms and called them cells (like monks' cells or prison cells).

1800s Robert Brown from Scotland discovered the nucleus.

Rudolf Virchow discovered that the nucleus controls the cell's activities.

Germans Schleiden and Schwann learned that all living things are made of one or more cells.

Write *the three main ideas of the cell theory. Then write a short sentence for each one describing some fact or observation from your previous knowledge that supports each idea.* Accept all reasonable paragraphs that support each theory.

1. All living things are made of one or more cells. Sample response: I have seen that an onion is made of cells and I know an onion was alive because it was a plant.

2. Cells are the basic units of structure and function in living things. Sample response: I know our muscles are all made of muscle cells. I have seen that plants are made of plant cells.

3. All cells come from other cells. Sample response: We learned that living things only come from other living things. You cannot make a cell in a laboratory.

A View of the Cell 59

Section 7.1 The Discovery of Cells (continued)

Main Idea ——— **Details** ——————————————————————

Two Basic Cell Types

I found this information on page _____.
SE, pp. 173–174
RE, p. 69

Summarize *information about electron microscopes by creating an outline.* Accept all reasonable responses.

• Microscopes improved in the 1930s–1940s.

• Microscopes allowed scientists to magnify objects up to 500 000 times.

• They use a beam of electrons instead of a beam of light.

• Scanning (SEM) can show a cell's 3-D shape.

• Transmission (TEM) help see inside a cell.

Compare and contrast *eukaryotic and prokaryotic cells by putting the phrases in the Venn diagram.*

• bacteria
• contain organelles
• have loose strands of DNA
• have a nucleus
• have membrane-bound organelles

• multicellular organisms
• unicellular organisms
• do not have membrane-bound organelles

Eukaryotic cells
• have membrane-bound organelles
• multi-cellular organisms
• have a nucleus

Both
• contain organelles
• unicellular organisms
• have loose strands of DNA

Prokaryotic cells
• do not have membrane-bound organelles
• bacteria

SYNTHESIZE

Explain how more sophisticated microscopes have allowed scientists to advance their knowledge of cells.

Accept all reasonable responses. Increased magnification has enabled scientists to study cells in greater detail.

A View of the Cell
Section 7.2 The Plasma Membrane

Main Idea	Details
	Infer *Considering that a cell's environment is extremely watery, why might lipids be important to the composition of the plasma membrane?*
	Accept all reasonable responses.

Review Vocabulary *Use your book to define the following term.*

ion	an atom or group of atoms with a positive or negative electrical charge

New Vocabulary *Use your book to define each term.*

fluid mosaic model	structural model of the plasma membrane where phospholipids and proteins float within the surface of the membrane
phospholipid	a large molecule with a glycerol backbone, two fatty acid chains, and a phosphate group
plasma membrane	the flexible boundary of a cell
selective permeability	a process in which a membrane allows some molecules to pass through while keeping others out
transport proteins	proteins that move needed substances or waste materials through the plasma membrane into or out of the cell

Academic Vocabulary *Define the following terms.*

transport	to convey from one place to another; carry
passive	influenced, acted upon, or affected by some external force, cause, or agency; opposite of active

Section 7.2 The Plasma Membrane (continued)

Main Idea ———— **Details** —————————————————————

Maintaining a Balance

I found this information on page _____.
SE, p. 175
RE, p. 71

Hypothesize *what would happen if the cell membrane was not selectively permeable. Give reasons for your answer.*

Accept all reasonable hypotheses. Sample response: The cell might be

destroyed because wastes could not leave and inappropriate molecules

might enter the cell.

Describe *how a window screen is selectively permeable.*

The screen lets air blow through, but insects are kept out.

List *five ways that the membrane can deal with materials.*

1. It can keep molecules out.

2. It can allow molecules in at any time.

3. It can allow molecules in only at certain times.

4. It can allow molecules in only in limited amounts.

5. It can expel wastes from inside the cell.

Structure of the Plasma Membrane

I found this information on page _____.
SE, pp. 177–178
RE, pp. 71–72

Draw *a phospholipid and label its parts. Describe how the phospholipid functions to make up the fluid membrane.*

Accept all reasonable responses. The

phosphate group forms the polar head of

the molecule. It points outward to interact

with the watery environment outside

the cell. The nonpolar fatty acid tails point

inwards toward each other (since two

layers make up each membrane) away

from the water outside the cell. A barrier is

created that is water-soluble on the

outside but water-insoluble on the inside.

Diagrams should resemble those in the book.

Section 7.2 The Plasma Membrane (continued)

(Main Idea) —— **(Details)** ——————————————

Structure of the Plasma Membrane

I found this information on page _____.
SE, pp. 177–178
RE, p. 71–72

Create *a detailed and accurate drawing of the plasma membrane. Write captions that label each part and describe the function of that part in detail.*

Diagrams should clearly show and explain phospholipids, proteins, and cholesterol. The RE and the SE show different models, so some students may explain transport and surface proteins and carboyhdrate chains.

phospholipids: polar phosphate heads allow membrane to interact with surface water; nonpolar tails are on inside of membrane and make it difficult for water-soluble particles to move through membrane not fixed in one place, but to float in membrane

transport proteins: regulate what is allowed to enter and exit the cell through the membrane

cholesterol: keeps phospholipids fluid, prevents them from sticking together

surface proteins: help identify chemical signals, part of structure

Explain *how the words fluid and mosaic describe the plasma membrane.*

Fluid: It is fluid because the phospholipids, proteins, and cholesterol float in the membrane.

Mosaic: It is a mosaic because it has many parts. The proteins create patterns on the membrane's surface.

ANALOGY Think of a real-life situation to make an analogy of how the fluid membrane of a cell functions. Identify real-life roles similar to the functions of each type of molecule in the membrane.

Accept all reasonable responses. Sample response: The membrane is like a circus tent. The tent can move

in the wind or if someone bumps against the inside or outside. The gatekeeper lets in people who have

tickets as long as there is space inside. It keeps out people who don't have tickets or if there are already too

many people inside. There are different ways to get in: spectators get in and out through the front gate, and

performers, animals, and equipment move in and out through the back gates and stage doors.

Name_____   Date _____

A View of the Cell
Section 7.3 Eukaryotic Cell Structure

Main Idea ————   **Details** ———————————————

Skim *Section 3 of your book. Write three questions that come to mind from reading the headings and the illustration captions.*

Accept all reasonable responses._____

_____

_____

_____

New Vocabulary   *Write each term in the table under the heading that best describes it. (Hint: The number of words that should go in each column is indicated in parentheses.)*

cell wall

chlorophyll

chloroplast

chromatin

cilia

cytoplasm

cytoskeleton

endoplasmic reticulum-
flagella

Golgi apparatus

lysosome

microfilament

microtubule

mitochondria

nucleolus

plastid

ribosome

vacuol

Cell Structure (6)	Related to Genetic Material (3)	Food, Storage, & Waste (6)	Energy (3)
cell wall	chromatin	cytoplasm	chlorophyll
cilia	nucleolus	endoplasmic reticulum	chloroplast
cytoskeleton	ribosome	Golgi apparatus	mitochondria
flagella		lysosome	
microfilament		plastid	
microtubule		vacuole	

Compare and contrast each pair of terms by defining them and noting their differences.

Chloroplast	Mitochondria
plant organelles that capture light and convert it to a chemical	in plants and animals, converts energy to a form cells can use
Vacuole	**Plastid**
storage compartments in all cells	storage compartments in plant cells
Cilia	**Flagella**
many short hairlike projections that aid in locomotion	few long hairlike projections that aid in locomotion

Section 7.3 Eukaryotic Cell Structure (continued)

Main Idea	Details

Cellular Boundaries

I found this information on page _____.
SE, p. 179
RE, p. 74

List *four types of cells that have walls and describe the function of the cell wall.*

plants, fungi, bacteria, and some protists;

It gives extra support and protection to the cell.

The Nucleus and Cell Control

I found this information on page _____.
SE, pp. 180–181
RE, p. 74

Summarize *three facts about chromatin.*
Accept all reasonable responses.

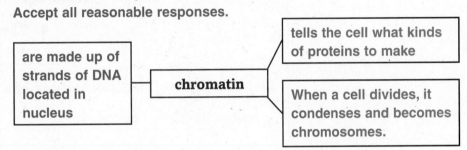

are made up of strands of DNA located in nucleus → chromatin
tells the cell what kinds of proteins to make
When a cell divides, it condenses and becomes chromosomes.

Describe *the role and path of a ribosome by completing the paragraph.*

Ribosomes are the sites where cells produce __proteins__ according to the direction of the __DNA__. Ribosomes are created by the __nucleolus__ in the __nucleus__. Ribosomes are made of __RNA and protein__, and have no __membrane around them__. After they are made, __ribosomes__ and __copies of the DNA__ move through __the nuclear envelope__ into the __cytoplasm__.

Assembly, Transport, and Storage

I found this information on page _____.
SE, pp. 181–183
RE, p. 75

Compare and Contrast *smooth endoplasmic reticulum and rough endoplasmic reticulum.*

Smooth Endoplasmic Reticulum	Rough Endoplasmic Reticulum
does not have ribosomes	has ribosomes
site of cellular chemical reactions, such as producing lipids	site of cellular chemical reactions, ribosomes produce proteins

Section 7.3 Eukaryotic Cell Structure (continued)

Main Idea	Details

Assembly, Transport, and Storage

I found this information on page _____ .
SE, pp. 181–183
RE, p. 75

Explain *the formation of a protein and its transport to where it is needed by completing the flow chart.*

1. Protein is created in the
   <u>rough endoplasmic reticulum</u> .

2. The proteins move to the
   <u>Golgi apparatus</u>

3. There, they are packed into
   structures called <u>vesicles</u> .

4. They are sent to where they are needed.

List *three types of material that can be stored in vacuoles.*

1. <u>materials needed by the cell</u>

2. <u>food and enzymes</u>

3. <u>waste products</u>

Analyze *how a lysosome helps certain types of vacuoles.*

Lysosomes are organelles filled with digestive enzymes. They join a

vacuole and send their enzymes in to digest the contents of the vacuole.

Create *a sketch to compare and contrast the organelles listed. Then write an observation about organelles.* Accept all reasonable responses. Sample response: All of the organelles are membrane-bound.

Golgi apparatus smooth endoplasmic reticulum rough endoplasmic reticulum lysosomes	Students should sketch all of the organelles listed. Encourage clarity over artistic merit.

Section 7.3 Eukaryotic Cell Structure (continued)

Main Idea	Details
Energy Transformers *I found this information on page _____.* SE, pp. 184–185 RE, p. 75	**Make** *a concept web with facts about mitochondria and chloroplasts.* Accept all reasonable responses. Facts to include: Both provide energy for cells. Chloroplasts are plastids, which store energy as sugar. Mitochondria change sugar into other energy that cells can use quickly and easily. Both have an outer membrane and a tightly folded inner membrane. Molecules for storing energy are on the surface of the folds.
Organelles for Support and Locomotion *I found this information on page _____.* SE, pp. 184–185 RE, p. 76	**Create** *an image of what you think the cilia, flagella, microtubules, microfilaments, centrioles, and cytoskeleton look like. Make captions on your diagram to explain how each works and how they all work together.* Accept all reasonable sketches. Information to be included: For movement: cilia are hairlike projections that move in wavelike motions and flagella are longer projections that move like whips. Centrioles come in pairs and are made of microtubules, and are important in helping the cell to divide when it is time. Microtubules and microfilaments are protein fibers that make a framework through the cytoplasm to support organelles and help move materials.

COMPARE
List some similarities and differences between plant and animal cells.

Accept all reasonable responses. Plant cells have walls, animal cells don't. Plant cells have

chloroplasts that make energy from sunlight. Both animal cells and plant cells get their energy

from mitochondria which need sugar to operate. Plants store materials in plastids as well as

vacuoles. Animal cells can move with cilia and flagella but plant cells are stuck in their wall.

A View of the Cell Chapter Wrap-Up

In the "What I Wanted to Find Out" column, copy the questions you listed in the Chapter Preview. In the "What I Learned" column, write down the answers you discovered as you worked through the chapter.

W What I Wanted to Find Out	L What I Learned
1. Accept all reasonable entries.	1.
2.	2.
3.	3.

Use this checklist to help you study.

- ☐ Study your Science Notebook for this chapter.
- ☐ Study the definitions of vocabulary words.
- ☐ Review daily homework assignments.
- ☐ Reread the chapter and review the tables, graphs, and illustrations.
- ☐ Review the Section Assessment questions at the end of each section.
- ☐ Look over the Study Guide at the end of the chapter.

SUMMARIZE After reading this chapter, list three things you have learned about cells.

Accept all reasonable responses.

_____

_____

Cellular Transport and the Cell Cycle
Before You Read

Use the "What I Know" column to list three things you know about how cells work. Then list three questions you have about how cells work in the "What I Want to Find Out" column.

K What I Know	W What I Want to Find Out
1. Accept all reasonable entries. _____	1. _____ _____
2. _____ _____	2. _____ _____
3. _____ _____	3. _____ _____

Science Journal

Write about the molecules that you think are moved in and out of cells. What types of molecules would be large? What types of molecules would be small?

Accept all reasonable responses. An example of large molecules would be

proteins. An example of a small molecule would be water.

_____

_____

_____

_____

_____

_____

_____

Cellular Transport and the Cell Cycle
Section 8.1 Cellular Transport

Main Idea ——   **Details** ——————————————————————

Scan *the titles, boldfaced words, pictures, figures, and captions in Section 1. Write two facts you discovered about cellular transport as you scanned the section.*

1. _____

2. _____

New Vocabulary   *Use your book to define each term.*

active transport

endocytosis

exocytosis

facilitated diffusion

hypertonic solution

hypotonic solution

isotonic solution

osmosis

passive transport

The diffusion of water across a selectively permeable membrane depending on the concentration of solutes on either side of the membrane is called ____osmosis____. A solution in which the concentration of dissolved substances outside the cell is the same as the concentration of dissolved substances inside the cell is called a(n) ____isotonic____ ____solution____ . A(n) ____hypotonic____ ____solution____ is a solution in which the concentration of dissolved substances outside the cell is lower than the concentration inside the cell. A(n) ____hypertonic____ ____solution____ is a solution in which the concentration of dissolved substances outside the cell is higher than the concentration inside the cell.

____Passive____ ____transport____ is the movement of particles across cell membranes by diffusion or osmosis, where the cell uses no energy to move the particles. The passive transport of materials across a plasma membrane by transport proteins embedded in the plasma membrane is called ____facilitated____ ____diffusion____. An energy-expending process called ____active____ ____transport____ involves cells transporting materials across the cell membrane against a concentration gradient. Active transport where a cell engulfs materials with a portion of the cell's plasma membrane and releases the contents inside of the cell is ____endocytosis____ . Active transport where materials are secreted or expelled from a cell is called ____exocytosis____ .

Name _____ Date _____

Section 8.1 Cellular Transport (continued)

Main Idea	Details

Osmosis: Diffusion of Water

I found this information on page _____ .
SE, pp. 195–197
RE, p. 79

Create *a diagram to show the definition of "selectively permeable."* Diagrams should show some kind of membrane or wall, with some things getting through and other things being blocked or rejected.

Summarize *the relationship between water and the plasma membrane by completing the concept web below.*

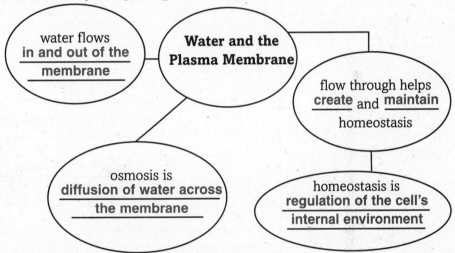

Examine *the figures in your book that show a cell after it has been in an isotonic, hypotonic, and hypertonic solution. Then answer the questions below.*

In an isotonic solution, how does the concentration of the dissolved substances inside and outside of the cell compare?

The concentration of the dissolved substances is the same both

inside and outside of the cell.

What happens to the size of a cell after being placed in a hypotonic solution?

The cell gets larger, or swells.

What happens to the pressure inside of a cell after being placed in a hypertonic solution?

The pressure inside of the cell decreases.

Section 8.1 Cellular Transport (continued)

(Main Idea) ——

(Details) —————————————————————

Passive and Active Transport/ Transport of Large Particles

I found this information on page _____.
SE, pp. 198–200
RE, p. 80

Teacher's Note:
For the analogy, encourage creative and original thought that synthesizes the concepts at hand.

Classify and Summarize *the five ways particles move through the membrane. Make notes and sketches in the rectangle for each one.* Sample answers shown. Accept all reasonable variations and diagrams.

Passive Transport

simple diffusion
cell uses no energy to move particles, they just diffuse through membrane

facilitated diffusion
transport proteins, assist passive transport

active transport
cell uses carrier proteins to help move particles, requires energy

Transport of Large Particles

exocytosis
requires energy, active transport; membrane capsule joins cell membrane and expels material

endocytosis
requires energy, active transport, cell engulfs materials with a portion of the cell's plasma membrane and releases the contents within the cell

ANALOGY
Think of real-life movement between locations and make analogies of the five different kinds of transport that occurs through the cell membrane. Explain how each type of transport works in your analogy.

Accept all reasonable responses. Simple diffusion is like walking through an entryway of

streamers; facilitated diffusion is like taking an escalator; active transport is like entering

through a subway gate using a ticket; endocytosis is like receiving shipping; and exocytosis

is like taking out the garbage.

Cellular Transport and the Cell Cycle

Section 8.2 Cell Growth and Reproduction

Main Idea | Details

Compare *cells in multicellular and unicellular organisms that undergo cell division. Contrast the two types of cells by explaining which one is more specialized.*

Accept all reasonable responses. Since there are many different

kinds of cells in a multicellular organism, they are probably more

specialized than ones in a unicellular organism in which one cell

must perform a variety of functions.

Review Vocabulary

Use your book to define the following term.

organelle | the membrane-bound structures within eukaryotic cells

New Vocabulary

Compare *the terms centromere, chromatin, chromosomes, and sister chromatids.*

centromere
chromatin
chromosomes
sister chromatid

Chromatin coils up to form chromosomes. Sister chromatids are the

identical halves of a duplicated chromosome, held together by a

centromere.

Describe *the relationships between organ, organ system, and tissue.*

organ
organ system
tissue

Organs are a group of two or more tissues organized to perform

complex activities within an organism, and an organ system is multiple

organs that work together to perform a specific function of life.

Complete *the concept map with the vocabulary words at left.*

anaphase
cell cycle
cytokinesis
interphase
metaphase
mitosis
prophase
telophase

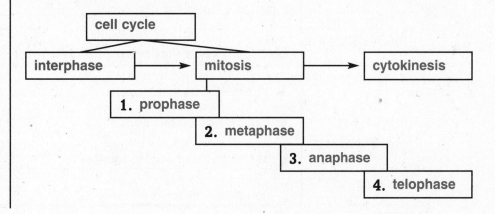

Section 8.2 Cell Growth and Reproduction (continued)

Main Idea ————— **Details** ——————————————————

Cell Size Limitations

I found this information on page _____.
SE, pp. 201–203
RE, p. 83

Analyze *movement of nutrients and wastes as cell size increases.*
Accept all reasonable responses.

| If a <u>cell</u> gets too <u>large</u> , | transport of <u>nutrients and wastes</u> **by** <u>diffusion</u> slows down . | **Therefore, cells** <u>divide</u> **before** <u>they become too large</u> . |

Cell Reproduction

I found this information on page _____.
SE, pp. 203–204
RE, p. 83

Summarize *information about chromosomes in the concept web.*
Accept all reasonable responses.

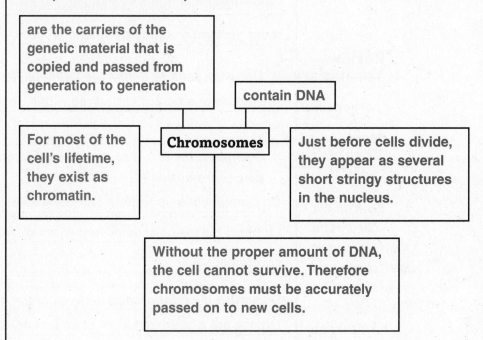

are the carriers of the genetic material that is copied and passed from generation to generation

contain DNA

For most of the cell's lifetime, they exist as chromatin.

Chromosomes

Just before cells divide, they appear as several short stringy structures in the nucleus.

Without the proper amount of DNA, the cell cannot survive. Therefore chromosomes must be accurately passed on to new cells.

The Cell Cycle, Interphase

I found this information on page _____.
SE, p. 204
RE, pp. 83–84

Identify *two periods of a cell's life cycle.*

a period of growth: ____interphase____

a period of nuclear division: ____mitosis____

List *four events that occur in a cell during interphase.*

1. cell grows _____

2. cell carries on metabolism _____

3. cell duplicates chromosomes _____

4. cell prepares for division _____

Section 8.2 Cell Growth and Reproduction (continued)

Main Idea ——— **Details** ——————————————————————

Phases of Mitosis/ Cytokinesis

I found this information on page _____.
SE, pp. 206–209
RE, p. 85

Model *and summarize the four stages of mitosis and the process of cytokinesis. Draw and label a cell in each stage, name each stage, and describe what is happening to the cell and its genetic material at each stage.*

Sketches should resemble those in the text. Accept all reasonable variations.

Name of Phase	Sketch of Cell	Description
prophase		chromatin coils to form chromosomes
metaphase		chromosomes move to the center of the cell
anaphase		centromeres split and sister chromatids are pulled to the opposite sides of the cell
telophase		two new nuclei are formed and a double membrane begins to form between them.
cytokinesis		cells cytoplasm divides and separates into two new identical cells

Results of Mitosis

I found this information on page _____.
SE, p. 210
RE, p. 85

Sequence *each type of life material from smallest to largest and give an example of each.*

• cell   • organ   • organ system   • tissue

Type	cell	tissue	organ	organ system
Example	muscle cell	muscle tissue	heart	circulatory system

COMPARE Choose two phases of mitosis and describe their similarities and differences in the Venn diagram. Accept all reasonable responses.

Metaphase
chromosomes move to the center of the cell and line up

sister chromatids are visible

Anaphase
centromeres split and sister chromatids are pulled to the opposite sides of the cell

Cellular Transport and the Cell Cycle
Section 8.3 Control of the Cell Cycle

Main Idea ———— **Details** ————————————————————

Study and Organize *Section 3 notes by answering the following questions as you read.*

1. What is a cause of uncontrolled cell division? **changes in**
   enzyme production inside the cell or by some outside factor

2. What are two environmental factors that contribute to the development of cancer? List possible ways you can influence these factors.
   cigarette smoke, air pollution; don't smoke, don't use aerosol cans

3. How does a person's diet relate to the chances of getting cancer?
   Diets low in fat and high in fiber reduce the risk of cancer.

Review Vocabulary

Use your book to define the following term.

protein   **a large complex polymer composed of carbon, hydrogen, oxygen,**
            nitrogen, and sometimes sulfur

New Vocabulary

Use your book to define the following term. Then write three sentences about what you already know about cancer and/or genes.

cancer   **uncontrolled cell division that may be caused by environmental**
           factors and/or changes in enzyme production in the cell cycle

gene   **segment of DNA that controls protein production and the cell cycle**
           Accept all reasonable responses.

_____

_____

Academic Vocabulary

Define the following term.

restrict   **to confine or keep within limits, such as limits of space, action,**
             choice, intensity, or quantity

Section 8.3 Control of the Cell Cycle (continued)

Main Idea ——— **Details** ——————————————————————————

Normal Control of the Cell Cycle

I found this information on page _____.
SE, p. 211
RE, p. 87

Explain *the cell cycle by completing the paragraph.*

The cell cycle is controlled by ___conditions inside the cell___ and

___the cell's environment___. When something goes wrong with

___cell conditions___, cells lose ___control of the cell cycle___.

Cancer occurs when there is ___uncontrolled cell division___.

Note to the Teacher: Have students look for magazine or internet pictures of cancerous growths.

Create *a drawing of what uncontrolled cell division, which causes cancer, might look like.*
Accept all reasonable drawings. The sketch should show rampant cell growth and division, until cells are piled up all over each other.

Cancer: A Mistake in the Cell Cycle

I found this information on page _____.
SE, pp. 212–213
RE, p. 87

Analyze *the causes and effects of cancer by completing the flow chart below.*

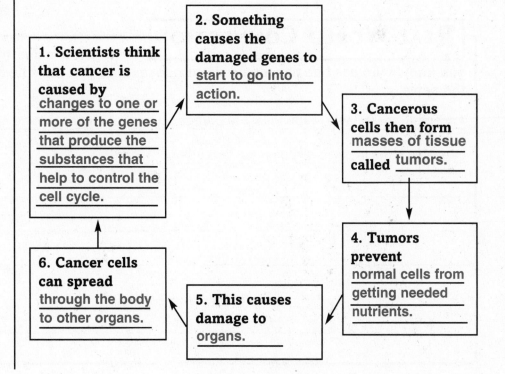

1. Scientists think that cancer is caused by changes to one or more of the genes that produce the substances that help to control the cell cycle.

2. Something causes the damaged genes to start to go into action.

3. Cancerous cells then form masses of tissue called tumors.

4. Tumors prevent normal cells from getting needed nutrients.

5. This causes damage to organs.

6. Cancer cells can spread through the body to other organs.

Section 8.3 Control of the Cell Cycle (continued)

(Main Idea) ——— **(Details)** ——————————————————————

Cancer: A Mistake in the Cell Cycle

I found this information on page _____.
SE, pp. 212–213
RE, p. 87

List *four environmental factors and one genetic factor that cause cancer.*

1. cigarette smoke _____

2. air pollution _____

3. water pollution _____

4. ultraviolet radiation _____

5. genetic damage through a viral infection _____

Hypothesize *the order of importance of the main factors that prevent cancer. Give reasons to support your order.* Accept all reasonable ordering arrangements, but encourage students to support their choices.

The factors that should be included are exercising, eating fruits and

vegetables, maintaining a diet low in fat and high in fiber, living a

generally healthy lifestyle, and not smoking or being around

secondhand smoke.

REAL-WORLD CONNECTION

Write a journal entry about someone you know who has had cancer, or about information you have heard about cancer in the news.

Accept all reasonable responses. Encourage students to be accepting and supportive of their

peers' feelings in class discussions that arise.

_____

_____

_____

_____

_____

Tie-It-All-Together

Make a concept web to show the main ideas and important details in this chapter, and the relationships between the facts you learned. Hint: You may find it easier to list the facts or topics you want to include first, then decide how to connect them in the web.

Cellular Transport and the Cell Cycle Chapter Wrap-Up

In the "What I Wanted to Find Out" column, copy the questions you listed in the Chapter Preview. In the "What I Learned" column, write down the answers you discovered as you worked through the chapter.

W What I Wanted to Find Out	L What I Learned
1. Accept all reasonable entries. 2. 3.	1. 2. 3.

Use this checklist to help you study.

☐ Study your Science Notebook for this chapter.

☐ Study the definitions of vocabulary words.

☐ Review daily homework assignments.

☐ Reread the chapter and review the tables, graphs, and illustrations.

☐ Review the Section Assessment questions at the end of each section.

☐ Look over the Study Guide at the end of the chapter.

SUMMARIZE After reading this chapter, list three things you have learned about how cells work.

Accept all reasonable responses._____

_____

_____

Energy in a Cell

Before You Read

Use the "What I Know" column to list three things you know about energy in cells. Then list three questions you have about cell energy in the "What I Want to Find Out" column.

K What I Know	W What I Want to Find Out
1. Accept all reasonable entries. _____	1. _____ _____
2. _____ _____	2. _____ _____
3. _____ _____	3. _____ _____

Science Journal

How does energy get to cells? How do cells use energy? Write your own ideas.

Accept all reasonable responses.

_____

_____

_____

_____

_____

_____

_____

_____

Energy in a Cell
Section 9.1 The Need for Energy

Main Idea ———— **Details** ————————————————————————

Summarize *Scan this section and make a list of three general ways in which cells use energy.*

1. Accept all reasonable responses._____

2. _____

3. _____

Review Vocabulary

Use your book to define the following term.

active transport

movement of materials through a membrane against a concentration

gradient; requires energy from the cell

New Vocabulary

Use your book to define each term. Then write a sentence that describes the relationship of the two words.

ADP (adenosine diphosphate)

molecule formed from the release of a phosphate group from ATP, a

process which releases energy that is used for biological reactions

ATP (adenosine triphosphate)

energy-storing molecule in cells, made of an adenosine molecule, a

ribose sugar, and three phosphate groups; energy is stored in the

molecule's chemical bonds and can be used quickly and easily by

cells

Academic Vocabulary

Define the following terms.

energy

the ability to cause change; used by organisms to perform biological

functions

transform

to change in form, appearance, or structure; metamorphose

Section 9.1 The Need for Energy (continued)

| Main Idea | Details |

Cell Energy

I found this information on page _____.
SE, pp. 221–222
RE, p. 89

List *at least seven of your body's cell processes that require energy. Use both information from your book and your previous knowledge.*

Accept all reasonable responses. Examples: cell processes, muscles

contracting, heart pumping, cell division, breathing, growing, reading,

thinking.

Forming and Breaking Down ATP

I found this information on page _____.
SE, pp. 222–224
RE, pp. 89–90

Compare *ATP and ADP.*

Explain what your body uses ATP for, and list the two parts besides ribose sugar. Adenosine triphosphate provides quick energy for cells when they need it. It is made of an adenosine molecule, and three phosphate groups.

Explain how ADP is made from ATP. Adenosine diphosphate is made when ATP loses a phosphate group of an adenosine molecule, and two phosphate groups.

Create *a cycle diagram to show ATP, ADP, phosphate groups, and energy.*

Diagrams may resemble those in the book. Accept all reasonable variations that show the same information.

Section 9.1 The Need for Energy (continued)

Main Idea —— **Details** _____

Forming and Breaking Down ATP

I found this information on page _____.
SE, pp. 222–224
RE, pp. 89–90

Sequence *the steps when a protein gets the energy out of an ATP molecule.*

ATP   Protein

1. A protein binds to ATP and breaks the chemical bond.

↓

2. Energy and a phosphate group are released.

↓

3. ATP becomes ADP and is released from the protein.

↓

4. **ADP** binds to another phosphate to form ATP again.

Uses of Cell Energy

I found this information on page _____.
SE, p. 224
RE, p. 90

Create *a concept web to show at least six uses of cell energy.*
Accept all reasonable responses.
Webs may include making new molecules, building membranes and cell organelles, maintaining homeostasis, kidneys eliminating wastes from the blood, and keeping needed substances in the bloodstream. Encourage students to make detailed notes and to connect their concepts logically.

SUMMARIZE
Make a concept map to show the three most important ideas from this section.

Encourage students to choose concise but meaningful phrases for their maps.

_____

_____

_____

_____

Energy in a Cell
Section 9.2 Photosynthesis: Trapping the Sun's Energy

Main Idea ——— | **Details** ————————————————————

Scan *Section 2 of your book. Write two questions that come to mind from reading the headings and the illustration captions.*

1. Accept all reasonable responses. _____

2. _____

New Vocabulary | *Use your book to define each term.*

Calvin cycle

series of reactions during the light-independent phase of

photosynthesis in which simple sugars are formed from carbon

dioxide using ATP and hydrogen from the light-dependent reactions

chlorophyll

light-absorbing pigment in plants and other green organisms

required for photosynthesis; absorbs most lightwaves except green

electron transport chain

series of proteins embedded in a membrane along which energized

electrons are transported; as electrons are passed from molecule to

molecule, energy is released

light-dependent reactions

phase of photosynthesis where light energy is converted to chemical

energy in the form of ATP; results in the splitting of water and the

release of oxygen

light-independent reactions

phase of photosynthesis where energy from light-dependent

reactions is used to produce glucose and additional ATP molecules

photosynthesis

process by which plants and other green organisms trap energy

from sunlight with chlorophyll and use this energy to convert carbon

dioxide and water into simple sugars

pigments

molecules that absorb specific wavelengths of sunlight

Section 9.2 Photosynthesis: Trapping the Sun's Energy (continued)

Main Idea ———— **Details** ————————————————

Trapping Energy from Sunlight

I found this information on page _____.
SE, pp. 225–226
RE, p. 92

Summarize *the functions of the light-dependent and light-independent reactions and photosynthesis in general by completing the sentences.*

Plants and other green organisms <u>trap light energy</u> from <u>the Sun</u>.

The energy must be stored in a form that <u>can be used by cells</u>.

This form is called <u>ATP</u>.

The light-dependent reactions change <u>light energy</u> into <u>chemical energy</u>.

The light-dependent reactions result in <u>the splitting of water</u> and <u>release of oxygen</u>.

The light-independent reactions produce <u>simple sugars</u>, which are then made into <u>complex carbohydrates</u> such as <u>starch</u>, which stores energy in plants.

Create *a concept web to summarize what you know about chloroplasts and chlorophyll.* Accept all reasonable responses.

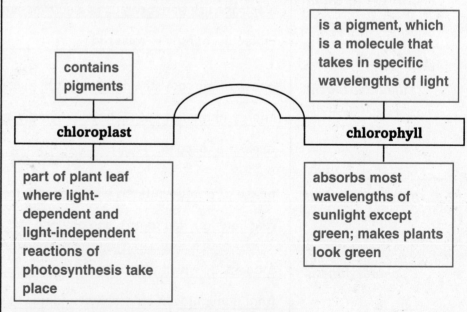

| contains pigments | | is a pigment, which is a molecule that takes in specific wavelengths of light |

| **chloroplast** | **chlorophyll** |

| part of plant leaf where light-dependent and light-independent reactions of photosynthesis take place | absorbs most wavelengths of sunlight except green; makes plants look green |

Analyze *why leaves change color in the fall.*

<u>Leaves stop producing chlorophyll, so other pigment colors become visible.</u>

Section 9.2 Photosynthesis: Trapping the Sun's Energy (continued)

Main Idea	Details

Light-Dependent Reactions

I found this information on page _____.

SE, pp. 226–228
RE, p. 93

Model *light-dependent reactions in a flow chart. Use the diagram in your book to help you.*

Diagrams should be similar to the one on SE p. 227, RE p. 93. Accept variations that show the same information.

Light-Independent Reactions

I found this information on page _____.

SE, pp. 228–230
RE, p. 93

Compare *light-dependent and light-independent reactions by putting each phrase into the correct part of the Venn diagram.*

- forms stored energy
- makes NADPH
- makes sugar
- needs sunlight

- occurs in the chloroplast
- occurs in the dark
- uses Calvin cycle
- uses electron transport chain

light-dependent
needs sunlight, uses electron transport chain, makes NADPH

both
occurs in the chloroplast, forms stored energy

light-independent
occurs in the dark, uses Calvin cycle, makes sugar

ANALOGY Create an original analogy for the electron transport chain.

Accept all reasonable responses. An electron transport chain is like passing a lump of

clay around a circle of people. Each time it passes between two people, a bit of the

clay falls off, so the lump gets smaller and smaller. This is the same as the electron transport

chain, where the electron's energy gets smaller and smaller as it is passed from one protein to

another to another.

Energy in a Cell
Section 9.3 Getting Energy to Make ATP

⟨Main Idea⟩ ———— **⟨Details⟩** ————————————————————

Identify *in which organelle sugars are converted to ATP.*

<u>Accept all reasonable responses.</u>

_____

⟨Review Vocabulary⟩ *Use your book to define the following term.*

mitochondria   <u>eukaryotic membrane-bound organelles that transform energy stored</u>

<u>in food molecules</u>

⟨New Vocabulary⟩ *Read the definitions below and write the matching vocabulary term in the blank.*

<u>anaerobic</u>   chemical reactions that do not require oxygen

<u>citric acid cycle</u>   in cellular respiration, a series of chemical reactions that break down glucose and produce ATP; energizes electron carriers that pass the energized electrons on to the electron transport chain

<u>lactic acid fermentation</u>   a series of anaerobic chemical reactions in which pyruvic acid uses NADH to form lactic acid and NAD+, which is then used in glycolysis; supplies energy when oxygen for aerobic respiration is scarce

<u>alcoholic fermentation</u>   anaerobic process in which cells convert pyruvic acid into carbon dioxide and ethyl alcohol; carried out by many bacteria and fungi such as yeasts

<u>cellular respiration</u>   chemical process where mitochondria break down food molecules to produce ATP; the three stages of cellular respiration are glycolysis, the citric acid cycle, and the electron transport cycle

<u>glycolysis</u>   in cellular respiration, a series of anaerobic chemical reactions in the cytoplasm that break down glucose into pyruvic acid; forms a net profit of two ATP molecules

⟨Academic Vocabulary⟩ *Define the following term.*

cycle   <u>a sequence of changing states that produces a final state equal to</u>

<u>the original one</u>

Section 9.3 Getting Energy to Make ATP (continued)

Main Idea ———   **Details** ———————————————————————

Cellular Respiration

I found this information on page _____.
SE, pp. 231–234
RE, p. 96

Compare and summarize *the three stages of cellular respiration.*
Make your own notes about each process.
Accept all reasonable responses.

Glycolysis	Citric Acid Cycle	Electron Transport Chain
a series of chemical reactions	a series of chemical reactions	like electron transport in photosynthesis
takes place in the cytoplasm of the cell	takes place in the mitochondria	takes place in mitochondrion inner membrane
breaks down glucose	also called the Krebs cycle	also called the Krebs cycle
produces two ATP molecules for every glucose molecule that is broken down	produces one ATP and two CO_2	provides energy for ATP production final acceptor is oxygen

Fermentation

I found this information on page _____.
SE, pp. 235–236
RE, p. 97

Sequence *events that lead to fermentation by completing the prompts.*

Cause: Cells can't get enough oxygen.

Fermentation follows glycolysis. It replaces the electron transport chain for a while. The electron transport chain will be backed up because oxygen is not available as the final acceptor.

Results in: muscle fatigue

List *the steps of lactic acid fermentation.*

1. Pyruvic acid uses NADH to form lactic acid and NAD+.

2. NAD+ is used in glycolysis. Lactic acid is transferred from muscle cells to liver.

3. Liver converts lactic acid back to pyruvic acid.

Section 9.3 Getting Energy to Make ATP (continued)

Main Idea	Details

Fermentation

I found this information on page _____.

SE, pp. 235–236
RE, p. 97

Name and describe *a process that bacteria and yeast do that is useful to humans and give an example.*

Alcoholic fermentation is a process used by some types of bacteria and yeast to make CO_2 and ethyl alcohol from pyruvic acid (which is made during glycolysis from glucose). This produces bubbles in bread and alcoholic beverages.

Comparing Photosynthesis and Cellular Respiration

I found this information on page _____.

SE, p. 237
RE, p. 98

Create *your own Venn diagram to compare photosynthesis and respiration. Use similarities as well as differences.*

Encourage students to make detailed notes. Differences are listed in the table on SE, p. 237, and RE, p. 98. Accept all reasonable responses.

photosynthesis

food is made; energy from the Sun is stored as sugar; CO_2 is used; O_2 is produced; produces sugars from PGAL; needs light; occurs only in presence of chlorophyll

both

use electron carriers and a cycle of chemical reactions to form ATP; use electron transport chains in their processes

respiration

food is broken down; sugar energy is used; CO_2 and H_2O are produced; O_2 is used; does not need light; occurs in all cells, both plant and animal

SUMMARIZE List all of the molecules in the section. Make a concept web to summarize their relationships, including the processes that transform one into another.

Accept all reasonable responses.

Tie-It-All-Together

Think *about the interactions and relationships in nature that involve cellular respiration and photosynthesis. How do the processes of one organism affect another? Make a diagram or write a journal entry to explain your ideas. Include at least one example of how plants and animals interact.*

Accept all reasonable responses. Students may mention that plants provide oxygen for animals, and animals provide carbon dioxide for plants. They may describe an aquarium or pond system. Encourage logical and correct synthesis of the facts and further research if the students are motivated to pursue the topic.

Energy in a Cell Chapter Wrap-Up

In the "What I Wanted to Find Out" column, copy the questions you listed in the Chapter Preview. In the "What I Learned" column, write down the answers you discovered as you worked through the chapter.

W What I Wanted to Find Out	L What I Learned
1. Accept all reasonable entries.	1.
2.	2.
3.	3.

Use this checklist to help you study.

- ☐ Study your Science Notebook for this chapter.
- ☐ Study the definitions of vocabulary words.
- ☐ Review daily homework assignments.
- ☐ Reread the chapter and review the tables, graphs, and illustrations.
- ☐ Review the Section Assessment questions at the end of each section.
- ☐ Look over the Study Guide at the end of the chapter.

SUMMARIZE After reading this chapter, list three things you have learned about energy in cells.

Accept all reasonable responses. _____

_____

_____

Mendel and Meiosis

Before You Read

Use the "What I Know" column to list three things you know about genetics. Then list three questions you have about genetics in the "What I Want to Find Out" column.

K What I know	W What I want to find out
1. Accept all reasonable entries. _____	1. _____
2. _____	2. _____
3. _____	3. _____

Science Journal

Genetics explains why you have inherited certain characteristics from your parents. Write about some characteristics that you have inherited from your own parents, or similarities that you see in other families or in animals or plants that you think might have been inherited.

Accept all reasonable responses. _____

_____

_____

_____

_____

_____

_____

Mendel and Meiosis
Section 10.1 Mendel's Laws of Heredity

(Main Idea) —— **(Details)** ——————————————————————

Skim *Section 1 of your book, write three questions that come to mind from reading the headings and illustration captions.*

1. Accept all reasonable responses._____

2. _____

3. _____

New Vocabulary   *Use terms in the left margin to complete the paragraph below.*

allele

fertilization

gamete

genetics

heredity

hybrid

law of independent assortment

law of segregation

pollination

trait

zygote

Genetics is the branch of biology that studies heredity , which is the passing on of characteristics, known as traits , from parents to offspring. Male and female sex cells, called gametes , unite during fertilization (which is called pollination in plants) to form a fertilized cell, called a zygote . Hybrid offspring result from parents that have different forms of alleles for certain traits. Mendel's law of segregation states that every individual has two alleles of each gene and when gametes are produced, each gamete receives one of these alleles. Mendel's law of independent assortment states that genes for different traits are inherited independently of each other.

Compare and contrast each pair of terms by defining them and/or noting their differences.

Accept all reasonable responses.

dominant

genotype

heterozygous

homozygous

phenotype

recessive

dominant trait	recessive trait
an observed trait that masks the recessive form of a trait	trait that can be observed if the dominant trait is not present
genotype	**phenotype**
the allele combination an organism behaves, contains	the way an organism looks and regardless of its genes
homozygous	**heterozygous**
an organism's two alleles for a trait are the same	an organism's two alleles for a trait are different

Section 10.1 Mendel's Laws of Heredity (continued)

Main Idea ——— **Details** ——————————————————————————

Why Mendel Succeeded

I found this information on page _____ .
SE, pp. 253–254
RE, p. 100

Describe *how a plant self-pollinates.*

A plant self-pollinates when its male and female gametes come from the

same plant. Its own male sex cells pollinate its own female sex cells.

Describe *how Mendel cross-pollinated pea plants. Why did Mendel use this technique to study inheritance?*

Mendel opened the petals of a flower and removed the male reproductive

organs. He then dusted the female reproductive organ with pollen from the

plant he wished to cross it with. The seeds that develop from cross-

pollination have traits of both plants. He did this so he could be sure of

the parents in his cross.

Mendel's Monohybrid Crosses

I found this information on page _____ .
SE, pp. 255–257
RE, pp. 101-102

Summarize *Mendel's first experiment.*

Mendel crossed: two true-breeding plants.

He controlled variables by: studying just one trait at a time.

The first trait he studied: height.

Results: When a six-ft-tall plant was crossed with a less than

two-ft-tall plant, all offspring were 6 ft tall.

When the offspring were allowed to self-pollinate: Three-fourths

of the plants were tall, and one-fourth of the plants were short.

The dominant allele was: tall.

The recessive allele was: short.

The number of monohybrid crosses he eventually tried: 7

His conclusion: Each organism has two alleles for each trait.

Phenotypes and Genotypes

I found this information on page _____ .
SE, p. 258
RE, p. 103

Compare *genotypes and phenotypes for pea plants.*

genotype	homozygous or heterozygous	phenotype
TT	homozygous	tall plant
Tt	heterozygous	tall plant
tt	homozygous	short plant

Section 10.1 Mendel's Laws of Heredity (continued)

Main Idea ————— **Details** ————————————————

Mendel's Dihybrid Crosses

I found this information on page _____.
SE, pp. 259–260
RE, p. 103

Demonstrate *the law of independent assortment by listing the four alleles that are produced when a pea plant with the genotype RrYy produces gametes.*

1. __R__   2. __Y__   3. __r__   4. __y__

List *two things that can be predicted by a Punnett square.*

possible genotypes of offspring

probable proportions of each genotype

Punnett Squares, Probability

I found this information on page _____.
SE, pp. 260–262
RE, p. 105

Complete *the Punnett squares for height in the F_1 and F_2 generations. Write the expected genotypes and the probability for each.*

F_1

	T	T
t	Tt	Tt
t	Tt	Tt

Tt 100%

F_2

	T	t
T	TT	Tt
t	Tt	tt

TT 25%

Tt 50%

tt 25%

Identify *the locations, within the Punnet square showing Mendel's F_2 dihybrid results, of genotypes that satisfy each description.*

	RY	ry	Ry	rY
RY	A	B	C	D
ry	E	F	G	H
Ry	I	J	K	L
rY	M	N	O	P

1. peas with only dominant alleles __A__
2. green peas __F, G, J, K__
3. wrinkled yellow peas __H, N, P__
4. round green peas __G, J, K__
5. peas with only recessive alleles __F__
6. round peas __A, B, C, D, E, G, I, J, K, L, M, O__
7. homozygous for color __A, D, F, G, J, K, M, P__
8. heterozygous for roundness __B, D, E, G, J, L, M, O__

REAL-WORLD CONNECTION

Discuss the effects of Mendel's two laws (segregation and independent assortment). Give an example. Accept all reasonable responses.

The law of segregation states that every individual has two alleles of each gene and each gamete receives one of these alleles. The law of independent assortment states that genes for different traits are inherited independently of each other. For example, when a pea plant with the genotype RrYy produces gametes, the alleles R and r will seperate from each other as well as from the alleles Y and y. Every individual is a unique combination of the traits of its parents.

Mendel and Meiosis

Section 10.2 Meiosis

(Main Idea)——— **(Details)**———————————————————————

Organize Information *As you read Section 2, list the ways in which meiosis explains Mendel's results.*

Accept all reasonable responses. Sample response: Meiosis produces haploid

cells which each have one allele of each gene. Chromosomes follow the law of

independent assortment. Genes for traits can be seen now with microscopes.

(Review Vocabulary) *Use your text to define the following term.*

mitosis   period of nuclear cell division in which two daughter cells are

formed, each containing a complete set of chromosomes

(New Vocabulary) *Use the terms in the left margin to complete the graphic organizer below.*

crossing over

diploid

egg

genetic recombination

haploid

homologous chromosome

meiosis

nondisjunction

sexual reproduction

sperm

A first step in sexual reproduction occurs when

a diploid cell with homologous chromosomes, or two of each pair, undergoes meiosis

which produces four cells containing half the number of chromosomes, haploid cells, called

egg and sperm .

Describe three things that can happen to homologous chromosomes during meiosis. Accept all reasonable responses.

	crossing over	**genetic recombination**	**nondisjunction**
What happens	non-sister chromatids from homologous chromosomes break and exchange genetic material	reassortment of chromosomes and genetic information during meiosis	failure of homologous chromosomes to separate properly during meiosis
Results in	new combinations of alleles on a chromosome	variation among organisms	gametes with too many or too few chromosomes

Section 10.2 Meiosis (continued)

Main Idea	Details

Genes, Chromosomes, and Numbers

I found this information on page _____.
SE, pp. 263–265
RE, p. 108

Summarize *at least six pieces of information about chromosomes by creating a concept map below.*

Accept all reasonable responses. Sample concept map:

thousand or more genes
lined up
one of each — chromosome — two of each
haploid cell
gametes
one from each parent gamete
diploid cell

The Phases of Meiosis

I found this information on page _____.
SE, pp. 266–269
RE, p. 109

Compare and contrast *the phases of Meiosis I and Meiosis II. Sketch each phase.* Accept all reasonable responses. Sketches should be similar to those in the text.

Sketch	Description	Sketch	Description	Compare and Contrast
Prophase I		**Prophase II**		
	DNA of chromosomes coil up, pair up with homologous chromosomes, spindle forms		a spindle forms in each of the new cells and chromosomes are pulled to center of cell	in Prophase II, the chromosomes are already coiled
Metaphase I		**Metaphase II**		
	centromere attaches to spindle fiber, pulls chromosomes to center of cell, lines up tetrads		chromosomes line up randomly at center of cell	Metaphase I is more organized
Anaphase I		**Anaphase II**		
	chromosomes move apart from each other toward "poles" of cell		centromere of each chromosome splits, sister chromatids move to opposite poles of cell	Anaphase II is forming two haploid cells, Anaphase I forms two diploid cells
Telophase I		**Telophase II**		
	spindle is broken down, chromosomes uncoil, cytoplasm divides		nuclei re-form, spindle breaks down, cytoplasm divides	in Telophase II, haploid cells are formed, in Telophase I, diploid cells are formed

Section 10.2 Meiosis (continued)

⟨Main Idea⟩	⟨Details⟩

The Phases of Meiosis

I found this information on page _____.
SE, pp. 266–269
RE, p. 109

Identify *the phase of meiosis when crossing over may occur. Describe the process.*

During Prophase I, the two sister chromatids in a tetrad pair tightly.

Non-sister chromatids from homologous chromosomes break off

and change places.

Meiosis Provides for Genetic Variation

I found this information on page _____.
SE, pp. 269–270
RE, p. 111

List *two factors that increase genetic variation. Name the process.*

1. cell division

2. crossing over

Process: genetic recombination

Nondisjunction

I found this information on page _____.
SE, p. 271
RE, p. 111

Identify *an advantage and a disadvantage of nondisjunction.*

Advantage	Disadvantage
Plants with more than the normal number of chromosomes produce flowers and fruits that are often larger than normal and the plant is healthier.	Organisms lacking one or more chromosomes often do not survive.

Gene Linkage and Maps

I found this information on page _____.
SE, pp. 272–273
RE, p. 111

Explain *gene linkage by completing the paragraph below.*

- chromosomes
- farther
- inherited
- sequence
- crossing over
- genes
- linked

Genes close together on the same chromosome are usually __linked__.

Linked genes are usually __inherited__ together. __Chromosomes__,

not __individual genes__, follow Mendel's law of independent

assortment. Linked genes might become separated, as a result of

__crossing over__. Crossing over is more likely to happen if

genes are __farther__ apart on a chromosome. Scientists use

the __frequencies of new gene combinations__ to map the

__relative locations of the genes__ on a chromosome.

Mendel and Meiosis Chapter Wrap-Up

In the "What I Wanted to Find Out" column, copy the questions you listed in the Chapter Preview. In the "What I Learned" column, write down the answers you discovered as you worked through the chapter.

W What I Wanted to Find Out	L What I Learned
1. Accept all reasonable entries.	1.
2.	2.
3.	3.

Use this checklist to help you study.

☐ Study your Science Notebook for this chapter.

☐ Study the definitions of vocabulary words.

☐ Review daily homework assignments.

☐ Reread the chapter and review the tables, graphs, and illustrations.

☐ Review the Section Assessment questions at the end of each section.

☐ Look over the Study Guide at the end of the chapter.

SUMMARIZE After reading this chapter, list three things you have learned about genetics.

Accept all reasonable responses.

DNA and Genes

Before You Read

Use the "What I Know" column to list three things you know about genes and DNA. Then list three questions you have about DNA and genes in the "What I Want to Find Out" column.

K What I Know	W What I Want to Find Out
1. Accept all reasonable entries.	1.
2.	2.
3.	3.

Science Journal

Ponies on the Shetland Islands in Scotland have short structure, thick hair, strength, and hardiness so they can thrive in their harsh environment. How do you think the DNA of their population has changed over time?

Accept all reasonable responses._____

_____

_____

_____

_____

_____

_____

_____

DNA and Genes

Section 11.1 DNA: The Molecule of Heredity

Main Idea ———— **Details** ————————————————

List *current events and issues concerning DNA that you have read about in a newspaper or magazine. As you read this section, refer to your list and add explanations from the book.*

Accept all reasonable responses.

_____

_____

_____

Review Vocabulary   *Use your book to define the following term.*

nucleotide   subunit of a nucleic acid formed from a simple sugar, a phosphate

group, and a nitrogenous base

New Vocabulary   *Use your book to define each term. In the box to the right, make a sketch to help you remember each term.* **Accept all reasonable sketches.**

DNA replication   process in which the DNA in the

chromosome is copied

double helix   shape of a DNA molecule

consisting of two strands of

nucleotides that are twisted into

a coil and held together by the

nitrogenous bases

nitrogenous base   carbon ring structure found in

DNA molecules that contains one

or more atoms of nitrogen

Section 11.1 DNA: The Molecule of Heredity (continued)

Main Idea	Details

What is DNA?

I found this information on page _____.

SE, pp. 281–284
RE, pp. 114–115

Write *the correct information to complete each list.*

Accept all reasonable responses.

Actions That Depend on Enzymes 1. eating 2. running 3. thinking	Types of Information in DNA 1. information for life 2. instructions to make all the different proteins an organism needs
Pieces of a Nucleotide 1. a simple sugar 2. a phosphate group 3. a nitrogenous base	Nitrogenous Bases 1. adenine 2. guanine 3. cytosine 4. thymine

Create *a memory device to help you remember how the nitrogenous bases are always paired.*

Accept all reasonable responses that pair adenine with thymine and

cytosine with guanine. Sample response: Aunt Tillie and Cousin Gus

Describe *the DNA molecule by explaining how each word applies to the molecule. Use a sketch to back up your explanation in each case.*

Word and What it Means	Sketch of Effect
zipper: The phosphate groups and sugar form the backbone of the strand and the nitrogenous bases stick out like the teeth of a zipper.	Accept all reasonable sketches.
helix: A helix is something twisted into a coil.	
double (as in "double helix"): DNA is made of two strands that are twisted into a coil.	

Explain *why the four nitrogenous bases in DNA provide so much variety in life.*

Though there are only four bases, different sequences or orders of

the bases result in thousands of organisms.

Section 11.1 DNA: The Molecule of Heredity (continued)

Main Idea	Details

Replication of DNA

I found this information on page _____.
SE, pp. 284–287
RE, pp. 115–116

Identify *when DNA replication occurs as a step in cell reproduction.*
before cells divide

Sequence and model *each step in the replication of a DNA molecule. Write about what happens, and draw a DNA molecule going through each step.*

A. The model unzips Drawing should resemble Part A, separation of strands on SE, p. 286, RE p. 116.	C. The molecule continues to unzip and base pairs continue to match and join. Drawing should resemble Part C, bonding of bases.
B. Nucleotides that are floating free in the cell attach to the unzipped chains (A to T and C to G). Drawing should resemble Part B, base pairing.	D. Two new strands will be formed. Drawing should resemble Part D, results of replication.

State *how a DNA molecule acts like a template.*
As it unzips, it dictates the bases that will come and match up, so

the two new molecules turn out exactly like their parent molecule.

SYNTHESIZE

Compare and contrast the processes of cell division and DNA replication.

Accept all reasonable responses. DNA replication is a process that must occur before cell

division can take place. Cell division: cells replicate all parts but they grow before dividing.

DNA replication: DNA doesn't grow; it just unzips and doubles.

DNA and Genes
Section 11.2 From DNA to Protein

Main Idea ——— **Details** ————————————————————

Scan *the headings and boldfaced words for the section. Predict three things that you think might be discussed.*

1. Accept all reasonable responses._____

2. _____

3. _____

Review Vocabulary *Use your book to define the following term.*

polymer a large molecule formed from smaller sub-units that are bonded

together

New Vocabulary *Use your book to define the following term.*

codon a group of three nitrogenous bases in mRNA that code for one

amino acid

Compare and contrast the three types of RNA by describing the function of each.

Messenger RNA	Ribosomal RNA	Transfer RNA
messenger RNA — carries information from DNA in the nucleus to the cell's cytoplasm	makes up the ribosomes; binds to mRNA and uses its information to assemble amino acids in the right order	delivers amino acids to the ribosomes to be assembled into proteins

(row labels in left margin: messenger RNA, ribosomal RNA, transfer RNA)

Compare and contrast transcription and translation.

Transcription	Translation
process in the cell nucleus where a copy of RNA is made from part of a DNA strand	process of changing the information in the mRNA into an amino acid chain in a protein

(row labels in left margin: transcription, translation)

Academic Vocabulary *Define the following term as a verb.*

code to translate a message into a code; to encode

_____

Section 11.2 From DNA to Protein (continued)

Main Idea	Details

Genes and Proteins, RNA

I found this information on page _____.

SE, p. 288
RE, p. 118

Analogy *If DNA and RNA were employees in a factory, what would their jobs be? Explain the function of each type of molecule.*

Accept all reasonable responses. DNA would be the engineer—it gives the

instructions. RNA would be the worker—it carries out the instructions.

Compare and contrast *RNA and DNA by writing at least five characteristics in the Venn diagram.* Accept all reasonable responses.

RNA
single strand; has ACUG for bases; uracil binds with adenine

Both
are nucleic acids; have sugars, but different ones

DNA
double strand; has ACTG for bases; thymine binds with adenine

Transcription

I found this information on page _____.

SE, pp. 290–291
RE, p. 119

Sequence *the steps in transcription of RNA.*

1. A portion of the DNA molecule unzips.

2. Free RNA nucleotides pair with the nucleotides on the DNA strand.

3. The mRNA strand breaks away and the DNA strands rejoin.

4. The mRNA leaves the nucleus and enters the cytoplasm.

Model *the movement of tRNA molecules during the translation process.*

Diagrams should show tRNA molecules moving to a ribosome while carrying amino acids, then as soon as each amino acid bonds, the tRNA moves away to bring another amino acid.

Section 11.2 From DNA to Protein (continued)

⟨**Main Idea**⟩ ——— ⟨**Details**⟩ ————————————————

The Genetic Code

I found this information on page _____.

    SE, pp. 291–292
    RE, pp. 120–121

Identify *four examples of codons.*

1. (GCU) alanine

2. (AAA) lysine

3. the codon that tells mRNA that this is the start of the amino acid chain

4. the codon that says this is the end of the amino acid chain

Translation: From mRNA to Protein

I found this information on page _____.

    SE, pp. 293–295
    RE, pp. 121–122

Describe *amino acid chains by completing the diagram.*

(They twist and curl into complex 3-dimensional shapes.)

(Each type of chain forms the same shape every time it is produced.)

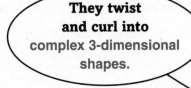

(Amino Acid Chains)

(Amino acid chains become proteins when they are freed from the ribosome.)

(Proteins become enzymes and cell structures.)

SUMMARIZE

Create a flow chart to describe the formation of a protein. Describe the activities of DNA and the three types of RNA. Accept all reasonable responses. Sample response shown.

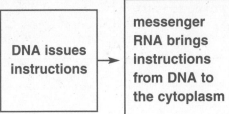

| DNA issues instructions | → | messenger RNA brings instructions from DNA to the cytoplasm | → | ribosomal RNA binds to the mRNA | | transfer RNA delivers amino acids to the ribosome to be made into a protein |

the rRNA uses the instructions to assemble the amino acids in the right order

DNA and Genes
Section 11.3 Genetic Changes

Main Idea ——— **Details** —————————————————————

Recognize Cause and Effect *Why might a mutation have little or no harmful effect on an organism?*

Accept all reasonable responses.
_____

Review Vocabulary *Use your book to define the following term.*

cancer   diseases believed to be caused by changes in the genes that control

the cell cycle
_____

New Vocabulary *Complete the sentence with two vocabulary words.*

mutagen   _____Mutagens_____, which include high temperatures, radiation, and

chemicals, can cause _____mutations_____, which are changes in the

mutation   DNA sequence.

Compare and contrast the three types of mutations by defining them side-by-side.

Chromosomal Mutation	Frameshift Mutation	Point Mutation
mutation that occurs when parts of the chromosomes break off during mitosis or meiosis and join to the wrong chromosome, or join backwards or in the wrong place on the chromosome	mutation that occurs when a single nitrogenous base is added or deleted from the DNA sequence; causes a shift in the reading of codons by one base	a change in a single base pair in DNA

chromosomal mutation

frameshift mutation

point mutation

Academic Vocabulary *Define the following term.*

error   a deviation from accuracy or correctness; a mistake
_____

Section 11.3 Genetic Changes (continued)

⟨Main Idea⟩———— ⟨Details⟩———————————————————————————

Mutations

I found this information on page _____ .
SE, pp. 296–299
RE, pp. 124–125

Outline *the important facts about mutations.*

A. internal causes of mutations:

1. errors in replication

2. errors in transcription

3. errors in cell division

B. outside forces that can cause mutations in DNA:

1. radiation from the sun

2. X rays

3. radioactive materials

C. types of cells affected by mutations from outside forces:

1. skin cells

2. muscle cells

3. bone cells

D. why mutations from outside forces on those three types of cells are not passed on to offspring:

They are not sex cells.

E. possible effects of mutations from outside forces on those three types of cells:

The mutated cell can divide and pass the mutation on to other cells (for example, a mutated stomach lining cell that has lost its ability to make the acid needed to digest food). Sometimes cells grow and divide too quickly, causing cancer.

Compare and contrast *a point mutation and a frameshift mutation by defining each mutation stating its consequence.*

Point mutation happens when there is a change in a single base pair in the DNA.	consequence: One protein is changed.
Frameshift mutation occurs when a single nitrogenous base is added or deleted from the whole DNA sequence.	consequence: The whole sequence is changed. It is more harmful to an organism than a point mutation.

Section 11.3 Genetic Changes (continued)

Main Idea ——— **Details** ——————————————————————

Mutations

I found this information on page _____.
SE, pp. 296–299
RE, pp. 124–125

Model *each of the following.* Students' diagrams should resemble those in the book.

a normal strip of DNA	
the same DNA strip, with a point mutation	
the same DNA strip, with a frameshift mutation	

Chromosomal Alterations

I found this information on page _____.
SE, pp. 299–300
RE, p. 126

List four examples of how chromosomes can change. Use your imagination to draw a sketch of what each change might look like. Accept all reasonable responses for sketches.

Example	Sketch
Pieces may join to the wrong chromosome.	
Pieces may join backwards.	
Pieces may join in the wrong place.	
Broken pieces may get lost.	

Section 11.3 Genetic Changes (continued)

Main Idea ———— **Details** ————————————————

Chromosomal Alterations

I found this information on page _____.
SE, pp. 299–300
RE, p. 126

Causes of Mutations

I found this information on page _____.
SE, pp. 300–301
RE, p. 126

Describe *two ways in which chromosomal alterations occur in plants.*

Gametes that should have a complete set of genes may end up with

too many or too few of a particular gene.

Examine *the types and effects of mutagens by completing the concept web.*

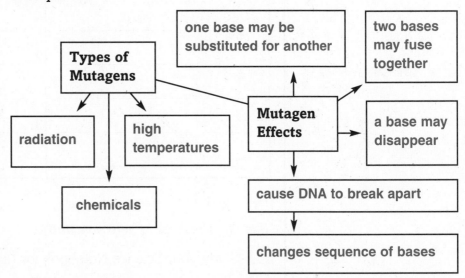

Summarize *how mistakes and mutations in DNA are repaired by cells and state the effectiveness of the mechanism.*

Cells contain enzymes that check the DNA sequence. If the enzymes

find an incorrect sequence of nucleotides, they replace it with the

correct sequence. The mechanism usually works very well.

CONNECT Write about genetic mutations you have heard about in the the news or daily life. Hypothesize what caused the mutation in each case.

Accept all reasonable responses. calves with 2 heads (probably an error

in cell division as it was differentiating as a fetus); "Conjoined twins" (joined at a body part)

(probably an error in cell division); pet breeds with 6 toes (e.g. Maine Coon cats) (a mutation

in DNA that is passed along)

DNA and Genes Chapter Wrap-Up

In the "What I Wanted to Find Out" column, copy the questions you listed in the Chapter Preview. In the "What I Learned" column, write down the answers you discovered as you worked through the chapter.

W What I Wanted to Find Out	L What I Learned
1. Accept all reasonable entries. _____	1. _____ _____
2. _____ _____	2. _____ _____
3. _____ _____	3. _____ _____

Use this checklist to help you study.

☐ Study your Science Notebook for this chapter.

☐ Study the definitions of vocabulary words.

☐ Review daily homework assignments.

☐ Reread the chapter and review the tables, graphs, and illustrations.

☐ Review the Section Assessment questions at the end of each section.

☐ Look over the Study Guide at the end of the chapter.

SUMMARIZE

After reading this chapter, list three things you have learned about DNA and genes. Accept all reasonable responses.

_____

_____

_____

Patterns of Heredity and Human Genetics

Before You Read

Use the "What I Know" column to list three things you know about heredity and genetics. Then list three questions you have about these topics in the "What I Want to Find Out" column.

K What I Know	W What I Want to Find Out
1. Accept all reasonable entries.	1. _____
2. _____	2. _____
3. _____	3. _____

Science Journal

Describe how you think a child's DNA is different from his or her mother's DNA and father's DNA.

Accept all reasonable responses.

_____

_____

_____

_____

_____

_____

_____

Patterns of Heredity and Human Genetics
Section 12.1 Mendelian Inheritance of Human Traits

Main Idea ——— **Details** ————————————————————————

Scan *Section 1 of your book. Use the checklist as a guide.*

- ☐ Read all section titles.
- ☐ Read all boldfaced words.
- ☐ Read all tables and graphs.
- ☐ Look at all pictures and read the captions.
- ☐ Think about what you already know about patterns of heredity and human genetics.

Write three facts you discovered about patterns of heredity and human genetics as you scanned the section.

1. Accept all reasonable responses._____

2. _____

3. _____

Review Vocabulary) *Use your book to define the following term.*

trait | any characteristic that is inherited

New Vocabulary) *Use your book to define each term.*

carrier | an individual heterozygous for a specific trait

pedigree | graphic representation of genetic inheritance used by geneticists to

map genetic traits

Explain why pedigrees are needed to identify the carriers of a recessive trait in a family.

Pedigrees are necessary to find carriers because the recessive traits

are not readily apparent by looking at the phenotype.

Academic Vocabulary) *Define the following term.*

dominate | to have a prevailing influence on somebody or something

Section 12.1 Mendelian Inheritance of Human Traits (continued)

| Main Idea | Details |

Making a Pedigree

I found this information on page _____.
SE, pp. 309–311
RE, pp. 128–129

Summarize *the pedigree symbols by naming them and then drawing them in the right-hand column of the table. The first two boxes have been completed for you. Sketches should resemble those in the book.*

	Description of Symbol	Sketch of Symbol
male	square	
female	circle	
affected male	shaded square	
affected female	shaded circle	
known heterozygotes	half–shaded symbol	
death	a line through the symbol	
parents and offspring siblings	circle joined to square, line down, circles or squares on second row	
mating	circle joined to square	

Simple Recessive Heredity

I found this information on page _____.
SE, pp. 311–313
RE, p. 129

Write *three facts about recessive heredity using the concept map below.* Accept all reasonable responses.

Simple Recessive Heredity

Most genetic disorders are caused by recessive alleles.

Diseases that can be predicted by the use of pedigree are cystic fibrosis, Tay-Sachs disease, phenylketonuria.

For an offspring to inherit a recessive trait, both parents must have the allele.

Section 12.1 Mendelian Inheritance of Human Traits (continued)

⊂Main Idea⊃———— **⊂Details⊃**————————————————————

Simple Dominant Heredity

I found this information on page _____.
SE, pp. 313–314
RE, p. 129

List *five examples of dominant traits in humans.* Accept all reasonable responses.

1. cleft chin

2. widow's peak hairline

3. freely hanging earlobes

4. almond-shaped eyes

5. thick lips

Summarize *the facts about Huntington's disease by completing the concept map below.*

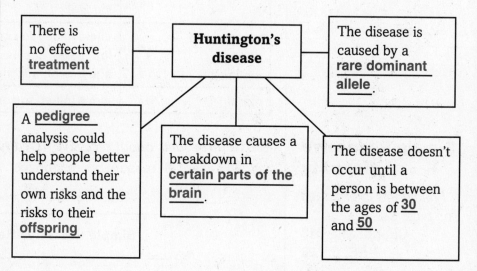

There is no effective **treatment**.

Huntington's disease

The disease is caused by a **rare dominant allele**.

A **pedigree** analysis could help people better understand their own risks and the risks to their **offspring**.

The disease causes a breakdown in **certain parts of the brain**.

The disease doesn't occur until a person is between the ages of <u>30</u> and <u>50</u>.

CONNECT Make your own pedigree diagram for a family. Pick a trait and designate it as dominant, then shade the boxes to show who has recessive genes, who has dominant genes, and who is likely heterozygous. Accept all reasonable diagrams.

Patterns of Heredity and Human Genetics

Section 12.2 When Heredity Follows Different Rules

Main Idea ——— **Details** ————————————————————

Analyze *Corn kernels can be many different colors and patterns. Think about what you know about Mendelian inheritance. Explain how you know that the inheritance of kernel color in corn is not simply Mendelian.*

The kernels of the corn can be many different colors and patterns.

With simple Mendelian inheritance, there would only be two possible

phenotypes of kernels.

Review Vocabulary   *Use your book to define the following term.*

allele   an alternative form of a gene

New Vocabulary   *Use your book to define each term.*

autosomes   pairs of homologous chromosomes in somatic cells

codominant alleles   pattern where phenotypes of both homozygote parents are produced

in heterozygous offspring so that both alleles are equally expressed

incomplete dominance   inheritance pattern where the phenotype of a heterozygote is

intermediate between those of the two homozygotes; neither allele

of the pair is dominant but combine and display a new trait

multiple alleles   presence of more than two alleles for a genetic trait

polygenic inheritance   inheritance pattern of a trait controlled by two or more genes; genes

may be on the same or different chromosomes

sex chromosomes   in humans, the 23rd pair of chromosomes; determine the sex of an

individual and carry sex-linked characteristics

sex-linked traits   traits controlled by genes located on sex chromosomes

Section 12.2 When Heredity Follows Different Rules (continued)

Main Idea ——— **Details** ——————————————————————

Complex Patterns of Inheritance

I found this information on page _____.

SE, pp. 315–320
RE, pp. 131–133

Analyze *the ratios of offspring of the following snapdragon pairs by writing the genotype of each phenotype given, then filling in the Punnett square. The first row has been done for you. Hint: To write the genotypes, designate the dominant red allele as R and the recessive white allele as R'.*

Parent Flowers	Genotypes of Parent Flowers	Punnett Square		Ratio of Offspring
red and white	RR × R'R'	R R	R' RR' RR' R' RR' RR'	4 pink
pink and white	RR' × R'R'	R R'	R' RR' R'R' R' RR' R'R'	2 pink: 2 white
red and pink	RR × RR'	R R	R RR RR R' RR' RR'	2 red: 2 pink
pink and pink	RR' × RR'	R R'	R RR RR' R' RR' R'R'	1 red: 2 pink: 1 white

Compare *incomplete and codominant traits.*

A trait that is incompletely dominant will be fully expressed if it is

homozygous or partially expressed if it is heterozygous. In

codominant inheritance, both traits show up equally.

Analyze *how the following pairs of multiple alleles for pigeon feathers would be expressed. The first one has been done for you.*

wild-type blue + chocolate-brown = blue

wild-type blue + ash-red = ___ash-red___

ash-red 1 chocolate-brown 5 ___ash-red___

Sequence *the multiple alleles (ash-red, wild-type blue, and chocolate-brown) for pigeon feathers from most dominant to most recessive.*

___ash-red___   ___wild-type blue___   ___chocolate-brown___
dominant   recessive

Section 12.2 When Heredity Follows Different Rules (continued)

Main Idea	Details

Complex Patterns of Inheritance

I found this information on page _____.
SE, pp. 315–320
RE, pp. 131–133

Contrast *the two given items in each line below.*

1. sex chromosomes with the 22 pairs of autosomes

   Sex chromosomes are not identical pairs but the other

   autosomes are.

2. traits of sex-linked inheritance with polygenic inheritance

   Sex-linked traits may only be passed to males if they are on the

   Y chromosome (Y-linked), or to both sexes if they are on the

   X chromosome (X-linked). Polygenic traits are inherited through

   many genes at once and vary over a wide range.

Environmental Influences

I found this information on page _____.
SE, pp. 321–322
RE, p. 133

Identify *environmental factors that influence the way genes are expressed.*

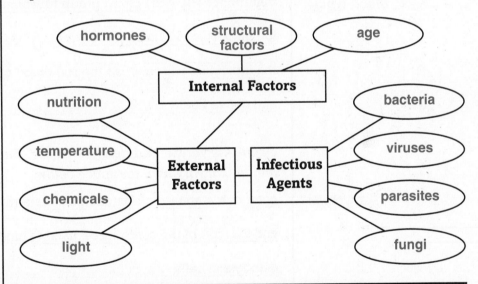

CONNECT Think of some traits in people, plants, or animals. Describe one trait and tell whether you think the trait is dominant/recessive, multiple allele, codominant, incompletely dominant, sex-linked, or polygenic trait. Explain your reasoning.

Accept all reasonable responses. Eye color; some people have blue eyes, some have green,

and some have brown. I think this is a multiple allele situation because there are so many

possible colors, and some colors seem dominant over others.

Patterns of Heredity and Human Genetics
Section 12.3 Complex Inheritance of Human Traits

Main Idea ————— **Details** ——————————————————

Organize Information *As you read Section 3, make a list of some physical characteristics that appear in your family members or friends. Try to determine how each trait is inherited by examining its inheritance pattern.*

Accept all reasonable responses.

_____

_____

Review Vocabulary

Use your book to define the following term.

homozygous

having two identical alleles for a particular gene

New Vocabulary

Define blood typing and tell why it is important.

blood typing

determines the ABO blood group to which an individual belongs

It is important because if the wrong ABO type is given, antibodies in

the individual will react so the red blood cells could clump together

and cause death.

Define karyotype and describe its use. Then make a sketch of a human karyotype in the space below.

karyotype

chart of metaphase chromosome pairs arranged according to length

and location of the centromere; used to pinpoint unusual chromosome

numbers in cells

It is used to identify an abnormal number of chromosomes.

Accept all reasonable sketches.

Academic Vocabulary

Define the following term.

link

anything serving to connect one part or thing with another; a bond

or tie

Section 12.3 Complex Inheritance of Human Traits (continued)

Main Idea	Details

Codominance in Humans

I found this information on page _____.

SE, pp. 323–324
RE, p. 135

Describe *the effects of sickle-cell anemia for people who are heterozygous for the disease and for people who are homozygous for the disease.*

Heterozygous
They produce normal and sickle-shaped red blood cells. They do not have serious health problems and can lead relatively normal lives.

Homozygous
Abnormal sickle-shaped cells are produced instead of normal disc-shaped cells. They slow blood flow, block small vessels, and cause tissue damage and pain. Individuals have short life spans and several related disorders.

Predict *how the offspring may be affected if two people who are heterozygous for sickle-cell anemia but lead normal lives have a child. It may be helpful to make a Punnett square to show the genotypes of the offspring.*

People who are heterozygous for sickle-cell anemia may have children

who have no alleles for the disease, who are also heterozygous, or

who are homozygous for the disease. The offspring who are

homozygous for the disease will not be able to live normal lives.

Multiple Alleles Govern Blood Type

I found this information on page _____.

SE, pp. 324–326
RE, p. 136

Identify *the phenotype that results from each combination of genotypes. The first one has been done for you.*

Possible Genotype Combinations	Phenotypes
A and A	A
A and B	AB
A and O	A
B and B	B
B and O	B
D and O	O

Section 12.3 Complex Inheritance of Human Traits (continued)

Main Idea	Details

Multiple Alleles Govern Blood Type

I found this information on page _____.
SE, pp. 324–326
RE, p. 136

Consider *in each case whether the father could possibly have the blood type given. Circle your choice.*

mother: type O	child: type A	father: type AB	(yes)	no
mother: type B	child: type A	father: type A	(yes)	no
mother: type AB	child: type O	father: type AB	yes	(no)
mother: type A	child: type B	father: type O	yes	(no)
mother: type O	child: type O	father: type B	(yes)	no
mother: type B	child: type O	father: type A	(yes)	no

Sex-Linked Traits in Humans

I found this information on page _____.
SE, pp. 326–327
RE, pp. 136–137

Explain *how a boy can have red-green color blindness with just one recessive allele, but a girl must have two recessive alleles to have this trait.*

Red-green color blindness is a recessive trait found on the

X chromosome. Girls receive one X chromosome from each parent

and would have to receive a recessive gene from both parents to get

the disease. Boys have an X chromosome and a Y chromosome.

Since there are no matching alleles on the Y chromosome, the

recessive allele will be expressed if the boy carries it on the X

chromosome he received from his mother.

Create *a pedigree diagram to show how a boy could inherit his grandfather's hemophilia even if neither of his parents have the disease. Review pedigree diagrams from Section 12.1 if you need help.*
The pedigree diagram should show that the grandfather is affected (shaded square), the mother is heterozygous (half shaded circle), and the boy is a shaded square again. The rest of the diagram may vary, but encourage students to use the proper symbols from the last section.

Section 12.3 Complex Inheritance of Human Traits (continued)

Main Idea	Details

Polygenic Inheritance in Humans

I found this information on page _____.

SE, pp. 327–328
RE, p. 137

Create *a flow chart to show polygenic inheritance of skin color. In the first generation a light-skinned person mates with a dark-skinned person. Show the possible skin colors of the next three generations.*

1. light skinned and dark skinned
   ↓
2. _____ intermediate _____
   ↓
3. _____ range from light to dark _____
   ↓
4. _____ most have intermediate skin color

Changes in Chromosome Numbers

I found this information on page _____.

SE, pp. 328–329
RE, pp. 137–138

Summarize *the following facts about chromosomes.*

• how an abnormal number of chromosomes is identified

   A sample of cells is taken from an individual or fetus.

• four possible results of abnormal chromosome numbers

   embryo death, Down syndrome, infertility, and various levels of

   mental retardation.

CONNECT

Consider a genetic disorder such as cystic fibrosis. Explain why genetic disorders like cystic fibrosis appear more often among certain ethnic groups.

Accept all reasonable responses. Adults are more likely to marry within their own ethnic

group, which causes recessive alleles to appear more frequently in the offspring of these

groups.

Patterns of Heredity and Human Genetics Chapter Wrap-Up

In the "What I Wanted to Find Out" column, copy the questions you listed in the Chapter Preview. In the "What I Learned" column, write down the answers you discovered as you worked through the chapter.

W What I Wanted to Find Out	L What I Learned
1. Accept all reasonable entries.	1. _____
2. _____	2. _____
3. _____	3. _____

Use this checklist to help you study.

☐ Study your Science Notebook for this chapter.

☐ Study the definitions of vocabulary words.

☐ Review daily homework assignments.

☐ Reread the chapter and review the tables, graphs, and illustrations.

☐ Review the Section Assessment questions at the end of each section.

☐ Look over the Study Guide at the end of the chapter.

SUMMARIZE
After reading this chapter, list three things you have learned about heredity and human genetics.

Accept all reasonable responses._____

_____

_____

Genetic Technology

Before You Begin

Use the "What I Know" column to list three things you know about genetic technology. Then list three questions you have about this topic in the "What I Want to Find Out" column.

K What I Know	W What I Want to Find Out
1. Accept all reasonable entries. _____ _____	1. _____ _____
2. _____ _____	2. _____ _____
3. _____ _____	3. _____ _____

Science Journal

Describe two examples of genetic technology that have affected your life or that you have read about in the news.

Accept all reasonable responses. _____

_____

_____

_____

_____

_____

_____

_____

Genetic Technology
Section 13.1 Applied Genetics

(Main Idea) ——— **(Details)** ————————————————————

Scan *Section 1 of your book. Use the checklist as a guide.*

☐ Read all section titles.

☐ Read all boldfaced words.

☐ Read all tables and graphs.

☐ Look at all pictures and read the captions.

☐ Think about what you already know about communicating in science.

Write three facts you discovered about genetic technology.

1. Accept all reasonable responses. _____

2. _____

3. _____

(Review Vocabulary) *Use your book to define the following term.*

Hybrid an organism whose parents have different forms of a trait

(New Vocabulary) *Use your book to define each term. Then look through the section to find a sentence with each term and write the sentence.* **Sentences will vary.**

inbreeding mating between closely related individuals; ensures that offspring

are homozygous for most traits, but also brings out harmful,

recessive traits

test cross mating of an individual of unknown genotype with an individual of

known genotype; can help determine the unknown genotype of the

parent

(Academic Vocabulary) *Define the following term.*

select to make a choice; pick

Section 13.1 Applied Genetics (continued)

| Main Idea | Details |

Selective Breeding

I found this information on page _____.
SE, pp. 337–338
RE, pp. 140–141

Summarize *selective breeding by completing the prompts.*
Accept all reasonable responses.

Time frame: several generations

Reason it takes that long: several generations need to be bred
before the desired trait becomes common in the population

Goal: increase the frequency of desired traits or alleles in a population

Successful example: Dairy cows today produce three times more
milk on average than 50 years ago.

The offspring of parents that have different forms of a trait:
hybrids .

Analyze *inbreeding by identifying the effect, an advantage, and a disadvantage.*

Inbreeding

advantage:
eliminates undesired traits, makes sure breeds have desired traits

effect:
creates individuals who are homozygous for most traits

disadvantage:
sometimes harmful recessive traits appear

Determining Genotypes

I found this information on page _____.
SE, p. 339
RE, p. 141

Interpret *information about genotypes by completing the paragraph below.*

For selective breeding , breeders select plants or
animals with the greatest chance of passing on desired traits .
To do this, breeders must determine the genotype, (homozygous
or heterozygous), for a trait . The method of doing so is
a test cross , which crosses an individual of
known genotype with an individual of unknown genotype .

Section 13.1 Applied Genetics (continued)

Main Idea	Details

Determining Genotypes

I found this information on page _____.

SE, p. 339
RE, p. 141

Create *a flow chart or other concept diagram to describe how a breeder would determine the genotype of an Alaskan malamute. Include the type of information that is known and what the possible outcomes are (including Punnett Squares).*

Encourage detailed responses and a logical, progressional presentation of the information, such as: An unknown dog is bred to a dwarf dog. The dwarf dog is homozygous recessive and the unknown might be heterozygous or homozygous.

Possible results—one dog is dwarf and one is normal. Then the unknown dog is heterozygous.

If both dogs are normal, the unknown dog is homozygous dominant and can be bred.

Punnett squares for this situation:

Dd	Dd
Dd	Dd

Dd	dd
Dd	dd

Generalize *the process of determining genotypes by inferring a general step from the process for Alaskan malamute dogs.*

Alaskan Malamute Dog	General Description
Step 1: Choose dwarf dog.	Step 1: Choose a specimen with the recessive trait.
Step 2: Cross it with unknown dog.	Step 2: Cross specimen with known recessive trait with specimen that you are testing.
Step 3: Observe the offspring to determine whether the unknown dog was homozygous or heterozygous.	Step 3: If the offspring all exhibit the dominant trait, then the unknown specimen was homozygous dominant. If there is a mixture, the unknown specimen was heterozygous.

CONNECT Selective breeding practices have been used in agriculture since ancient times. Provide a specific example where selective breeding has resulted in an improved agricultural product.

Accept all reasonable responses. Grains are now much larger than the first ones humans cultivated. Cows produce more milk.

Genetic Technology
Section 13.2 Recombinant DNA Technology

Main Idea	Details

Think Critically *Predict why a gene from a firefly can function in a tobacco plant.*

Accept all reasonable responses._____

_____

_____

New Vocabulary *Use your book to define each term.*

clone | genetically identical copy of an organism or gene_____

genetic engineering | method of cutting DNA from one organism and inserting the DNA

fragment into a host organism of the same or different species

plasmid | small ring of DNA found in a bacterial cell that is used as a biological

vector

recombinant DNA | DNA made by recombining fragments of DNA from different

sources

restriction enzyme | DNA-cutting enzyme that can cut both strands of a DNA molecule at

a specific nucleotide sequence

transgenic organism | organism that contains functional recombinant DNA from a different

organism

vector | means by which DNA from another species can be carried into the

host cell; may be biological or mechanical

Academic Vocabulary *Define the following term.*

insert | to put or introduce into the body of something; to put in

Section 13.2 Recombinant DNA Technology (continued)

Main Idea	Details

Genetic Engineering

I found this information on page _____.
SE, pp. 341–345
RE, pp. 144–146

Identify *one transgenic organism from your book and the two original organisms that went into it. Then use your imagination to think of two other possible transgenic organisms that could be made and give the original organisms that could be used to make it.*

A glowing plant (a plant and firefly genes). Accept all imagined

transgenic organisms, for example, horses with wings, (a horse and

an eagle) fish that can fly (fish and bird), vegetarian spiders (inch

worms and spiders).

Sequence *the three steps to produce a transgenic organism. Explain how each step is carried out.* Accept all reasonable responses.

1. Cut a DNA fragment out of one organism; use restriction

   enzymes.

2. Connect the DNA fragment to a carrier called a vector. Vectors

   can be plasmids or viruses.

3. Insert the DNA fragment and its carrier into a new organism.

Explain *what happens after the transgenic organism is produced.*
The plasmid produces multiple copies of itself. When the host cell

divides, clones are produced.

Identify *two types of experiments scientists perform with gene clones.* Accept all reasonable responses.

1. Insert recombinant DNA into host cells. This DNA has a code to

   make a certain type of protein. Scientists study what that protein

   does in cells that don't normally make it.

2. Produce mutant forms of protein, and observe the effects on cells.

State *the benefit of agricultural animal cloning.*
Farmers will be able to clone the most productive, healthy animals to

increase the food supply.

Section 13.2 Recombinant DNA Technology (continued)

Main Idea	Details

Genetic Engineering

I found this information on page _____.
SE, pp. 341–345
RE, pp. 144–146

Describe *how a PCR machine works.*

A PCR machine uses heat to separate DNA strands. An enzyme from

a heat-loving bacterium is used to replicate the DNA. Correct

nucleotides must be added to the machine during the process. The

PCR machine can make millions of copies of DNA in a day.

Applications of DNA Technology

I found this information on page _____.
SE, p. 345
RE, p. 146

Summarize *advances that have been made in genetic technology.*

Accept all reasonable responses.

Area	Recent Advances
industry	E. coli bacteria have been used to produce the blue dye to color blue jeans
medicine	1. production of insulin and human growth hormone 2. production of human clotting protein through sheep to help hemophiliacs
agriculture	1. development of corn that contains as much protein as beef 2. discovery of ways to increase the amount of vitamins in certain crops 3. plants that have toxins to make them resistant to insects to limit pesticide use

SYNTHESIZE Make a flow chart showing the process of making recombinant DNA. List any advantages or disadvantages of the process.

Accept all reasonable responses.

Genetic Technology

Section 13.3 The Human Genome

Main Idea —— **Details** ——————————

Research *As a class, build a reference file of the latest discoveries by the Human Genome Project. Use library resources or visit bdol.glencoe.com to collect information. Update the file throughout the school year.*

New Vocabulary *Use your book to define each term. Then skim the section to find one extra interesting fact related to each vocabulary word.*

gene therapy

insertion of normal genes into human cells to correct genetic disorders

Sample: research is being done to find help for cystic fibrosis,

sickle-cell anemia, and hemophilia

human genome

map of the thousands of genes on 46 human chromosomes that when

mapped and sequenced may provide information on the treatment

and cure of genetic disorders; Sample: the Human Genome Project

began in 1990 to sequence the 35 000 or 40 000 genes on the 46

human chromosomes

linkage map

genetic map that shows the relative locations of genes on a

chromosome; Sample: crossover data helps scientists form a

linkage map

Academic Vocabulary *Define each of the following terms as a noun and as a verb.*

cycle

noun: a series of occurrences that repeats

verb: to move or revolve in cycles

sequence

noun: the following of one thing after another; succession

verb: to place in a sequence or determine the order of units in a chain

Section 13.3 The Human Genome (continued)

Main Idea	Details

Mapping and Sequencing the Human Genome

I found this information on page _____.
SE, pp. 349–350
RE, pp. 148–149

Create *a linkage map for your state and the surrounding eight states or combination of states and bodies of water.*

Maps will vary depending on the state. Example: North Carolina.

<table>
<tr><td>_____ West Virginia _____</td><td>_____ Maryland _____</td><td></td></tr>
<tr><td>_____ Kentucky _____</td><td>_____ Virginia _____</td><td></td></tr>
<tr><td>_____ Tennessee _____</td><td>_____ North Carolina _____</td><td>_____ Atlantic Ocean _____</td></tr>
<tr><td>_____ Alabama _____</td><td>_____ South Carolina _____</td><td></td></tr>
<tr><td></td><td>_____ Georgia _____</td><td></td></tr>
<tr><td></td><td>_____ Florida _____</td><td></td></tr>
</table>

Describe *methods used to find linkage data on chromosomes by completing the sentences below.*

Originally, information used to assign genes to particular chromosomes came from ___ linkage data of human pedigrees ___.

Scientists know that genes are farther apart when ___ the genes experience crossover during meiosis more often ___.

The original method was not efficient because ___ scientists had to wait for individual humans to reproduce and mature to identify which genes were passed on ___.

A more efficient method that is used now is ___ the polymerase chain reaction (PCR) ___.

Using this reaction, ___ millions of copies of DNA fragments are cloned in a day ___.

The locations of ___ the known genes and segments of DNA ___ are used as markers to track ___ the inheritance pattern of a gene that has not yet been identified ___.

Sequence *the steps in gene sequencing by writing the steps in order.*

1. DNA is cut with restriction enzymes.

2. Fragments are cloned.

3. Fragments are put into order by matching overlapping sequences.

Section 13.3 The Human Genome (continued)

Main Idea ———— **Details** ——————————————

Applications of the Human Genome Project

I found this information on page _____.
SE, pp. 351–353
RE, p. 149

Create *an outline of applications of the Human Genome Project.*

A. Diagnosing disorders in unborn fetuses:

Doctors take fluid surrounding fetus and analyze DNA to determine if the fetus will develop a genetic disorder.

B. Gene therapy is the insertion of normal genes into human cells to correct genetic disorders.

C. Doctors are experimenting with treating

  i. cystic fibrosis   **iv.** cancer

  ii. sickle-cell anemia   **v.** heart disease

  iii. hemophilia   **vi.** AIDS

D. Law enforcement: officers can solve crimes using DNA fingerprinting

  1. Samples can be used from

    i. skin   **iii.** blood

    ii. hair   **iv.** other body tissues

  2. The method works because

    i. all individuals have a unique DNA fingerprint.

    ii. all of an individual's cells have the exact same DNA.

E. Studying ancient life:

  1. Geneticists use the DNA polymerase chain reaction (PCR) to clone DNA from mummies.

  2. DNA from fossils is studied to compare

    i. extinct fossilized species with living species

    ii. extinct fossilized species with other extinct species

SYNTHESIZE Hypothesize about the future of genetic technology. Write about applications you think might touch your life in the next ten or twenty years, and the limitations you think there will be on DNA technology.

Accept all reasonable responses.

_____

_____

_____

Tie-It-All-Together

Create a concept web or mini-poster to tie together what
you learned in this chapter about advances in genetic technology. Use pictures and words to
show the most important ideas.

Accept all reasonable responses. Students may find it easier to list the most important ideas
before combining them in a concept web.

Genetic Technology Chapter Wrap-Up

In the "What I Wanted to Find Out" column, copy the questions you listed in the Chapter Preview. In the "What I Learned" column, write down the answers you discovered as you worked through the chapter.

W What I Wanted to Find Out	L What I Learned
1. Accept all reasonable entries. 2. 3.	1. 2. 3.

Use this checklist to help you study.

- ☐ Study your Science Notebook for this chapter.
- ☐ Study the definitions of vocabulary words.
- ☐ Review daily homework assignments.
- ☐ Reread the chapter and review the tables, graphs, and illustrations.
- ☐ Review the Section Assessment questions at the end of each section.
- ☐ Look over the Study Guide at the end of the chapter.

SUMMARIZE
After reading this chapter, list three things you have learned about genetic technology.

Accept all reasonable responses.

_____

_____

_____

The History of Life

Before You Read

Use the "What I Know" column to list three things you know about the history of life. Then list three questions you have about the history of life in the "What I Want to Find Out" column.

K What I Know	W What I Want to Find Out
1. Accept all reasonable entries. _____	1. _____ _____
2. _____ _____	2. _____ _____
3. _____ _____	3. _____ _____

Science Journal

Think about early life on Earth. Describe the physical conditions that needed to be present in order for life to begin to form.

Accept all reasonable responses.

_____

_____

_____

_____

_____

_____

_____

The History of Life

Section 14.1 The Record of Life

Main Idea	Details

Skim *Section 1 of your book. Write three questions that come to mind from reading the headings and the illustration captions.*

1. Accept all reasonable responses. _____

2. _____

3. _____

Review Vocabulary *Use your book to define the following term.*

isotope   atoms of a given element that have different numbers of neutrons

New Vocabulary *Use your book to define each term.*

fossil   physical evidence of an organism that lived long ago that scientists

use to study the past; evidence may appear in rocks, amber, or ice

plate tectonics   geological explanation for the movement of continents over Earth's

thick, liquid interior

Academic Vocabulary *Define the following terms.*

method   orderly thought, action, or technique

evident   easy or clear to see or understand

Section 14.1 The Record of Life (continued)

Main Idea	Details

Early History of Earth

I found this information on page _____.

SE, p. 369
RE, p. 151

Complete *the organizer below by listing the order of events that led to the formation of life in the oceans. The last step has been done for you.*

> Over 4 billion years ago, Earth cooled enough for water vapor in the atmosphere to condense.

↓

> This led to millions of years of thunderstorms. Enough water fell to create oceans.

↓

> Life forms in the oceans between 3.9 and 3.5 billion years ago.

History in Rocks

I found this information on page _____.

SE, pp. 370–375
RE, pp. 151–153

Name *three types of materials in which fossils are found.*

1. sedimentary rock

2. ice

3. amber

Compare *relative and radiometric dating using the table below. Provide three facts for each type of dating.*

Accept all reasonable responses.

Relative Dating	Radiometric Dating
1. used with sedimentary rocks	1. measures rate of decay of radioactive isotopes
2. youngest rock on top of older rocks	2. gives exact age of fossil
3. does not give exact age of fossil	3. cannot be used with sedimentary rocks; must date other rocks near sedimentary fossils

Section 14.1 The Record of Life (continued)

Main Idea	Details

A Trip Through Geologic Time

I found this information on page _____.
SE, pp. 375–379
RE, pp. 153–156

Summarize *the four eras of the geologic time scale using the following table. The first row has been done for you.*

Geologic Era	Dates	Organisms	Other Facts
Precambrian	4.6 billion – 544 million years ago	unicellular life forms, jellyfish, sponges	makes up about 87% of Earth's history
Paleozoic	544 million – 245 million years ago	fish, amphibians, ferns, reptiles	divided into 6 periods; mass extinction at end of era
Mesozoic	245 million – 66 million years ago	dinosaurs, flowering plants, birds, small mammals	split into 3 periods; mass extinction at end of era; lost 2/3 of living species
Cenozoic	66 million years ago – present	humans, large mammals	modern humans appeared about 200 000 years ago

Describe *the current theory on the cause of the mass extinction at the end of the Mesozoic era.* Accept all reasonable responses.

Scientists propose that Earth was struck by a giant meteor, which

caused a tremendous amount of dust to enter the atmosphere. This

led to climate change, which caused fewer species to survive.

COMPARE
Explain how paleontologists helped create the geologic time scale.
Accept all reasonable responses.

Paleontologists are scientists who study ancient life. They use fossils to learn about ancient

climate, geography, and the kinds of organisms from long ago. Radiometric dating allows

scientists to accurately date fossils. These findings were helpful in determining the exact

dates of the geologic time scale. It also helped lead to descriptions of the life on Earth and

position of the continents during different eras.

The History of Life
Section 14.2 The Origin of Life

Main Idea ———   **Details** ———————————————

Using Prior Knowledge *Before you read Section 2, explain why mold forms on food that has been left in your refrigerator for a long period of time.*

Accept all reasonable responses.

_____

_____

_____

Review Vocabulary   *Use your book to define the following term.*

prokaryotes   unicellular organisms that lack internal membrane-bound structures

New Vocabulary   *Use your book to define each term.*

archaebacteria   chemosynthetic prokaryotes that live in deep-sea vents and

hot springs

biogenesis   idea that living things only come from other living things

protocell   large, ordered structure, enclosed by a membrane, that carries out

some life activities, such as growth and division

spontaneous generation   mistaken idea that living things can arise from nonliving materials

Academic Vocabulary   *Define the following terms.*

complex   involved or intricate

conclude   to form an opinion or make a logical judgment about something

after considering everything you know about it

Section 14.2 The Origin of Life (continued)

⟮Main Idea⟯———— **⟮Details⟯**————————————————————————

Origins: The Early Ideas

I found this information on page _____ .
SE, pp. 380–381
RE, pp. 158–159

Draw *a diagram that illustrates how Redi's experiment was used to disprove spontaneous generation.*
Diagrams will vary but should include at least two different jars. One jar should be open with a piece of meat on the bottom, and a second jar should be covered with a piece of meat on the bottom. Students should show that there are flies and later maggots on the meat that is uncovered. The flies may be shown circling around the covered jar of meat but no maggots should be shown.

Origins: The Modern Ideas

I found this information on page _____ .
SE, pp. 381–383
RE pp. 159–160

Compare *spontaneous generation and biogenesis by describing one way that the two are alike and one way that the two are different.*
Accept all reasonable responses.

Both spontaneous generation and biogenesis tried to explain how

living things are formed. Spontaneous generation stated that some-

thing alive could come from an object that is not alive. Biogenesis is

the idea that living things come only from other living things.

Explain *the formation of simple organic molecules by filling in the graphic organizer below.*

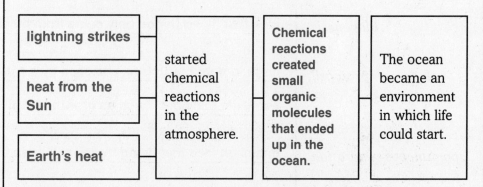

Identify *the gases believed to have been part of Earth's early atmosphere.*

1. water vapor _____

2. ammonia _____

3. methane _____

4. hydrogen gases _____

Section 14.2 The Origin of Life (continued)

Main Idea	Details

The Evolution of Cells

I found this information on page _____ .
SE, pp. 383–385
RE, pp. 160–161

Explain *why early organisms on Earth were anaerobic.*

Accept all reasonable responses. There was no oxygen in the early atmosphere, therefore any organism that lived on Earth at that time had to be able to survive without oxygen. Organisms that can survive without oxygen are called anaerobic.

Describe *the impact that the addition of oxygen to the atmosphere had on the organisms that lived on Earth.*

Accept all reasonable responses. Oxygen allowed an increased number of prokaryotes to evolve due to the change of conditions in the atmosphere. Oxygen in the upper atmosphere became ozone. This ozone helps to protect Earth's surface from harmful ultraviolet radiation, allowing more complex organisms to evolve.

Summarize *Refer to the figure in your book to summarize the evolution of the eukaryote. One step has been done for you.*

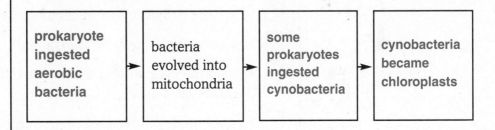

| prokaryote ingested aerobic bacteria | → | bacteria evolved into mitochondria | → | some prokaryotes ingested cynobacteria | → | cynobacteria became chloroplasts |

COMPARE Create a cartoon that describes the difference between a prokaryote and a eukaryote. Accept all reasonable responses.

Students' cartoons need to express the idea that prokaryotes are very simple, an example would be archaebacteria. Students should also include information about eukaryotes, which may include the fact that they are more complex, and may have evolved into either animal or plant cells.

The History of Life Chapter Wrap-Up

In the "What I Wanted to Find Out" column, copy the questions you listed in the Chapter Preview. In the "What I Learned" column, write down the answers you discovered as you worked through the chapter.

W What I Wanted to Find Out	L What I Learned
1. Accept all reasonable entries. _____	1. _____ _____
2. _____ _____	2. _____ _____
3. _____ _____	3. _____ _____

Use this checklist to help you study.

☐ Study your Science Notebook for this chapter.

☐ Study the definitions of vocabulary words.

☐ Review daily homework assignments.

☐ Reread the chapter and review the tables, graphs, and illustrations.

☐ Review the Section Assessment questions at the end of each section.

☐ Look over the Study Guide at the end of the chapter.

SUMMARIZE

After reading this chapter, list three things you have learned about the history of life.

Accept all reasonable responses.

_____

_____

_____

Name _____ Date _____

The Theory of Evolution
Before You Read

Use the "What I Know" column to list three things you know about evolution. Then list three questions you have about evolution in the "What I Want to Find Out" column.

K What I Know	W What I Want to Find Out
1. Accept all reasonable entries. _____	1. _____ _____
2. _____ _____	2. _____ _____
3. _____ _____	3. _____ _____

Science Journal

Life has evolved slowly on Earth. Certain organisms evolved in response to changes in their environment. Describe an adaptation of an organism that you see around you. How has the organism become better suited to its environment as a result of this adaptation?

Accept all reasonable responses. _____

_____

_____

_____

_____

_____

_____

_____

The Theory of Evolution

Section 15.1 Natural Selection and the Evidence for Evolution

Main Idea ———— **Details** —————————————————

Skim *Section 1 of your book. Write three questions that come to mind from reading the headings and the illustration captions.*

1. Accept all reasonable responses.

2. _____

3. _____

Review Vocabulary *Use your book to define the following term.*

evolution   the changes in populations over time

New Vocabulary *Use your book to define each term.*

analogous structure   structures that do not have a common evolutionary origin but are

similar in function

artificial selection   process of breeding organisms with specific traits to produce

offspring with the same traits

camouflage   structural adaptation that enables a species to blend with their

surroundings

embryo   earliest stage of growth and development of a plant or an animal

homologous structure   structures with common evolutionary origin

mimicry   structural adaptation that enables one species to resemble another

species

natural selection   occurs in nature when organisms with favorable variations survive,

reproduce, and pass their variations to the next generation

vestigial structure   a structure in a present-day organism that no longer serves its

original purpose but was probably useful to an ancestor

Section 15.1 Natural Selection and the Evidence for Evolution (continued)

Main Idea ——— **Details** —————————————————————

Charles Darwin and Natural Selection

I found this information on page _____.
SE, pp. 393–397
RE, pp. 163–164

Describe *three observations that Darwin made in his research with pigeons.*

1. small variations in traits of individual pigeons

2. traits inherited by offspring

3. pigeons bred for certain traits passed these traits to offspring

Summarize *natural selection by completing the sentences below.*

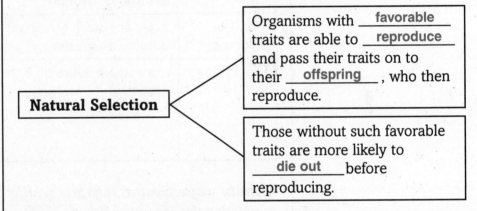

Natural Selection

Organisms with ___favorable___ traits are able to ___reproduce___ and pass their traits on to their ___offspring___, who then reproduce.

Those without such favorable traits are more likely to ___die out___ before reproducing.

Adaptations: Evidence for Evolution

I found this information on page _____.
SE, pp. 397–399
RE, pp. 164–165

Apply *Give separate examples of how animals use camouflage and mimicry in order to protect themselves. Use examples that are not given in your book.* Accept all reasonable responses.

Camouflage	Structural Adaptations	Mimicry
_____		_____
_____		_____
_____		_____
_____		_____
_____		_____

Explain *how medicines can lose their effectiveness over time.*

The bacteria can undergo physiological adaptations to keep them

from being killed by various medications.

Section 15.1 Natural Selection and the Evidence for Evolution (continued)

Main Idea ———— **Details** ————————————————————————

Other Evidence for Evolution

I found this information on page _____.
SE, pp. 399–403
RE, pp. 165–167

Summarize *the role that anatomy plays in teaching us about evolution by completing the table below.*

Structure	What is it?	Example
Homologous Structure	structural features with common evolutionary origin	forelimbs of whale, crocodile, and bird are similar
Analogous Structure	body parts that are similar in function but evolved differently	birds and butterflies both have wings
Vestigial Structure	body structure no longer serving a purpose	eyes of mole rats
Embryology	the earliest stage of growth and development of a plant or animal	embryos of fishes, birds, reptiles, and mammals have structures that suggest they had common ancestors

Identify *ways scientists interpret relationships among species by completing the organizer below.*

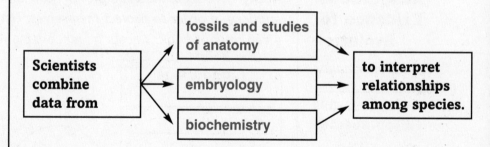

Scientists combine data from → fossils and studies of anatomy / embryology / biochemistry → to interpret relationships among species.

COMPARE Explain why fossils are such important tools in understanding evolution.

Accept all reasonable responses. Fossils are needed to learn about the structure of organisms

from the past. For example, evolution has been seen in such structures as vestigial structures,

homologous structures, and analogous structures. By studying fossil evidence, scientists

have a much more complete history to look back at and compare.

The Theory of Evolution
Section 15.2 Mechanisms of Evolution

Main Idea

Details

Infer *Suppose two species of birds live in the same area. What might prevent competition between them?*

Accept all reasonable responses.

Foods, mating rituals, territory, etc. are all important in reducing

competition between closely related species, such as meadowlarks.

New Vocabulary

Organize *the vocabulary terms. Find each term in your book and place it under the appropriate heading. Then define each term. The number of terms under each heading is given.*

adaptive radiation

allelic frequency

convergent evolution

divergent evolution

gene pool

genetic drift

genetic equilibrium

geographic isolation

gradualism

polyploid

punctuated equilibrium

reproductive isolation

speciation

Population, Genetics, and Evolution (4)	The Evolution of the Species (6)	Patterns of Evolution (3)
genetic equilibrium: frequency of alleles remains the same	*speciation*: process of evolution of new species that occurs when members of similar populations no longer interbreed to produce fertile offspring within their natural environment	*adaptive radiation*: divergent evolution where ancestral species evolve into an array of species to fit a number of diverse habitats
gene pool: all alleles in a population's genes	*geographic isolation*: occurs when a physical barrier divides a population, which results in individuals no longer being able to mate	*divergent evolution*: evolution in which species that were once similar to an ancestral species diverge
allelic frequency: percentage of any specific allele in a population's gene pool	*reproductive isolation*: occurs when formerly interbreeding offspring can no longer produce fertile offspring within their natural environment	*convergent evolution*: evolution in which distantly related organisms evolve similar traits
genetic drift: alteration of allelic frequencies in a population by chance events	*gradualism*: idea that species originate through a gradual change of adaptations	
	polyploid: any species with multiple sets of the normal set of chromosomes	
	punctuated equilibrium: idea that periods of speciation occur relatively quickly with long periods of genetic equilibrium in between	

Section 15.2 Mechanisms of Evolution (continued)

Main Idea ———— **Details** ————————————————

Population Genetics and Evolution

I found this information on page _____.
SE, pp. 404–409
RE, pp. 169–170

Organize *the steps associated with genetic equilibrium by completing the graphic organizer below.*

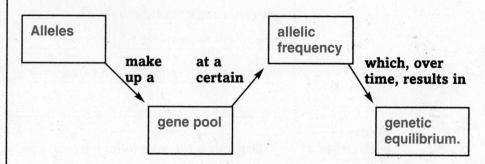

Identify *three ways that genetic equilibrium can be disrupted.*

1. genetic mutation

2. genetic drift

3. gene flow

The Evolution of the Species

I found this information on page _____.
SE, pp. 409–412
RE, pp. 170–172

Contrast *Briefly explain the difference between geographic isolation and reproductive isolation.*

Geographic isolation is when a new species develops after members

of a population are separated by a physical boundary. Reproductive

isolation occurs when organisms that used to mate and produce

fertile offspring no longer can do so.

Summarize *the current thoughts about the time it takes to develop a new species by completing the table below.*

Polyploidy	Gradualism	Punctuated Equilibrium
new species evolve in one generation; a mutation which occurs during meiosis and mitosis creating extra chromosomes	species originate through a gradual change of adaptations	speciation occurs rapidly, in bursts

Name_____ Date_____

Section 15.2 Mechanisms of Evolution (continued)

Main Idea — **Details** ——————————————————

Patterns of Evolution

I found this information on page_____.
SE, pp. 412–413
RE, pp. 172–173

Summarize *the idea of convergent evolution by completing the graphic organizer below. The first step has been done for you.*

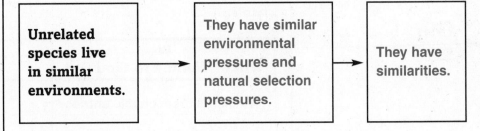

| Unrelated species live in similar environments. | → | They have similar environmental pressures and natural selection pressures. | → | They have similarities. |

Explain *adaptive radiation using the example of a Hawaiian honeycreeper.*

Hawaiian honeycreepers are similar in size and shape but have

different colors and beaks and live in different habitats. Despite the

differences, scientists believe that they came from a common

ancestor. This single ancestor gave way to a wide variety of

offspring though the process of adaptive radiation.

Label *each model as representing divergent evolution or convergent evolution.*

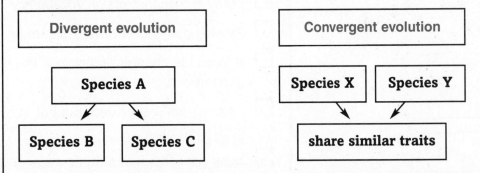

COMPARE

Explain how geographic isolation can lead to adaptive radiation.

Accept all reasonable responses. If a species becomes separated by a physical barrier as in

geographic isolation, the organisms will begin to evolve separately. These organisms will

begin to adapt to their unique conditions and will eventually become a new species through

adaptive radiation, a type of divergent evolution.

The Theory of Evolution Chapter Wrap-Up

In the "What I Wanted to Find Out" column, copy the questions you listed in the Chapter Preview. In the "What I Learned" column, write down the answers you discovered as you worked through the chapter.

W What I Wanted to Find Out	L What I Learned
1. Accept all reasonable entries.	1.
2.	2.
3.	3.

Use this checklist to help you study.

☐ Study your Science Notebook for this chapter.

☐ Study the definitions of vocabulary words.

☐ Review daily homework assignments.

☐ Reread the chapter and review the tables, graphs, and illustrations.

☐ Review the Section Assessment questions at the end of each section.

☐ Look over the Study Guide at the end of the chapter.

SUMMARIZE

After reading this chapter, list three things you have learned about evolution.

Accept all reasonable responses._____

_____

_____

Primate Evolution

Before You Read

Use the "What I Know" column to list three things you know about the way primates evolved. Then list three questions you have about primate evolution in the "What I Want to Find Out" column.

K What I Know	W What I Want to Find Out
1. Accept all reasonable entries. _____ _____	1. _____ _____
2. _____ _____	2. _____ _____
3. _____ _____	3. _____ _____

Science Journal

The ability of an organism to adapt to its surroundings is needed for survival. Describe the adaptations you think were most important to the survival of primates in a variety of climates.

Accept all reasonable responses. _____

_____

_____

_____

_____

_____

_____

_____

Primate Evolution

Section 16.1 Primate Adaptation and Evolution

Main Idea	Details

Predict *Read the title of Section 1. List three things that might be discussed in this section.*

1. Accept all reasonable responses. _____

2. _____

3. _____

Review Vocabulary

Use your book to define the following term.

speciation

the process of evolution of a new species that occurs when

members of similar populations no longer interbreed to produce

fertile offspring

New Vocabulary

Use your book to define each term.

anthropoids

humanlike primates that include New World monkeys, Old World

monkeys, and hominoids

opposable thumb

primate characteristic of having a thumb that can cross the palm and

meet the other fingertips; enables animal to grasp and cling to objects

prehensile tail

long muscular tail used as a fifth limb for grasping and wrapping

around objects; characteristics of many New World monkeys

primate

groups of mammals including lemurs, monkeys, apes, and humans

that evolved from a common ancestor; shared characteristics include

a rounded head, a flattened face, fingernails, flexible shoulder joints,

opposable thumbs or big toes, and a large, complex brain

Academic Vocabulary

Define the following term.

unique

being the only one of its kind

Section 16.1 Primate Adaptation and Evolution (continued)

Main Idea ——— **Details** ————————————

What is a primate?

I found this information on page _____.
SE, pp. 421–423
RE, pp. 175–176

Identify nine traits that make primates unique compared to other mammals.

1. rounded heads with flattened faces

2. large brains compared to body size

3. social behavior

4. complex brain

5. flexible shoulder and hip joints

6. nails instead of claws on fingers and toes

7. opposable thumbs

8. eyes face forward

9. seeing colors

Explain *why having eyes that face forward is an important adaptation for primates.*

Eyes that face forward allow the primate to see an object with both

eyes at the same time. This helps them to see depths and judge

distances.

Primate Origins

I found this information on page _____.
SE, pp. 423–427
RE, pp. 176–177

Compare *modern haplorhines and strepsirrhines by completing the table.*

Primate Group	Description	Location	Examples
Strepsirrhines	small primates, large eyes, sleep during the day, active at night	tropical forests of Africa and Southeast Asia	lemurs, lorises, pottos, galagos
Haplorhines	brains are more complex, skeletons are larger and more upright	worldwide	tarsiers, New/Old World monkeys, humans, orang-utans, gibbons, African apes

Section 16.1 Primate Adaptation and Evolution (continued)

Main Idea ——— Details ——————————————————————————

Primate Origins

I found this information on page _____.
SE, pp. 423–427
RE, pp. 176–177

Classify *the subgroups of the Anthropoids by completing the graphic organizer below.*

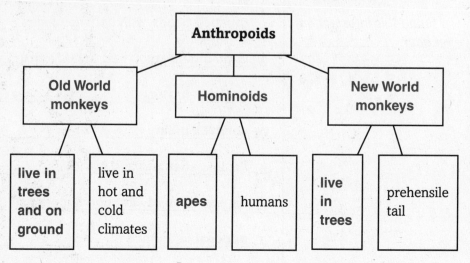

Summarize *the evolution of anthropoids by filling in the diagram below.*

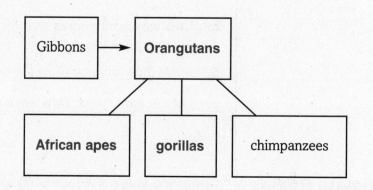

COMPARE Describe some similarities and differences among the members of the hominoid group.

Accept all reasonable responses. Hominoids are apes and humans. Apes do not have tails,

they live in trees, are social animals, and walk on two legs with support from their hands.

Humans do not live in trees, are social, and walk upright.

Primate Evolution

Section 16.2 Human Ancestry

(Main Idea)	(Details)

Details

Infer *Describe the parts of a skeleton you think would provide scientists with the most information about human ancestry.*

Accept all reasonable responses. Skulls provide information about

diet, brain volume, bipedalism, binocular vision, face shape, and

even height.

New Vocabulary *Use your book to define each term.*

australopithecine — early African hominid, genus *Australopithecus*, that had both apelike

and humanlike characteristics

bipedal — ability to walk on two legs; leaves arm and hands free for other

activities such as hunting, protecting, young, and using tools

Cro-Magnon — modern form of *Homo sapiens* that spread throughout Europe

between 35 000 to 40 000 years ago; were identical to modern

humans in height, skull and tooth structure, and brain size

hominid — a group of bipedal primates that includes modern humans and their

direct ancestors

hominoid — a group of primates that can walk upright on two legs; includes

gorillas, chimpanzees, bonobos, and humans

Neandertal — archaic *Homo sapiens* that lived from 35 000 to 100 000 years ago in

Europe, Asia, and the Middle East; had thick bones and large faces

with prominent noses and brains at least as large as those of

modern humans

Section 16.2 Human Ancestry (continued)

Main Idea ———— **Details** ————————————————

Hominids

I found this information on page _____.
SE, pp. 428–430
RE, pp. 179–180

Identify *key terms in the evolution from hominoid to hominid by completing the flow chart below.*

> Scientists suggest that the separation in the <u>hominoid</u> population is a result of <u>environmental</u> changes.

↓

> These changes caused hominoid ancestors to leave the <u>trees</u> and move onto the <u>ground</u> to find <u>food</u>.

↓

> It may have been helpful to be <u>bipedal</u>, or able to walk upright on two legs.

↓

> <u>Hominids</u> are bipedal primates that include modern <u>humans</u> and their direct <u>ancestors</u>.

The Emergence of Modern Humans

I found this information on page _____.
SE, pp. 431–435
RE, pp. 180–182

Identify *three characteristics of Lucy and other Australopithecus afarenis.*

1. <u>apelike shoulders and arms</u>

2. <u>pelvis indicates bipedal</u>

3. <u>small brain</u>

Compare *Homo habilis and Homo erectus by giving five characteristics of each species using the table below.*

Homo habilis	Homo erectus
"handy human"; made tools; lived in Africa; were scavengers; lived 1.5 to 2.5 million years ago	"upright human"; used fire; made axes; lived in caves; migrated from Africa to Asia and possibly Europe; lived 1.5 to 1.8 million years ago

Section 16.2 Human Ancestry (continued)

Main Idea ————

The Emergence of Modern Humans

I found this information on page _____.
SE, pp. 431–435
RE, pp. 180–182

Details————————————

Explain *how scientists formed their hypotheses relating to how modern humans may have emerged.*

Scientists studied the fossilized teeth and bones of ancient humans

as well as their DNA.

Identify *two different species that existed before Homo sapiens.*

1. Homo antecessor

2. Homo heidelbergensis

Compare *Neandertals and Cro-Magnons by completing the table below. The first box has been done for you.*

Characteristic	Neandertal	Cro-Magnon
brain size	at least as large as humans	same size as humans
bone structure	thicker, larger faces	same height, skull, and tooth structure
communication	spoken language	spoken language
home life	tools, cave dwellers, religion, carving	toolmakers, artists, cave paintings

SUMMARIZE Describe how the australopithecine adapted to its environment.

Accept all reasonable responses. Responses might include references to moving out of trees to find food on the ground and to travel. The adaptation for these new behaviors was bipedal species. Developing ways to scavenge for food resulted in larger brains. Larger brains were also needed for coming up with solutions to new problems such as cooking and providing shelter out of the trees.

Primate Evolution Chapter Wrap-Up

In the "What I Wanted to Find Out" column, copy the questions you listed in the Chapter Preview. In the "What I Learned" column, write down the answers you discovered as you worked through the chapter.

W What I Wanted to Find Out	L What I Learned
1. Accept all reasonable entries. _____	1. _____ _____
2. _____ _____	2. _____ _____
3. _____ _____	3. _____ _____

Use this checklist to help you study.

☐ Study your Science Notebook for this chapter.

☐ Study the definitions of vocabulary words.

☐ Review daily homework assignments.

☐ Reread the chapter and review the tables, graphs, and illustrations.

☐ Review the Section Assessment questions at the end of each section.

☐ Look over the Study Guide at the end of the chapter.

SUMMARIZE

After reading this chapter, list three things you have learned about primate evolution.

Accept all reasonable responses._____

_____

_____

Organizing Life's Diversity

Before You Read

Use the "What I Know" column to list three things you know about life's diversity. Then list three questions you have about diversity in the "What I Want to Find Out" column.

K What I Know	W What I Want to Find Out
1. Accept all reasonable entries. _____	1. _____ _____
2. _____ _____	2. _____ _____
3. _____ _____	3. _____ _____

Science Journal

Consider several living organisms that you see around you. Describe some characteristics that biologists might use when trying to classify, or organize, them into similar species.

Accept all reasonable responses.

_____

_____

_____

_____

_____

_____

_____

_____

Organizing Life's Diversity

Section 17.1 Classification

Main Idea ——— | **Details** ———————————————

Scan *Section 1 of your book. Write three questions that come to mind from reading the headings and the illustration captions.*

1. Accept all reasonable responses.

2. _____

3. _____

Review Vocabulary | *Use your book to define the following term.*

species | a group of organisms that can interbreed and produce

fertile offspring

New Vocabulary | *Classify each term at the left as being part of Linnaeus' two-word naming system or a taxonomic group. The number of terms in each column is given to you.*

binominal
nomenclature
class
division
family
genus
kingdom
order
phylum
specific epithet

Linnaeus' System (3)	Taxonomic Group (6)
binominal nomenclature	class
genus	division
specific epithet	family
	kingdom
	order
	phylum

Use your book to define each term.

classification | grouping of objects or information based on similarities

_____

taxonomy | branch of biology that groups and names organisms based on

studies of their shared characteristics; biologists who study

taxonomy are called taxonomists

Section 17.1 Classification (continued)

Main Idea	Details

How Classification Began

I found this information on page _____.
SE, pp. 443–445
RE, pp. 184–185

Identify *the parts of Linnaeus' two-word naming system by completing the graphic organizer below.*

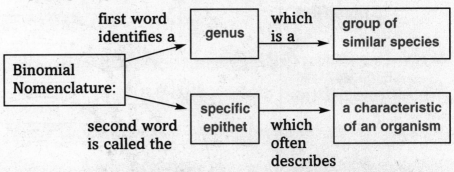

Name *the genus and specific epithet for the species name of modern humans.*

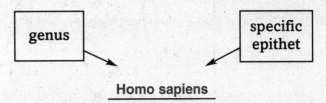

Homo sapiens

Modern Classification

I found this information on page _____.
SE, pp. 445–446
RE, p. 185

Explain *why scientists now think that dinosaurs are more closely related to birds than to reptiles.*

Some dinosaurs and birds have large internal spaces in their bones.

There are also other similarities between the skeletons of birds and

dinosaurs. These findings led to the conclusion that dinosaurs were

more closely related to birds than to reptiles as first thought.

Describe *three uses of taxonomy.*

1. a framework to study the relationships between living and extinct

   organisms

2. a useful tool for agriculture, forestry, and medicine

3. helps the economy by discovering new sources of lumber,

   medicines, and energy

Section 17.1 Classification (continued)

⟨ **Main Idea** ⟩——   ⟨ **Details** ⟩————————————

How Living Things are Classified

I found this information on page _____.
SE, pp. 447–449
RE, p. 186

Organize *the following taxa from most specific to least specific: family, genus, order, species. The first one has been done for you.*

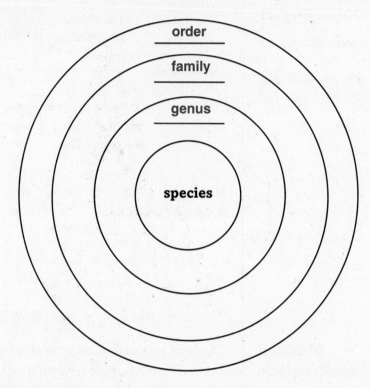

order
_____

family
_____

genus
_____

species

Examine *the figure of the taxonomic groups in your book. Then identify the kingdom, phylum, and class for humans.*

Kingdom: **Animalia** _____

Phylum: **Chordata** _____

Class: **Mammalia** _____

┌───┐
│ **ANALOGY** Create your own organizer that shows where you live in a similar way that a classification system works. For example, you may want to indicate the continent you live on, your country, state, county, and town in your "home" classification.

Accept all reasonable responses. For example, a student might create an organizer showing

the progression from North America to the United States to a specific state, county, city, street,

and house number.
└───┘

Organizing Life's Diversity

Section 17.2 The Six Kingdoms

(Main Idea)——— (Details)——————————————————————

Compare and contrast *What physical characteristics do you share with your parents? What physical characteristics make you different from them?*

Accept all reasonable responses. Students may include height, eye

or hair color, or similar characteristics; other students will identify

these same characteristics as differences. Be aware that some

students may not be able to discuss familial characteristics.

(**Review** **Vocabulary**) *Use your book to define the following term.*

archaebacteria   chemosynthetic prokaryotes that live in harsh environments

(**New** **Vocabulary**) *Use your book to define each term.*

cladistics   biological classification system based on phylogeny

cladogram   branching diagram that models the phylogeny of a species based on

the derived traits of a group of organisms

eubacteria   group of prokaryotes with strong cell walls and a variety of

structures

fungus   group of unicellular or multicellular heterotrophic eukaryotes that do

not move from place to place

phylogeny   evolutionary history of a species based on comparative relationships

of structures and comparisons of modern life forms with fossils

protist   diverse group of multicellular or unicellular eukaryotes that lack

complex organ systems and live in moist environments

Section 17.2 The Six Kingdoms

Main Idea ———— **Details** ——————————————————————

How are evolutionary relationships determined?

I found this information on page _____.
SE, pp. 450–451
RE, pp. 188–189

Identify *the five characteristics that are the basis for evolutionary relationships.*

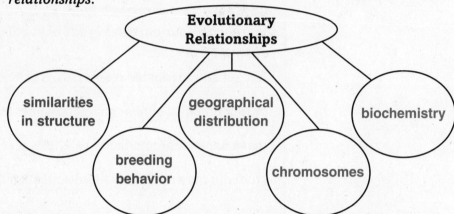

Explain *how scientists came to the conclusion that giant pandas and red pandas are not closely related to each other.* Accept all reasonable responses.

Scientists used biochemistry to study the relationship between giant

pandas and red pandas. Scientists study the DNA of a species and

find that species that are closely related have similar DNA.

Scientists suggest that the red panda is more closely related to the

raccoon while the giant panda is more closely related to the bear.

Phylogenic Classification: Models

I found this information on page _____.
SE, pp. 452–456
RE, pp. 189–190

Compare *two models that are used to show the phylogeny of a species by completing the table below. Write two facts about each model.*

Cladogram	Fan-Shaped Diagram
assumes that as groups of organisms evolve from a common ancestor, they keep unique inherited characteristics	may show the time organisms became extinct
	show number of species in a group
inherited characteristics called derived traits	
	uses information from fossils and structural, biochemical, and cladistic studies
branching diagram	

Section 17.2 The Six Kingdoms

Main Idea ——— **Details** ———————————————————————

The Six Kingdoms of Organisms

I found this information on page _____.

SE, pp. 456–459
RE, pp. 191–192

Identify *each kingdom with its description by placing the letters on the appropriate lines.*

a. animals   **c.** eubacteria   **e.** plants

b. archaebacteria   **d.** fungi   **f.** protists

__c__ have strong cell walls, cause diseases

__d__ are stationary unicellular or multicellular heterotrophs

__b__ live in extreme environments

__e__ are multicellular autotrophs, cells have walls

__f__ have simple organ systems

__a__ all are multicellular heterotrophs

Summarize *the main characteristics of organisms by writing at least one fact in each box.* Accept all reasonable responses.

Kingdom	Cell Structure	Energy Sources	Other Characteristics
Eubacteria	strong cell walls	heterotrophs, autotrophs, and chemosynthetic	live in most habitats
Archaebacteria	have cell walls that are different from eubacteria	autotrophs, chemosynthetic, and photosynthetic	live in extreme environments
Protists	unicellular or multicellular	autotrophs, heterotrophs	simple organ systems
Fungi	unicellular or multicellular	heterotrophs	stationary
Plants	have cell walls	autotrophs	stationary
Animals	no cell walls	heterotrophs	most able to move

COMPARE Provide one example of how chemosynthetic organisms are different from photosynthetic organisms.

Accept all reasonable responses. Chemosynthetic organisms such as archaebacteria and

eubacteria make their own energy through chemical reactions. Photosynthetic organisms like

plants and some eubacteria also make their own energy but from energy from the Sun.

Organizing Life's Diversity Chapter Wrap-Up

In the "What I Wanted to Find Out" column, copy the questions you listed in the Chapter Preview. In the "What I Learned" column, write down the answers you discovered as you worked through the chapter.

W What I Wanted to Find Out	L What I Learned
1. Accept all reasonable entries. _____	1. _____ _____
2. _____ _____	2. _____ _____
3. _____ _____	3. _____ _____

Use this checklist to help you study.

☐ Study your Science Notebook for this chapter.

☐ Study the definitions of vocabulary words.

☐ Review daily homework assignments.

☐ Reread the chapter and review the tables, graphs, and illustrations.

☐ Review the Section Assessment questions at the end of each section.

☐ Look over the Study Guide at the end of the chapter.

SUMMARIZE
After reading this chapter, list three things you have learned about organizing life's diversity.

Accept all reasonable responses.

_____

_____

_____

Viruses and Bacteria

Before You Read

Use the "What I Know" column to list three things you know about viruses and bacteria. Then list three questions you have about viruses and bacteria in the "What I Want to Find Out" column.

K What I Know	W What I Want to Find Out
1. Accept all reasonable entries. _____	1. _____ _____
2. _____ _____	2. _____ _____
3. _____ _____	3. _____ _____

Science Journal

Many viruses and bacteria can cause diseases in animals and plants. Write about a disease that you know of that is caused by a virus or a bacteria. Be sure to discuss how the disease is treated.

Accept all reasonable responses.

_____

_____

_____

_____

_____

_____

_____

_____

Name_____ Date _____

Viruses and Bacteria
Section 18.1 Viruses

Main Idea — **Details** —

Research *List three vaccines and the disease that each vaccine prevents.*

Students' lists may include DPT (Diptheria, Pertussis, Tetanus), Polio, Hepatitis A, Hepatitis B, MMR (Measles, Mumps, Rubella), and Chicken Pox.

New Vocabulary *Use your book to define the following terms.*

bacteriophage — virus that infects and destroys bacteria, also called phages

capsid — outer coat of protein that surrounds a virus's inner core of nucleic acid; arrangement of capsid proteins gives a virus its shape

host cell — living cell in which a virus replicates

prion — a virus-like infectious agent that is composed of only protein, with no genetic material

viroid — a virus-like infectious agent that is composed of only a single, circular strand of RNA

virus — disease-causing, nonliving particle composed of an inner core of nucleic acids surrounded by a capsid

Use the terms at the left to complete the following paragraph.

lysogenic cycle
lytic cycle
provirus
retovirus
reverse transcriptase

During a ___lytic cycle___ a virus takes over a host cell's genetic material and uses its structures and energy to replicate until the host cell bursts. A virus's nucleic acid integrates into the host cell's chromosome, during a ___lysogenic cycle___. It is then called a ___provirus___. It replicates each time the host cell reproduces. A ___retrovirus___ makes DNA from its RNA using ___reverse transcriptase___, an enzyme it carries inside its capsid. The viral DNA is then integrated into the host cell's chromosome.

170 *Viruses*

Section 18.1 Viruses (continued)

⟨Main Idea⟩——— ⟨Details⟩——————————————————————

What is a virus?

I found this information on page _____.

SE, pp. 475–478
RE, pp. 193–194

Sketch *a model of a virus in the space below. Be sure to label the following parts in your sketch.*

• Capsid • Nucleic Acid • Envelope

Check students' drawings. Students should accurately draw a model of a virus and label the capsid, nucleic acid, and envelope.

Describe *how a virus enters a host cell.*

The virus must recognize and attach to a receptor site on the plasma

membrane of the host cell. Each virus has a specifically shaped

attachment protein. Therefore, each virus can attach only to a few

kinds of cells. Once attached to the host cell, the virus enters the cell.

Viral Replication Cycles

I found this information on page _____.

SE, pp. 478–482
RE, pp. 194–197

Label *steps A, B, C, D, and E of a lytic cycle in the figure below. Use the following terms.*

• Assembly • Attachment • Entry
• Lysis and Release • Replication

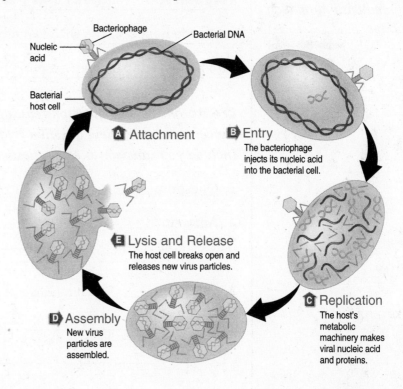

Section 18.1 Viruses (continued)

Main Idea	Details

Viral Replication Cycles

I found this information on page _____.
SE, pp. 478–482
RE, pp. 194–197

Sequence *the steps of a lysogenic cycle.*

1. A virus <u>attaches to a host cell</u> .

↓

2. The viral <u>nucleic acid</u> enters the cell.

↓

3. Viral DNA is <u>included in the host cell's chromosome</u> .

↓

4. The provirus replicates along the host cell's chromosome.

Cancer and Viruses, and Origin of Viruses

I found this information on page _____.
SE, pp. 482–483
RE, p. 197

Explain *the role of reverse transcriptase.*

Reverse transcriptase is an enzyme that is contained in the capsid of

a retrovirus. The retrovirus uses it to make DNA from its RNA once

inside the host cell. The DNA is integrated into the host cell's

chromosome and becomes a provirus.

Create *one review question relating to the link between viruses and cancer and one review question relating to the origin of viruses. Include your answer to each question.*

1. Question:_____

   Answer: _____

   _____

2. Question:_____

   Asnwer: _____

   _____

Viruses and Bacteria

Section 18.2 Archaebacteria and Eubacteria

⟨**Main Idea**⟩——   ⟨**Details**⟩———————————————————————

Scan *Section 2 of your book. Write two facts you discovered as you scanned the section.*

1. Accept all reasonable responses. _____

2. _____

⟨**New Vocabulary**⟩   *Use your book to define each term.*

binary fission   asexual reproduction process in which one cell divides into two

separate genetically identical cells

chemosynthesis   autotrophic process where organisms obtain energy from the

breakdown of inorganic compounds containing sulfur and nitrogen

conjugation   form of sexual reproduction in some bacteria where one bacterium

transfers all or part of its genetic material to another through a

bridgelike structure called a pilus

endospore   structure formed by bacteria during unfavorable conditions that

contains DNA and a small amount of cytoplasm encased by a

protective outer covering

nitrogen fixation   metabolic process in which bacteria use enzymes to convert

atmospheric nitrogen (N_2) into ammonia (NH_3)

obligate aerobe   bacteria that require oxygen for cellular respiration

obligate anaerobe   bacteria that are killed by oxygen and can only survive in

oxygen-free environments

toxin   poison produced by a bacterium

Section 18.2 Archaebacteria and Eubacteria (continued)

Main Idea	Details

Diversity of Prokaryotes

I found this information on page _____ .
SE, pp. 484–486
RE, pp. 200–201

Describe *Give a general description of the three types of environments where archaebacteria live. With each general description, also provide one specific example of the environment.*

1. oxygen-free environments; marshes, lake bottoms, some mammal digestive tracts, and sewage disposal plants

2. water with high concentrations of salt; Great Salt Lake and the Dead Sea

3. hot, acidic waters; near cracks in the ocean floor

Organize *information about the three types of eubacteria by completing the graphic organizer below. Label the three types, and describe how they obtain food.*

type: heterotrophic	type: photosynthetic autotroph	type: chemosynthetic autotroph
food: obtain food as parasites and saprophytes	food: use the sun's energy to make food	food source: use chemosynthesis to make food

What is a bacterium?

I found this information on page _____ .
SE, pp. 486–490
RE, pp. 201–203

Draw *and label a bacterial cell in the space below. Use the figure in your book for help. Be sure to include the following parts.*

- capsule
- cell wall
- chromosome
- flagellum
- pilus
- plasma membrane
- plasmid

Students drawings should be appropriately labeled.

Section 18.2 Archaebacteria and Eubacteria (continued)

| Main Idea | Details |

What is a bacterium?

I found this information on page _____.
SE, pp. 486–490
RE, pp. 201–203

Compare *bacterial reproduction by completing the table below.*

	Binary Fission	**Conjugation**
Type of Reproduction	asexual	sexual
How It Occurs	a bacterium makes a copy of its chromosome and splits in two	one bacterium transfers chromosomes to another bacterium through pili
Description of Cells Produced	genetically identical	new genetic combination

Adaptations in Bacteria

I found this information on page _____.
SE, pp. 490–493
RE, pp. 203–204

Summarize *information about endospores by answering the questions below.*

What are they? Endospores are structures that contain a bacterium's DNA and a small amount of cytoplasm in a tough outer shell.

How do they germinate? When environmental conditions improve, endospores produce cells that grow and reproduce.

How can they cause problems for humans? Endospores can produce toxins. For example, botulism causes food poisoning, and anthrax is a disease caused by a bacterium that lives in soil.

The Importance of Bacteria

I found this information on page _____.
SE, pp. 493–495
RE, pp. 204–205

List five ways that bacteria are helpful to humans.
Accept all reasonable responses.

1. fixation nitrogen
2. return nutrients to the environment
3. produce oxygen
4. produce products such as cheese, yogurt, and pickles
5. produce antibiotics

SYNTHESIZE Assess whether bacteria are more harmful than helpful to humans. Defend your answer.

Accept all reasonable responses. Bacteria are more helpful than harmful. Life would be

impossible without bacteria because they produce the oxygen that is necessary for life.

Viruses and Bacteria Chapter Wrap-Up

In the "What I Wanted to Find Out" column, copy the questions you listed in the Chapter Preview. In the "What I Learned" column, write down the answers you discovered as you worked through the chapter.

W What I Wanted to Find Out	L What I Learned
1. Accept all reasonable entries. _____	1. _____ _____
2. _____ _____	2. _____ _____
3. _____ _____	3. _____ _____

Use this checklist to help you study.

☐ Study your Science Notebook for this chapter.

☐ Study the definitions of vocabulary words.

☐ Review daily homework assignments.

☐ Reread the chapter and review the tables, graphs, and illustrations.

☐ Review the Section Assessment questions at the end of each section.

☐ Look over the Study Guide at the end of the chapter.

SUMMARIZE

After reading this chapter, list three things you have learned about viruses and bacteria.

Accept all reasonable responses.

_____

_____

Protists

Before You Read

Use the "What I Know" column to list three things you know about protists. Then list three questions you have about protists in the "What I Want to Find Out" column.

K What I Know	W What I Want to Find Out
1. Accept all reasonable entries.	1.
2.	2.
3.	3.

Science Journal

Protists are the base for most food chains in aquatic environments. Describe how protists might contribute to an important food source—fish and other seafood.

Accept all reasonable responses.

Protists

Section 19.1 The World of Protists

⟨Main Idea⟩	⟨Details⟩

Explain *Read Section 1 and then define a protist.*

Protists are eukaryotes that show variety in feeding relationships

(some are autotrophic, many are decomposers, some are parasitic),

reproduction (both asexual and sexual, many times within the same

group), and movement.

Review Vocabulary *Use your book to define the following term.*

eukaryote

unicellular or multicellular organism whose cells contain membrane-

bound organelles

New Vocabulary *Use your book to define each term.*

algae

photosynthetic, plantlike, autotrophic protists

asexual reproduction

type of reproduction where one parent produces one or more identical

offspring by dividing into two cells

ciliates

group of protozoans of the phylum Ciliophora that have a covering

of cilia that aids in locomotion

flagellates

protists that have one or more flagella

protozoans

unicellular, heterotrophic, animal-like protists

pseudopodia

in protozoans, cytoplasm-containing extensions of the plasma

membrane; aid in locomotion and feeding

spore

type of reproductive cell with a hard outer coat that forms

a new organism without fertilization

sporozoans

group of parasitic protozoans of the phylum Sporozoa that reproduce

by spore production

Section 19.1 The World of Protists (continued)

| Main Idea | Details |

What is a protist?

I found this information on page _____.

SE, pp. 503–504
RE, pp. 207–208

Organize *information about different types of protists by completing the concept web.*

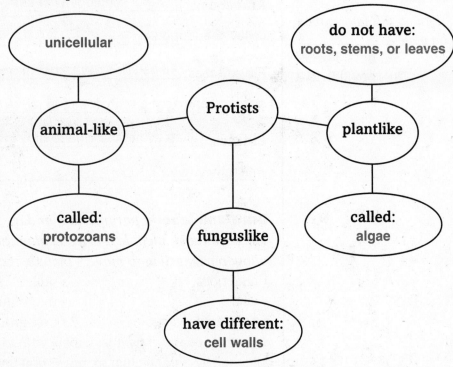

| unicellular |

| Protists |

| do not have: roots, stems, or leaves |

| animal-like |

| plantlike |

| called: protozoans |

| funguslike |

| called: algae |

| have different: cell walls |

What is a protozoan?

I found this information on page _____.

SE, p. 504
RE, p. 208

Summarize *information about protozoans by completing the table below.*

Protozoans
Protozoans are found in _____moist_____ environments.
Protozoans feed on __other organisms__ or __dead organic matter__ .
All protozoans are __heterotrophs__ .

Diversity of Protozoans

I found this information on page _____.

SE, pp. 504–509
RE, pp. 208–210

List *the four main groups of protozoans.*

1. amoebas

2. flagellates

3. ciliates

4. sporozoans

Section 19.1 The World of Protists (continued)

Main Idea	Details

Diversity of Protozoans

I found this information on page _____.
SE, pp. 504–509
RE, pp. 208–210

Describe *the ways that amoebas, flagellates, and ciliates move.*

Amoebas: Amoebas send out extensions of their plasma membranes called pseudopodia.

Flagellates: Flagellates have whip-like organelles that move side to side and enable the protozoans to move about.

Ciliates: Ciliates beat the cilia to move through watery places in which they live.

Draw and label *a paramecium and its parts in the space below. For each label, include a brief explanation. For example, "Cilia— allow paramecium to move." Include the following labels.*
- anal pore
- cilia
- contractile vacuole
- gullet
- micronucleus and macronucleus
- oral groove

Check students' drawings. Labels should include the following: cilia—allow paramecium to move; oral groove—where food enters; gullet—breaks down food; micronucleus—involved in sexual reproduction; macronucleus—controls cell functions; anal pore— where waste is eliminated; contractile vacuole—pumps out excess water

---

CONNECT Malaria is a disease that is caused by a sporozoan. It is spread by certain types of mosquitoes. Consider which would have a greater benefit—developing a drug that would cure malaria or developing a drug eliminating mosquitoes' ability to carry it. Explain your reasoning.

Accept all reasonable responses. Eliminating mosquitoes' ability to carry malaria would be

more beneficial because people would no longer contract the disease, and therefore would not

require treatment.

Protists

Section 19.2 Algae: Plantlike Protists

Main Idea	Details

Skim *Section 2 of your book. Write two questions that come to mind from reading the headings and the illustration captions.*

1. Accept all reasonable responses._____

2. _____

Review Vocabulary *Use your book to define the following term.*

photosynthesis
process by which autotrophs trap energy from sunlight with

chlorophyll and convert carbon dioxide and water into simple sugars

New Vocabulary *Use your book to define each term.*

alternation of generations
type of life cycle found in some algae, fungi, and all plants where an

organism alternates between a haploid (*n*) gametophyte generation

and a diploid (2*n*) sporophyte generation

colony
group of unicellular or multicellular orgnanisms that live together in

a close association

fragmentation
type of asexual reproduction in algae where an individual breaks into

pieces and each piece grows into a new individual

gametophyte
haploid form of an organism in alternation of generations that

produces gametes

sporophyte
in algae and plants, the diploid (2*n*) form of an organism in alternation

of generations that produces spores

thallus
body structure produced by some plants and some other organisms

that lacks roots, stems, and leaves

Section 19.2 Algae: Plantlike Protists (continued)

⟨**Main Idea**⟩ —————— ⟨**Details**⟩ ————————————————————

What are algae?

I found this information on page _____.

    SE, p. 510
    RE, p. 212

Organize *information about algae by completing the table.*

Algae	
How they obtain energy: **Algae use chlorophyll to trap energy from the sun and convert carbon dioxide and water into simple sugars.**	The kinds of pigments they contain: **Algae contain four kinds of chlorophyll as well as other pigments.**
Phytoplankton produce: **Phytoplankton are a major producer of nutrients and oxygen in water environments.**	Seaweed is: **Seaweed is a multicellular algae. It looks like a plant, but is not. It does not have roots, stems, or leaves.**

Diversity of Algae

I found this information on page _____.

    SE, pp. 511–516
    RE, pp. 212–215

Describe *the ways that euglenoids are like plants and like animals.*

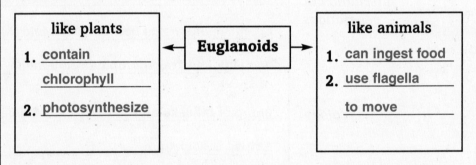

like plants
1. contain chlorophyll
2. photosynthesize

Euglanoids

like animals
1. can ingest food
2. use flagella to move

Sequence *the asexual and sexual reproductive cycles of diatoms by writing the letter for each step in the correct box. Use the figure in your book for help.*

a. fusion of gametes   **d.** sperm released

b. meiosis   **e.** wall formation around cell

c. mitosis   **f.** zygote

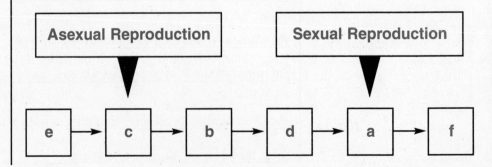

Asexual Reproduction   Sexual Reproduction

e → c → b → d → a → f

Section 19.2 Algae: Plantlike Protists (continued)

Main Idea ———— **Details** ————————————————————

Diversity of Algae

I found this information on page _____ .

SE, pp. 511–516
RE, pp. 212–215

Outline *information about red, brown, and green algae. Write three main points about each type on the lines provided.*

I. Red algae

   A. seaweeds

   B. use holdfasts to attach to rocks

   C. have photosynthetic pigments that absorb green, violet, and blue light

II. Brown algae

   A. found in cool ocean water

   B. have air bladders to keep them floating near the surface

   C. form huge underwater forests

III. Green algae

   A. most live in freshwater

   B. most diverse of all algae

   C. may live in colonies

Alternation of Generations

I found this information on page _____ .

SE, p. 516
RE, p. 216

Summarize *the alternation of generations by completing the organizer below.*

The haploid form of the algae, gametophyte, produces gametes.

⬇

The gametes join to form a zygote.

⬇

From the zygote, the diploid form of the algae will develop.

The diploid form is called sporophyte.

⬇

Certain cells in the sporophyte undergo meiosis.

⬇

These spores are haploid that develop into new gametophytes.

SYNTHESIZE Use the words *meiosis, fertilization, diploid,* and *haploid* in a sentence that demonstrates your understanding of alternation of generations in green algae.

Accept all reasonable responses. In meiosis, haploid spores of green algae develop, and in fertilization they are combined to produce the diploid form.

Protists

Section 19.3 Slime Molds, Water Molds, and Downy Mildews

(Main Idea) ——— **(Details)** ————————————————

Describe *As you read the section, write a description or draw your perception of how the funguslike protists appear physically and how they live. Compare and contrast these descriptions with how you would describe fungi.*

Accept all reasonable responses. Funguslike protists may be slimy or fuzzy in appearance. Water molds, with their fuzzy appearance, look much like the hyphae of fungi.

(Review Vocabulary) *Use your book to define the following term.*

heterotroph organisms that cannot make their own food and must feed on other

organisms for energy and nutrients

(New Vocabulary) *Use your book to define the following term.*

plasmodium in plasmodial slime molds, the mass of cytoplasm that contains

many diploid nuclei but no cell walls or membranes

(Academic Vocabulary) *Define the following term.*

consist to be made up of diverse elements

distinct clearly different and separate

Name _____ Date _____

Section 19.3 Slime Molds, Water Molds, and Downy Mildews (continued)

| Main Idea | Details |

What are fungus-like protists?

I found this information on page _____.

SE, p. 517
RE, p. 218

Slime Molds

I found this information on page _____.

SE, pp. 517–519
RE, pp. 218–219

Describe *funguslike protests by completing the paragraph below.*

The funguslike protists include ___slime molds___, ___water molds___, and ___downy mildews___. They are like fungi because they ___decompose___ organic material for ___food___. Two of the three phyla of funguslike protists are made up of ___slime molds___. The third phylum consists of ___water molds___ and ___downy mildews___.

Distinguish *between plasmodial slime molds and cellular slime molds by writing the letter for each phrase in the correct area of the Venn diagram.*

a. are animal-like during much of their life cycle

b. slimy mass forms many, separate stalks that produce spores

c. form a mass of cytoplasm with no cell walls or membranes

d. make spores to reproduce

e. move and surround food like amoebas

f. multicellular mass forms a single stalk that produces spores

g. spend part of their life cycle as single, amoeba-like cells

Plasmodial Slime Molds c, b — **Both** a, d, e — **Cellular Slime Molds** f, g

Compare and contrast *the life cycles of plasmodial slime and cellular slime. Identify two ways in which they are alike, and two ways in which they are different.*

Answers will vary. Both plasmodial slime and cellular slime form masses during parts of their life cycles. They both make spores to reproduce. But cellular slime takes the form of amoeba-like cells that feed and grow before they gather together to reproduce. Then the entire mass forms a single stalk that produces spores. Plasmodial slime remains in a slimy mass until it reproduces by changing into many separate stalks that each produce spores.

Section 19.3 Slime Molds, Water Molds, and Downy Mildews (continued)

Main Idea	Details

Water Molds and Downy Mildews

I found this information on page _____.

SE, p. 520
RE, pp. 219–220

Organize *information about water molds and downy mildews by filling in the prompts below.*

Where they live: water or moist places

What they feed on: dead organisms or plants

How they are different from fungi: at some point in their life cycle they produce reproductive cells with flagellates, which fungus never do

What they look like: most look like fuzzy, white growth on decaying matter

Problems they cause for humans: a downy mildew destroyed most of the potatoes in Ireland in the 1800s and caused a serious famine

Origin of Protists

I found this information on page _____.

SE, p. 520
RE, p. 220

Infer *how analyzing the RNA of ancient green algae lead biologists to believe that ancient green algae were probably the ancestors to modern plants.*

Biologists could recognize similarities in the RNA of ancient green algae and modern plants and determine that they are related.

SUMMARIZE

Create a simple organizer below that shows how the following are related.

- cellular slime mold
- funguslike protists
- plasmodial slime molds
- three phyla of funguslike protists
- water molds and downy mildew

Accept all reasonable responses. Organizers should show that the three phyla of funguslike protists are a subset of funguslike protists.

Tie-It-All-Together

SYNTHESIZE

The world of protists is large and complex. It contains organisms that resemble animals, plants, and fungi. In the space below, create a concept web that includes all the kinds of protists discussed in this chapter.

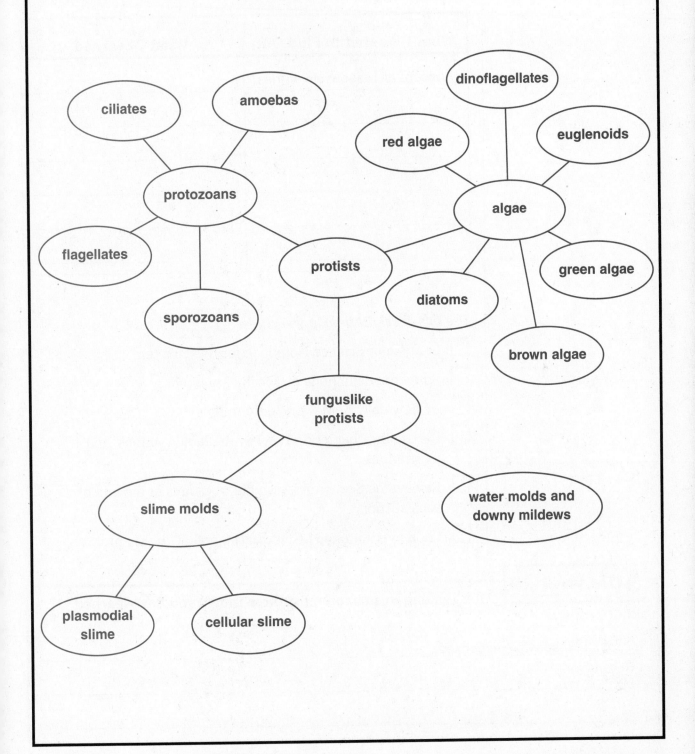

Protists Chapter Wrap-Up

In the "What I Wanted to Find Out" column, copy the questions you listed in the Chapter Preview. In the "What I Learned" column, write down the answers you discovered as you worked through the chapter.

W What I Wanted to Find Out	L What I Learned
1. Accept all reasonable entries.	1. _____
2. _____	2. _____
3. _____	3. _____

Use this checklist to help you study.

☐ Study your Science Notebook for this chapter.

☐ Study the definitions of vocabulary words.

☐ Review daily homework assignments.

☐ Reread the chapter and review the tables, graphs, and illustrations.

☐ Review the Section Assessment questions at the end of each section.

☐ Look over the Study Guide at the end of the chapter.

SUMMARIZE

After reading this chapter, list three things you have learned about protists.

Accept all reasonable responses.

_____

Fungi

Before You Read

Use the "What I Know" column to list three things you know about fungi. Then list three questions you have about fungi in the "What I Want to Find Out" column.

K What I Know	W What I Want to Find Out
1. Accept all reasonable entries.	1.
2.	2.
3.	3.

Science Journal

Fungi can be both helpful and harmful to humans. On the lines below, write two things that you already know about fungi.

Accept all reasonable responses.

Fungi

Section 20.1 What is a fungus?

Main Idea ———— **Details** ————————————————

Infer why mushrooms sometimes grow in a ring, given that thread-like filaments under the soil may grow a long distance before they produce the surface mushrooms.

Mushrooms are fruiting bodies that appear at the edges of the fungal

 colony. They began growing in one spot and the underground

mycelium grew outward until the mushrooms grew above the

surface.

Review Vocabulary *Use your book to define the following term.*

decomposer | organism that breaks down and absorbs nutrients from dead

organisms

New Vocabulary *Use your book to define each term.*

budding | type of asexual reproduction in unicellular yeasts and some other

organisms in which a cell or group of cells pinch off from the parent

to form a new individual

chitin | complex carbohydrate that makes up the cell walls of fungi

haustoria | in parasitic fungi, hyphae that grow into host cells and absorb

nutrients and minerals from the host

hyphae | threadlike filaments that are the basic structural units of multicellular

fungi

mycelium | in fungi, a complex network of branching hyphae; may serve to anchor

the fungus, invade food sources, or form reproductive structures

sporangium | in fungi, a sac or case of hyphae in which spores are produced

Name _____   Date _____

Section 20.1 What is a fungus? (continued)

Main Idea ——————   **Details** ————————————————————

The Characteristics of Fungi

I found this information on page _____.
SE, pp. 529–531
RE, pp. 222–223

Organize *information about the structure of multicellular fungi by completing the graphic organizer.*

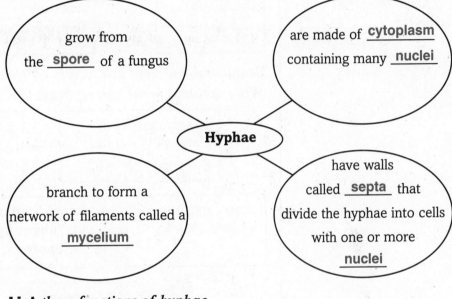

grow from the __spore__ of a fungus

are made of __cytoplasm__ containing many __nuclei__

Hyphae

branch to form a network of filaments called a __mycelium__

have walls called __septa__ that divide the hyphae into cells with one or more __nuclei__

List *three functions of hyphae.*

1. anchor the fungus _____

2. enter into the food source _____

3. reproduction _____

Adaptations in Fungi

I found this information on page _____.
SE, pp. 531–532
RE, pp. 223–224

Describe *how extracellular digestion allows fungi to obtain nutrients.*

Hyphae release digestive enzymes that break down large organic

molecules into smaller molecules. These small molecules are

absorbed into the hyphae and move into the flowing cytoplasm.

Define *three types of fungi by writing how each obtains food.*

Saprophytes	feed on waste and dead organic material
Mutualists	have symbiotic relationship with another organism
Parasites	absorb nutrients from host cells

Section 20.1 What is a fungus? (continued)

Main Idea —— **Details** _____

Reproduction in Fungi

I found this information on page _____ .
SE, pp. 532–534
RE, pp. 224–225

Name *the two forms of asexual reproduction in fungi in the boxes below.*

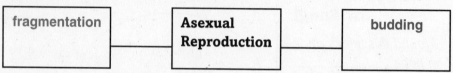

| fragmentation | **Asexual Reproduction** | budding |

Sequence *the steps involved in reproduction of fungi by spores. Write the steps in the correct boxes.*

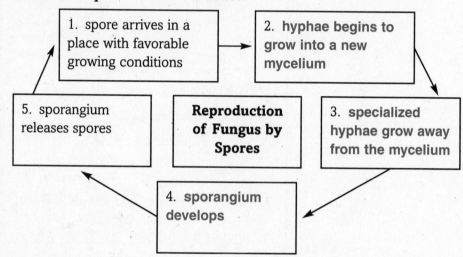

1. spore arrives in a place with favorable growing conditions
2. hyphae begins to grow into a new mycelium
5. sporangium releases spores
Reproduction of Fungus by Spores
3. specialized hyphae grow away from the mycelium
4. sporangium develops

Describe *three ways that reproduction by spores gives fungi an adaptive advantage.*

1. The sporangia protect the spores until they are ready to be released.

2. A large number of spores are produced at one time.

3. Spores are small, lightweight, and can be carried long distances by wind, water, and animals.

ANALYZE Explain where would you expect to find a greater number of fungal spores—in a desert or in a tropical forest.

Accept all reasonable responses. You would expect to find more fungal spores in a forest because many fungi grow in warm, moist conditions.

Fungi

Section 20.2 The Diversity of Fungi

Main Idea ———

Details ———————————————————————

Skim *Section 2 of your book. Write two questions that come to mind from reading the headings and the illustration captions.*

1. Accept all reasonable responses. _____

2. _____

New Vocabulary

Classify each vocabulary word in the table as relating to hyphae, spores, or the relationship between organisms. Write a brief definition for each term.

ascospores

ascus

basidia

basidiospores

conidia

conidiophores

gametangium

lichen

mycorrhiza

rhizoids

stolons

zygospores

Hyphae (5 terms)	Spores (5 terms)	Relationship Between Organisms (2 terms)
basidia: club shaped hyphae of basidiomycote fungi, produce spores	ascospores: sexual spore of ascomycote fungi that develop within an ascus	lichen: organism formed from a symbiotic association between a fungus and a photosynthetic green algae or cyanobacteria
conidiophores: in ascomycotes, elongated, upright hyphae that produce conidia at their tips	ascus: tiny, saclike structure in ascomycotes in which ascospores develop	
gametangium: structure that contains haploid nucleus, formed by the fusion of haploid hyphae	basidiospores: spores produced in basidia of basidiomycotes during sexual reproduction	mycorrhiza: mutualistic relationship in which a fungus lives symbiotically with a plant
rhizoids: fungal hyphae that penetrate food, anchor a mycelium, secrete enzymes for extracellular digestion and absorb nutrients	conidia: chains or clusters of asexual ascomycote spores that develop on the tips of conidiophores	
stolons: fungal hyphae that grow horizontally along a surface and rapidly produce a mycelium	zygospores: thick-walled spores of zygometes that can withstand unfavorable conditions	

Section 20.2 The Diversity of Fungi (continued)

Main Idea	Details

Zygomecotes

I found this information on page _____.
SE, pp. 535–536
RE, pp. 226–228

Explain *how zygomecotes reproduce sexually.*

Accept all reasonable responses. Haploid hypha from two compatible

mycelia, called plus and minus, fuse. Each of them forms a

gametangium, which is a structure containing a haploid nucleus.

When the haploid nuclei of two gametangia fuse, a diploid zygote

forms. This zygote is called a zygospore. It is dormant until the

conditions are right for it to germinate.

Ascomycotes

I found this information on page _____.
SE, p. 537
RE, p. 228

Organize *information about ascomycotes by completing the table below.*

How they reproduce sexually	How they reproduce asexually
Sexual spores develop in saclike structures, each called an ascus.	Hyphae grow from the mycelium. They become longer and form conidiophores. Chains or clusters of asexual spores called conidia develop from the conidiophores.
How they are helpful	**How they are harmful**
Yeasts are used to produce alcohol, bread, and vaccines.	They form mold on foods and cause plant diseases.

Basidiomycotes

I found this information on page _____.
SE, pp. 538–539
RE, pp. 228–229

Examine *the illustration of a basidiomycote's reproductive cycle in your book. Then make your own sketch of step D—hyphae fusion. Be sure to label the + and – mating types as well as the new mycelium.*
Drawings should resemble step D in the book, and should be properly labeled.

Section 20.2 The Diversity of Fungi (continued)

Main Idea ———— **Details** ————————————————————

Deuteromycotes

I found this information on page _____ .

SE, p. 540
RE, p. 229

Summarize *information about the uses of deuteromycotes by completing the organizer below.*

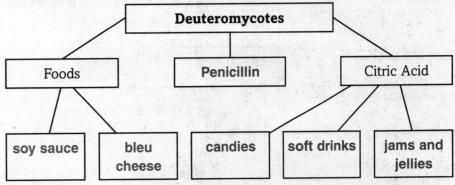

Mutualism: Mycorrhizae and Lichens

I found this information on page _____ .

SE, pp. 540–542
RE, pp. 230–231

Add to *each sentence that explains mycorrhizae.*

Fungi benefit from a mycorrhizal relationship because the <u>fungus</u> receives organic nutrients such as amino acids and sugars from the plant.

Plants benefit from a mycorrhizal relationship because <u>the hyphae</u> increase the surface area of the plant's roots, absorb minerals in the soil and release them into the roots, and help to maintain water around the roots.

Origins of Fungi

I found this information on page _____ .

SE, p. 543
RE, p. 231

Explain *why fossils of fungi are rare, and also give the approximate age of the oldest fungi fossils.*

Fossils of fungi are rare because fungi are made of soft materials.

The oldest fossils of fungi are over 400 million years old.

SYNTHESIZE

Describe one similarity and one difference between mycorrhizae and lichens.

Accept all reasonable responses. Both involve symbiotic relationships between a fungus and another organism. A mycorrhizae is made up of a fungus and a plant, while a lichen is made up of a fungus and an algae or cyanobacteria. In a mycorrhizae, the organisms remain separate, while a lichen appears to be a single organism.

Fungi Chapter Wrap-Up

In the "What I Wanted to Find Out" column, copy the questions you listed in the Chapter Preview. In the "What I Learned" column, write down the answers you discovered as you worked through the chapter.

W What I Wanted to Find Out	L What I Learned
1. Accept all reasonable entries.	1.
2.	2.
3.	3.

Use this checklist to help you study.

☐ Study your Science Notebook for this chapter.

☐ Study the definitions of vocabulary words.

☐ Review daily homework assignments.

☐ Reread the chapter and review the tables, graphs, and illustrations.

☐ Review the Section Assessment questions at the end of each section.

☐ Look over the Study Guide at the end of the chapter.

SUMMARIZE After reading this chapter, list three things you have learned about fungi.

Accept all reasonable responses.

_____

_____

_____

What is a plant?

Before You Read

Use the "What I Know" column to list three things you know about plants. Then list three questions you have about plants in the "What I Want to Find Out" column.

K What I Know	W What I Want to Find Out
1. Accept all reasonable entries.	1.
2.	2.
3.	3.

Science Journal

Plants are found in many different environments. Describe some of the plants you are familar with. Identify the environment in which each lives.

Accept all reasonable responses.

What is a plant?

Section 21.1 Adapting to Life on Land

Main Idea	Details

Scan *Section 1 of your book. Write two questions that come to mind from reading the headings and the illustration captions.*

1. Accept all reasonable responses.

2. _____

New Vocabulary *Use your book to define each term.*

cuticle — protective, waxy coating on the outer surface of the epidermis of most stems and leaves; important adaptation in reducing water loss

leaf — the plant organ that grows from a stem in which photosynthesis usually occurs

nonvascular plant — plants that do not have vascular tissues

root — plant organ that absorbs water and minerals usually from soil; contains vascular tissues; anchors plant; can be a storage organ

seed — a plant organ of seed plants consisting of an embryo, a food supply, and a protective coat; protects the embryo from drying out

stem — plant organ that provides support and growth; contains tissues that transport food, water, and other materials; organ from which leaves grow; can serve as a food storage organ; green stems can carry out photosynthesis

vascular plant — plants that have vascular tissues; enables taller growth and survival on land

vascular tissue — tissues found in vascular plants composed of tubelike, elongated cells through which food, water, and other materials are transported throughout the plant; include xylem and phloem

Section 21.1 Adapting to Life on Land (continued)

Main Idea	Details

Origins of Plants

I found this information on page _____ .
SE, pp. 559–560
RE, pp. 233–234

Sequence *the evolution of plants by placing the following information in the correct boxes below.*

- algae at edges of seas adapted to life on land
- algae in oceans
- no plants
- simple plants appear

no plants	algae in oceans	algae at edges of seas adapted to life on land	simple plants appear

↑ 1 billion years ago   ↑ 440 million years ago

Describe *the characteristics of the modern members of the algae and plant groups.*

These groups have cell walls with cellulose, use chlorophyll in

photosynthesis, and store food in the form of starch.

Adaptations in Plants

I found this information on page _____ .
SE, pp. 560–563
RE, pp. 234–236

Summarize *adaptations in plants by identifying four challenges that land-based plants face.*

1. obtaining water and food from the soil

2. reproducing in a way that prevents gametes from drying out

3. surviving exposure to wind and weather

4. developing structures to ensure growth against the force of gravity

Draw *a diagram of a plant and label the following parts: leaf, root, and stem.*
Drawings should clearly show the leaves, stem, and roots anchoring the plant to the ground.

Section 21.1 Adapting to Life on Land (continued)

| ⟨Main Idea⟩ ── | ⟨Details⟩ ────────────────────────────── |

Adaptations in Plants

I found this information on page _____.
SE, pp. 560–563
RE, pp. 234–236

Identify *an important structural adaptation of vascular plants. Then describe two ways that vascular plants benefit from this adaptation.*

Adaptation: vascular tissues

Benefits: enable vascular plants to live farther away from water;

fibers allow vascular plants to grow taller

Organize *the plant organs by completing the table below. The first row has been filled out for you.*

	Location	Purpose	Plant organ?	General Characteristic
cuticle	on stems and leaves	reduce water loss	no	allowed plant to move on land
leaf	grows from stem	photosynthesis	yes	each plant has unique leaves
root	bottom of stem	absorbs water and nutrients	yes	food storage, anchor
stem	middle of plant	provides support for growth	yes	tissues for transporting food and water
seed	on plant	protects embryo from drying	yes	contains embryo and food in protective cover

CONTRAST Explain how the sperm reaches the egg differently in seed plants than in non-seed plants.

Accept all reasonable responses. Seed plants sperm can reach the egg without needing water.

In non-seed plants the sperm need a film of water in order to reach the egg, and require a

wetter environment.

What is a plant?

Section 21.2 Survey of the Plant Kingdom

Main Idea	Details
	Infer *What structural and physiological adaptations do plants, such as cacti and mosses, have that would allow them to survive in different biomes on Earth? Compare and then evaluate the significance of these adaptations.*
	Some cacti store water for drier months. Modified leaves can be small or thornlike, thus reducing surface areas and reducing water loss. Some cacti have stems and waxy coatings that help reduce water loss. Mosses are small nonvascular plants that live in moist environments. Movement of materials by osmosis is satisfactory because of their small size.
Review Vocabulary	*Use your book to define the following term.*
evolution	gradual change in an organism through adaptations over time
New Vocabulary	*Use your book to define each term.*
cones	in coniferophytes; scaly structures that support male and female reproductive structures; scaly structures produced by some seed plants that support male or female reproductive structures and are the sites of seed production
frond	in fern leaves that grow upward from the rhizome; often divided into pinnae that are attached to a central rachis
Academic Vocabulary	*Define the following terms.*
diverse	made up of many different elements or kinds of things
environment	the conditions within which people, animals, and plants live

Section 21.2 Survey of the Plant Kingdom (continued)

Main Idea ——— ## Details ——————————————————

Phylogeny of Plants

I found this information on page _____ *.*

SE, p. 564
RE, p. 238

Describe *three causes for the phylogeny of plants.*

1. landmasses moved from place to place

2. climates changed

3. bodies of water have appeared and disappeared

Non-seed Plants

I found this information on page _____ *.*

SE, pp. 565–567
RE, pp. 239–240

Compare *the different types of non-seed plants by completing the table below. The first row has been done for you.*

	Vascular/ Nonvascular?	Characteristic	Example
Hepaticophytes	nonvascular	small, flattened bodies; grow in moist places	liverworts
Anthocerophytes	nonvascular	small, live in damp, shady habitats	hornworts
Bryophytes	nonvascular	some cells transport water and sugar	mosses
Psilophytes	vascular	no roots or leaves	whisk ferns
Lycophytes	vascular	very large during Paleozoic Era, now less than 25 cm high	club mosses
Arthrophytes	vascular	hollow, jointed stems; small now, but ancestors were as big as trees	horsetails
Pterophytes	vascular	abundant during Paleozoic and Mesozoic Eras	ferns

Section 21.2 Survey of the Plant Kingdom (continued)

Main Idea ———— **Details** ————————————————

Seed Plants

I found this information on page _____ .
SE, pp. 567–569
RE, pp. 240–241

Compare *the different types of seed plants by filling in the table below. Provide at least one description for each type of seed.*

Type	Description
Cycads	look like palm trees, have scaly trunks, and come in various heights, produce male and female cones on separate trees
Gnetophytes	divided into three groups: tropical trees, climbing vines; shrubs that grow in dry, desert regions; single species that lives in the deserts of southwest Africa
Ginkgophytes	small trees with fan-shaped leaves; have male and female cones on separate trees; female tree has unpleasant smell
Conifers	cone-bearing trees; produce seeds in cones; many have needlelike leaves
Anthophytes	are flowering plants; produce flowers from which fruit develops; broken into two classes

Explain *the difference between seeds and cones.*

Seeds contain the embryo of a plant and the food supply for the

embryo inside a protective shell. Cones are scaly structures that

support male or female reproductive structures. Seeds are produced

in female cones. Male cones produce clouds of pollen.

SYNTHESIZE Describe the differences between a seed plant and a non-seed plant. Include specific examples and labeled diagrams of each plant.

Accept all reasonable responses. Students should include information about vascular tissues, environments in which the plants live, methods of getting water and nutrients, and specific examples of each plant. You may wish to have students create a poster.

What is a plant? Chapter Wrap-Up

In the "What I Wanted to Find Out" column, copy the questions you listed in the Chapter Preview. In the "What I Learned" column, write down the answers you discovered as you worked through the chapter.

W What I Wanted to Find Out	L What I Learned
1. Accept all reasonable entries. _____	1. _____ _____
2. _____ _____	2. _____ _____
3. _____ _____	3. _____ _____

Use this checklist to help you study.

☐ Study your Science Notebook for this chapter.

☐ Study the definitions of vocabulary words.

☐ Review daily homework assignments.

☐ Reread the chapter and review the tables, graphs, and illustrations.

☐ Review the Section Assessment questions at the end of each section.

☐ Look over the Study Guide at the end of the chapter.

SUMMARIZE

After reading this chapter, list three things you have learned about plants.

Accept all reasonable responses.

_____

_____

The Diversity of Plants

Before You Read

Use the "What I Know" column to list three things you know about the diversity of plants. Then list three questions you have about plant diversity in the "What I Want to Find Out" column.

K What I Know	W What I Want to Find Out
1. Accept all reasonable entries.	1. _____
_____	_____
2. _____	2. _____
_____	_____
3. _____	3. _____
_____	_____

Science Journal

Plants can be categorized as either non-seed or seed plants. Think about the plants you see around you. Give an example of each type of plant, and briefly describe the difference between the two.

Accept all reasonable responses.

_____

_____

_____

_____

_____

_____

_____

_____

The Diversity of Plants

Section 22.1 Nonvascular Plants

Main Idea ——— **Details** ——————————————————————

Scan *Section 1 of your book. Use the checklist as a guide.*

☐ Read all section titles.

☐ Read all boldfaced words.

☐ Read all tables and graphs.

☐ Look at all pictures and read the captions.

☐ Think about what you already know about the diversity of plants.

Write three facts you discovered about the diversity of plants as you scanned the section.

1. Accept all reasonable responses. _____

2. _____

3. _____

Review Vocabulary *Use your book to define the following term.*

fertilization | fusion of male and female gametes

New Vocabulary *Use your book to define each term.*

antheridium | male reproductive structure in which sperm develop

archegonium | female reproductive structure in which eggs develop

Academic Vocabulary *Define the following term.*

adapt | to make or become used to a new environment or different conditions

Section 22.1 Nonvascular Plants (continued)

| Main Idea | Details |

What is a nonvascular plant?

I found this information on page _____.
SE, pp. 577–578
RE, p. 243

Explain *why nonvascular plants need to be near water.*

Nonvascular plants need water for life functions such as reproduction

and photosynthesis. A steady supply of water is not available

everywhere, so nonvascular plants need to be in moist habitats.

Sketch *and label an example of a sporophyte attached to a gametophyte.*

Sketches should resemble the figure in the book, with sporophyte and gametophyte properly labeled.

Adaptations in Bryophyta, Adaptations in Hepaticophyta, and Adaptations in Anthocerophyta

I found this information on page _____.
SE, pp. 578–580
RE, p. 244

Compare *the general characteristics of bryophytes, hepaticophytes, and anthocerophytes by completing the table below.*

Accept all reasonable responses.

	Description	Environment	Example
Bryophyta	small plants with leafy stems	variety of habitats	mosses, peat moss
Hepaticophyta	thallose body, shape of liverwort gametophyte looks like an animal's liver	grown on damp soil, tropical jungles, and places with lots of fog	liverworts
Anthocerophyta	thallose body, shape of hornwort sporophyte looks like an animal's horn	moist environments	hornworts

Name _____ Date _____

Section 22.1 Nonvascular Plants (continued)

Main Idea ———— Details ————

Adaptations in Bryophyta, Adaptations in Hepaticophyta, and Adaptations in Anthocerophyta

I found this information on page _____.
SE, pp. 578–580
RE, p. 244

Match *the following terms with the definitions below: sporophyte, gametophyte, thallus, rhizoid. Write the correct term next to the definition.*

____rhizoid____ colorless, multicellular structures found in nonvascular plants; used to help anchor the plants to the soil

____thallus____ broad shape resembling a fleshy lobed leaf

____sporophyte____ diploid generation; grow attached to gametophytes

____gametophyte____ haploid generation; dominant generation

Describe *how anthocerophytes became known as hornworts.*

The sporophyte of an anthocerophyte resembles the horn of an animal.

Origins of Nonvascular Plants

I found this information on page _____.
SE, p. 580
RE, p. 245

Create *your own graphic organizer that models the possible common ancestry of nonvascular and vascular plants.* Accept all reasonable responses.

common ancestor; probably had alternating sporophyte and gametophyte generations, cellulose in cell walls, and chlorophyll

nonvascular plants

vascular plants

COMPARE Draw a diagram of a liverwort and a hornwort. Label each part and include information on their environment and surroundings as part of your overall diagram. Use a separate sheet of paper if necessary.
Accept all reasonable responses. Student responses should include the general shape of each plant as well as the moist environment that they need to survive.

The Diversity of Plants
Section 22.2 Non-Seed Vascular Plants

Main Idea ———

Details ————————————

Concept Map *After you read about non-seed vascular plants, make a concept map that identifies and analyzes the relationships among these organisms.* Accept all reasonable responses.

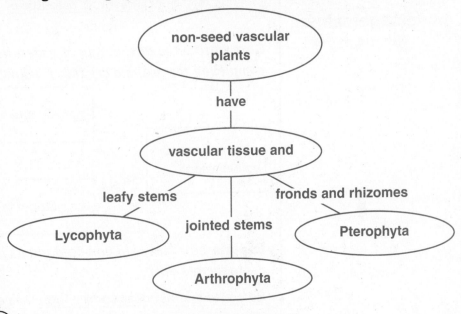

Review Vocabulary *Use your book to define the following term.*

alternation of generations

type of life cycle found in some algae, fungi, and all plants where an

organism alternates between a haploid (*n*) gametophyte generation

and a diploid (2*n*) sporophyte generation

New Vocabulary *Use your book to define each term.*

prothallus

fern gametophyte

rhizome

thick, underground stem of a fern and other vascular plants; often

functions as an organ for food storage

sorus

clusters of sporangia usually found on the surface of fern fronds

strobilus

compact cluster of spore-bearing leaves produced by some non-seed

vascular plants

Section 22.2 Non-Seed Vascular Plants (continued)

Main Idea	Details

What is a non-seed vascular plant?

I found this information on page _____.
SE, pp. 581–582
RE, pp. 246–247

Describe *vascular tissue.*

Vascular tissue is made of tubelike, long cells that carry and transport water and nutrients. Vascular tissue allows a plant to live in a variety of habitats, farther away from a source of water.

Summarize *the alternation of generations for vascular plants by completing the graphic organizer below.*

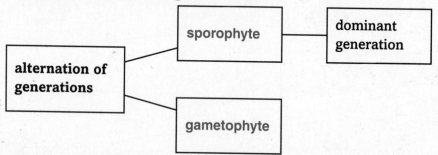

Explain *how leaves in non-seed plants protect the developing reproductive cells.*

Some leaves that bear spores form a cluster called a strobilus. The spores are then released from the strobilus to form gametophytes.

Reproductive structures develop on the gametophyte.

Adaptations in Lycophyta, Adaptations in Arthrophyta, and Adaptations in Pterophyta

I found this information on page _____.
SE, pp. 582–586
RE, pp. 247–248

Compare *the three divisions of non-seed vascular plants by completing the table below. Write at least two facts about each division.*

Lycophyta	Arthrophyta	Pterophyta
club moss or spike moss; sporophyte generation is dominant; sporophyte has roots, stems, and leaflike structures; a single vein of vascular tissue runs through each leaflike structure	horsetails; sometimes called scouring rushes; grow in damp soil, shallow ponds, marshes, stream banks; have ribbed, hollow and jointed stem; spores are produced in strobili; spores grow into gametophytes	ferns; become dormant when water is scarce; sporophyte generation has roots, stems and leaves; the main stem is underground; first of vasculr plants to have evolved leaves with veins of branching vascular tissue

Section 22.2 Non-Seed Vascular Plants (continued)

Main Idea —— **Details** ——————————————————

Adaptations in Lycophyta, Adaptations in Arthrophyta, and Adaptations in Pterophyta

I found this information on page _____.
SE, pp. 582–586
RE, pp. 247–248

Distinguish *between the non-seed vascular plants that appear in the fossil record and the ones found today by completing the organizer below.*

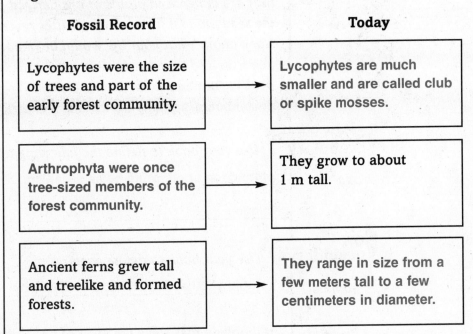

Fossil Record   **Today**

Fossil Record	Today
Lycophytes were the size of trees and part of the early forest community.	→ Lycophytes are much smaller and are called club or spike mosses.
Arthrophyta were once tree-sized members of the forest community.	→ They grow to about 1 m tall.
Ancient ferns grew tall and treelike and formed forests.	→ They range in size from a few meters tall to a few centimeters in diameter.

Origins of Non-Seed Vascular Plants

I found this information on page _____.
SE, pp. 586–587
RE, p. 248

Sequence *the evolution of the non-seed vascular plant in the sentences below. The first one has been done for you.*

___4___ Many non-seed vascular plants died out, leaving the ones that are dominant today.

___3___ Earth became cooler and drier 280 million years ago.

___1___ The earliest evidence of the non-seed vascular plants was from the Devonian Period 375 million years ago

___2___ During the Carboniferous Period, large, tree-sized lycophytes, arthrophytes, and pterophytes were abundant in warm forests.

┌───┐
│ **SYNTHESIZE** Use a separate sheet of paper to create your own drawings of the three main groups of non-seed vascular plants. Label the important features of each group and give an example of each one.

Accept all reasonable responses.
└───┘

The Diversity of Plants
Section 22.3 Seed Plants

(Main Idea)——— **(Details)**

Creative Writing *As a class, brainstorm and record items you use that are either seed plants or are derived from seed plants. Identify the seed plant(s) for each item. After reviewing your list, write a story about what your life would be like without seed plants.*
Items derived from seed plants might include books, dyes in clothing, pencils, furniture, baskets, rope, cosmetics, medicines, preservatives, poster board, sporting equipment, and certain buildings.

Review Vocabulary *Use your book to define the following term.*

reproduction | production of offspring by an organism; a characteristic of all living things

New Vocabulary *Use your book to define each term.*

annual | anthophyte that lives for one year or less

biennial | anthophyte that has a life span of two years

cotyledons | structure of seed plant embryo that stores or absorbs food for the developing embryo

deciduous plant | plants that drop all of their leaves each fall or when water is scarce or unavailable; an adaptation for reducing water loss when water is unavailable

dicotyledon | class of anthophytes that have two seed leaves

embryo | the young diploid sporophyte of a plant

fruit | seed-containing ripened ovary of an anthophyte flower; may be fleshy or dry

monocotyledon | class of anthophytes that have one seed leaf

Section 22.3 Seed Plants (continued)

Main Idea ——— **Details** ———————————————————————————

What is a seed plant?

I found this information on page _____.

SE, pp. 588–590
RE, pp. 250–251

Describe *a seed.*

A seed is a small sporophyte plant inside a protective coat. Seeds

may be surrounded by fruit or carried within the scales of a cone.

Sketch *a seed plant. Be sure to label the ovary and ovules. On the line below, describe what the ovule does.*

Sketches should resemble the one in the book, and the ovary and
ovules should be correctly labeled.

The ovule ___forms the seeds after fertilization_____.

Identify *three advantages of seeds.*

1. ___The seed contains food for the young plant until the leaves___
   ___develop enough to carry out photosynthesis.___

2. ___The embryo is protected during harsh conditions by the tough___
   ___seed coat.___

3. ___Some seeds have adaptations to help them move away from___
   ___parent plant, reducing the competition among plants.___

Compare *the two types of seed plants by completing the organizers below. Write at least two facts for each type of seed plant.*

Seeds not Protected by Fruit	**Seeds Protected by Fruit**
called gymnosperms; seeds released by pinecones are an example; divisions are Cycadophyta, Ginkgophyta, Gnetophyta, Coniferophyta	called angiosperms; a fruit includes the ripened ovary of a flower; the fruit protects the seeds and helps in seed dispersal; the Anthophyta division contains all fruit-producing plants

Section 22.3 Seed Plants (continued)

Main Idea —— **Details** ——————————————————

Adaptations in Cycadophyta, Ginkgophyta, Gnetophyta, Coniferophyta, and Anthophyta

I found this information on page _____.
SE, pp. 590–596
RE, pp. 252–255

Compare *the characteristics of the different divisions of seed plants by completing the table below. The first one has been done for you.*

	Reproduction	Environment	Examples
Cycadophyta	males produce pollen grains from cones, pollen produce motile sperm	tropics and subtropics	there are about 100 species today
Ginkgophyta	males produce pollen grains from cones, pollen produce motile sperm	male ginkgoes planted in cities—they tolerate smog and pollution	*Ginkgo biloba*
Gnetophyta	none given	found in deserts or mountains of Asia, Africa, North America, Central or South America	tropical climbing plants and shrub-like plants
Coniferophyta	reproductive structures produced in cones	found in many forest environments	pine, fir, spruce, juniper, cedar, redwood, yew, larch
Anthophyta	enclose seeds in a fruit	found in a variety of environments	fruit trees

Origins of Seed Plants

I found this information on page _____.
SE, pp. 596–597
RE, p. 255

Describe *one major event that took place in each period.*

Paleozoic: seed plants first appeared

Mesozoic: ancient relatives of ginkgoes and cycads shared forest with dinosaurs

Jurassic: conifers became the most common forest plant

CONNECT Suppose you want to plant a vegetable garden. Research the soil conditions and overall climate in your area. Then describe a plant that should be successful, and explain your reasoning.

Accept all reasonable responses.

Tie-It-All-Together

You have read about the three types of plants: nonvascular plants, non-seed vascular plants, and seed plants. Now create a quick identification guide to common plants in your area. Your plant guide should be easy to read, yet contain basic information about the reproduction, environment, general structure, and significant characteristics of each plant. Include one plant from each type. Remember that a good plant guide has well-labeled diagrams. When you are finished, share your plant guide with your class.

Accept all reasonable responses.

The Diversity of Plants Chapter Wrap-Up

In the "What I Wanted to Find Out" column, copy the questions you listed in the Chapter Preview. In the "What I Learned" column, write down the answers you discovered as you worked through the chapter.

W What I Wanted to Find Out	L What I Learned
1. Accept all reasonable entries.	1. _____
2. _____	2. _____
3. _____	3. _____

Use this checklist to help you study.

☐ Study your Science Notebook for this chapter.

☐ Study the definitions of vocabulary words.

☐ Review daily homework assignments.

☐ Reread the chapter and review the tables, graphs, and illustrations.

☐ Review the Section Assessment questions at the end of each section.

☐ Look over the Study Guide at the end of the chapter.

SUMMARIZE After reading this chapter, list three things you have learned about the diversity of plants.

Accept all reasonable responses.

_____

_____

Plant Structure and Function

Before You Read

Use the "What I Know" column to list three things you know about plant structure and function. Then list three questions you have about plant structure and function in the "What I Want to Find Out" column.

K What I Know	W What I Want to Find Out
1. Accept all reasonable entries. _____	1. _____
2. _____	2. _____
3. _____	3. _____

Science Journal

Describe some plants that you eat. Then describe some products that you use that come from plants.

Accept all reasonable responses. _____

_____

_____

_____

_____

_____

_____

_____

Plant Structure and Function

Section 23.1 Plant Cells and Tissues

Main Idea ——— **Details** ———————————————

Scan *Section 1 of your book. Write two questions that come to mind from reading the headings and the illustration captions.*

1. Accept all reasonable responses. _____

_____

2. _____

_____

_____

New Vocabulary **Classify** *each vocabulary word in the list to the left as being a plant cell or a plant tissue. Then give a short description.*

apical meristem

collenchyma

companion cells

cork cambium

epidermis

guard cells

lateral meristem

meristems

parenchyma

phloem

sclerenchyma

sieve tube members

stomata

tracheids

trichomes

vascular cambium

vessel elements

xylem

Cells (8 terms)	Tissues (10 terms)
collenchyma: long plant cells with unevenly thickened walls	apical meristem: regions of actively dividing cells near the tips of roots and stems
companion cells: cells with nuclei that help transport sugars and other organic compounds through sieve tubes	cork cambium: lateral meristem that produces a tough protective covering for the surface of stems and roots
guard cells: control the opening and closing of the stomata	epidermis: in plants, the outer-most layer of flattened cells that covers and protects all parts of the plant
parenchyma: most abundant type of plant cell, spherical cells with thin, flexible cell walls and a large central vacuole; important for storage and food production	lateral meristem: cylinders of dividing cells located in the roots and stems
	meristems: regions of actively dividing cells
sclerenchyma: plant cells with rigid, thick walls; die when mature, but still provide support	phloem: vascular plant tissue made of tubular cells joined end to end
sieve tube members: tubular cells in phloem; lack nucleus	stomata: openings in leaf tissues
tracheids: tubular cells in the xylem that have tapered ends; have small openings for tranport of water and minerals	trichomes: hairlike projections from the plant's epidermis
vessel elements: hollow, tubular cells in the xylem	vascular cambium: lateral meristem that produces new xylem and phloem cells in the stems and roots
	xylem: vascular plant tissue composed of tubular cells

Section 23.1 Plant Cells and Tissues (continued)

Main Idea ———— **Details** ——————————————————————————

Types of Plant Cells

I found this information on page _____ .
SE, pp. 605–606
RE, pp. 257–258

Point out *three ways that plant cells differ from animal cells.*

Plant cells have a cell wall, a central vacuole, and can contain
_____

chloroplasts.
_____

Label *the cell wall, central vacuole, and chloroplast in the figure below.*

The three parts of the plant cell should be accurately labeled.

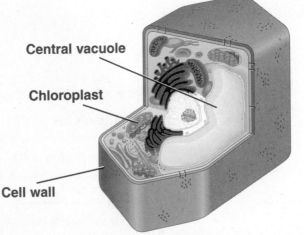

Central vacuole

Chloroplast

Cell wall

Compare *the three types of plant cells by completing the table below. Describe one characteristic and one function for each type of cell.*

	Parenchyma	Collenchyma	Sclerenchyma
Characteristic	sphere-shaped cells that have thin, flexible walls	long cells with unevenly thickened cell walls	thick and rigid cells that often die when they mature
Function	used for storage and food production	provide strength and support for surrounding tissue	provide support for plant

Plant Tissues

I found this information on page _____ .
SE, pp. 607–611
RE, pp. 258–260

Describe *the function of each of the following.*

epidermis: __covers and protects the body of a plant__

stomata: __control the exchange of gases__

guard cells: __control the opening and closing of stomata__

trichomes: __reduce the evaporation of water from the plant__

Section 23.1 Plant Cells and Tissues (continued)

Main Idea	Details

Plant Tissues

I found this information on page _____.

SE, pp. 607–611
RE, pp. 258–260

Draw *a sketch of phloem tissue. Label the following parts.*

• companion cell   • sieve plate   • sieve tube member

Sketches should resemble the one in the book, and the three parts should be accurately labeled.

Describe *ground tissue by completing the organizer below.*

Made up of:

| sclerenchyma cells |
| parenchyma cells |
| collenchyma cells |

Ground Tissue

Functions include:

| photosynthesis |
| storage |
| support |

Construct *two questions about meristematic tissues. Then give the answer to each question.* **Accept all reasonable responses.**

1. Question:_____

   Answer: _____

   _____

2. Question:_____

   Answer: _____

SYNTHESIZE

Use a separate sheet of paper to draw a diagram of a plant. Include captions that explain the three types of cells as well as the four types of tissues.

Accept all reasonable responses.

Plant Structure and Function

Section 23.2 Roots, Stems, and Leaves

Main Idea ———

Details ————————————————————

Experiment *After reading the first two sections of this chapter, design an investigation to demonstrate how vascular tissue is common to roots, stems, and leaves. Show your plan to your teacher and get permission to perform the investigation. Be sure to follow all laboratory safety rules. Share your findings with your class.*

Students might decide to investigate how colored water moves from

the root through a plant stem to the leaf or flower. When you examine

their plan, make sure they have incorporated a control and plan to

collect quantitative data.

_____

_____

New Vocabulary

Classify *each term at the left as relating to roots, stems, or leaves. Provide a brief definition for each term.*

cortex

endodermis

mesophyll

pericycle

petiole

root cap

sink

translocation

transpiration

Roots (4 terms)	Stems (2 terms)	Leaves (3 terms)
cortex: layer of ground tissue in the root that is involved in the transport of water endodermis: single layer of cells that forms a waterproof seal around a root's vascular tissue pericycle: the layer of cells just within the endodermis that gives rise to lateral roots root cap: tough, protective layer of parenchyma cells that covers the tip of a root	sink: any part of a plant that stores sugars produced during photosynthesis translocation: movement of sugars in the phloem of a plant	mesophyll: photosynthetic tissue of a leaf petiole: the stalk that joins the leaf blade to the stem transpiration: the loss of water through stomata

Section 23.2 Roots, Stems, and Leaves (continued)

Main Idea	Details

Roots

I found this information on page _____.

SE, pp. 612–615
RE, pp. 263–266

Organize *information about the two main types of root systems. Give a brief description of taproots and fibrous roots, then make a sketch of each type.*

taproots: single, thick structures with smaller branching roots

fibrous roots: have many small branching roots that grow from a

central point

Sketches should resemble those in RE p. 263

Identify *the layers of cells of roots beginning with the outermost layer. The first one has been done for you.*

__3__ endodermis __1__ epidermis __4__ pericycle __2__ cortex

Stems

I found this information on page _____.

SE, pp. 615–617
RE, pp. 266–268

Describe *three stems that store food.*

A tuber is a swollen stem that has buds from which new plants grow. A

corm is a short thickened stem surrounded by leaf scales. Rhizomes

also store food.

Summarize *the function of the stem by completing the model of the vascular tissues of a carrot.*

Leaf		Phloem

Xylem	Sink	carries dissolved sugars from photosynthetic cells in leaves to the sink

Xylem
moves water and dissolved minerals from the roots to the leaves

Section 23.2 Roots, Stems, and Leaves (continued)

Main Idea	Details

Leaves

I found this information on page _____ .
SE, pp. 617–621
RE, pp. 268–270

Organize *information about the shapes of leaves. Give a brief description of a simple and a compound leaf, and provide one example of each. Then make a sketch of each type.*

simple leaf: <u>blade that is not divided; maple leaf</u>

compound leaf: <u>blade that is divided into leaflets; walnut leaf</u>

Sketches should resemble those in SE p. 618, RE p. 268

Summarize *the role of mesophyll by completing the organizer below.*

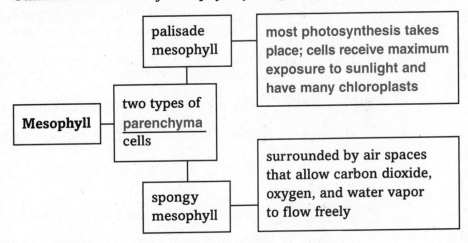

Mesophyll	two types of <u>parenchyma</u> cells	palisade mesophyll	most photosynthesis takes place; cells receive maximum exposure to sunlight and have many chloroplasts
		spongy mesophyll	surrounded by air spaces that allow carbon dioxide, oxygen, and water vapor to flow freely

Name *two plants with leaves that have functions besides photosynthesis. Briefly describe these functions.*

1. <u>Cacti spines help reduce water loss and provide protection from plant-eaters.</u>

2. <u>Carnivorous plants have leaves that can trap insects or small animals.</u>

CONNECT Plant roots, stems, and leaves all serve as food sources for humans. Give a specific example of a food we eat from each of the three categories.

<u>Accept all reasonable responses. Carrots are taproots, a white potato is an example of a tuber, and an onion is the immature leaf of a plant.</u>

Plant Structure and Function

Section 23.3 Plant Responses

Main Idea ———— **Details** ————————————————

Make and Use Tables *As you read this section, make a table of plant stimuli and responses. Include the source of the stimulus and describe how the plant responds.* **Accept all reasonable responses.**

Stimulus	Response
Gravity	roots grow down, stems grow up
Light	leaves and stems grow toward light
Touch	tendrils coil around fence; mimosa leaves fold; flytrap's leaves snap shut
Hormones	fruit ripening; growth; cell division

Review Vocabulary *Use your book to define the following term.*

stimulus   anything in an organism's internal or external environment that

causes the organism to react

New Vocabulary *Use your book to define each term.*

auxins   group of plant hormones that promote cell elongation

cytokinins   group of hormones that stimulate mitosis and cell division

ethylene   plant hormone that promotes the ripening of fruit

gibberellins   group of plant hormones that cause plants to grow taller by

stimulating cell elongation

hormone   chemical produced in one part of an organism and transported to

another part, where it causes a physiological change

nastic movement   responsive movement of a plant not dependent on the direction of

the stimulus

tropism   growth response of a plant to an external stimulus

Section 23.3 Plant Responses (continued)

Main Idea ———— **Details** ————————————————————

Plant Hormones

I found this information on page _____.
SE, pp. 622–623
RE, pp. 272–273

Compare *four plant hormones by completing the table below.*

Hormone	How This Hormone Regulates Growth	A Characteristic of This Hormone	Another Benefit of This Hormone
Auxins	causes cells to lengthen or elongate	produced in apical meristems	delays fruit formation and keeps side branches from growing
Gibberellins	helps cells elongate	some dwarf plants do not produce these	increases the rate at which seeds begin to grow and buds develop
Cytokinins	stimulates the production of proteins needed for mitosis	effects are enhanced by other hormones	plant cells would never divide without it
Ethylene	causes cell walls to weaken and soften	is a gas made of carbon and hydrogen	speeds ripening of fruits

Plant Responses

I found this information on page _____.
SE, pp. 624–625
RE, pp. 273–274

Summarize *the two types of tropisms by completing the organizer below.*

Tropism is a change in a plant's growth due to an external stimulus.

The tropism is positive if the plant grows toward the stimulus.

The tropism is negative if the plant grows away from the stimulus.

Plants respond to phototropism as they grow toward light.

Stems respond to gravitropism as they grow against gravity away from the ground.

Section 23.3 Plant Responses (continued)

Main Idea	Details

Plant Responses

I found this information on page _____.

SE, pp. 624–625
RE, pp. 273–274

Compare *tropism and nastic movement. Place each characteristic in the correct location in the Venn diagram below.*

- does not involve growth
- involves growth
- involves plant response
- is reversible
- is not reversible
- response can be positive or negative

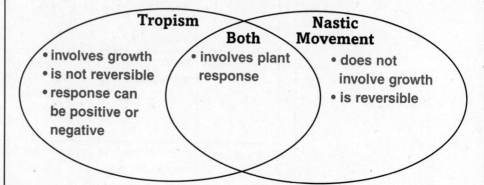

Tropism
- involves growth
- is not reversible
- response can be positive or negative

Both
- involves plant response

Nastic Movement
- does not involve growth
- is reversible

Classify *each of the following as examples of tropism or nastic movement.*

nastic movement — Venus's-flytrap closes on an insect.

tropism — Sweet pea tendrils climb a fence.

tropism — A plant grows toward a lamp.

nastic movement — Mimosa pudica leaflets become limp when touched.

tropism — Plant roots grow into the soil.

CONNECT Farmers often use hormones to improve their crop yield. Describe a hormone that a farmer might use and how the hormone can help increase crop output.

Accept all reasonable responses. Farmers use gibberellins to increase the formation of fruit.

Farmers may pick unripe fruit and use ethylene to ripen it later. Farmers may use auxins to

control the ripening of their fruits.

Tie-It-All-Together

SYNTHESIZE

You have read about the structure and function of plants.
Create a detailed and well-labeled diagram of a plant including the plant stem, roots, and
leaves. Beside each section, indicate the types of tissues and cells at work in these areas as well
as their functions. Your diagram may have smaller callouts where you draw a part of your dia-
gram in greater detail. Refer to the figure that shows the structure of roots in Section 2 for an
example of a callout. Be sure to indicate where growth and reproduction in the plant occur.
Accept all reasonable responses.

Plant Structure and Function Chapter Wrap-Up

In the "What I Wanted to Find Out" column, copy the questions you listed in the Chapter Preview. In the "What I Learned" column, write down the answers you discovered as you worked through the chapter.

W What I Wanted to Find Out	L What I Learned
1. Accept all reasonable entries.	1.
2.	2.
3.	3.

Use this checklist to help you study.

☐ Study your Science Notebook for this chapter.

☐ Study the definitions of vocabulary words.

☐ Review daily homework assignments.

☐ Reread the chapter and review the tables, graphs, and illustrations.

☐ Review the Section Assessment questions at the end of each section.

☐ Look over the Study Guide at the end of the chapter.

SUMMARIZE

After reading this chapter, list three things you have learned about plant structure and function.

Accept all reasonable responses. _____

_____

_____

Reproduction in Plants

Before You Read

Use the "What I Know" column to list three things you know about plant reproduction. Then list three questions you have about reproduction in plants in the "What I Want to Find Out" column.

K What I Know	W What I Want to Find Out
1. Accept all reasonable entries.	1. _____
	_____
2. _____	2. _____
	_____
3. _____	3. _____
	_____

Science Journal

Explain how you think life on Earth would be affected if plants were to stop reproducing.

Accept all reasonable responses.

_____

_____

_____

_____

_____

_____

_____

_____

Reproduction in Plants
Section 24.1 Life Cycles of Mosses, Ferns, and Conifers

Main Idea ———— **Details** ————————————

Skim *Section 1 of your book. Write three questions that come to mind from reading the headings and the illustration captions.*

1. Accept all reasonable responses._____

2. _____

3. _____

Review Vocabulary *Use your book to define the following term.*

gametophyte haploid form of an organism in alternation of generations that

produces gametes

New Vocabulary *Use your book to define each term.*

megaspore female spore formed by some plants that develops into a female

gametophyte

micropyle the opening in the ovule through which the pollen tube enters

microspore male spore formed by some plants that develops into a male

gametophyte

protonema in mosses, a small green filament of haploid cells that develops from

a spore; develops into the gametophyte

vegetative reproduction type of asexual reproduction in plants where a new plant is produced

from existing plant organs or parts of organs

Academic Vocabulary *Define the following terms.*

generation one of the successive phases that make up the life cycle of certain

organisms

release to set free from restraint, confinement, or servitude

Section 24.1 Life Cycles of Mosses, Ferns, and Conifers (continued)

Main Idea	Details

Alteration of Generations

I found this information on page _____.

SE, pp. 633–634
RE, pp. 276–277

Summarize *the alternation of generations found in plants by completing the flowchart below.*

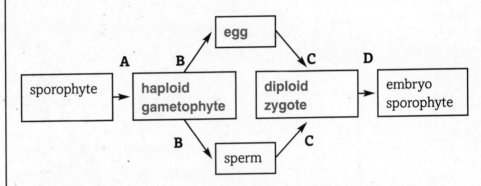

Identify *the steps in the alteration of generations that have been labeled in the flowchart above. Choose from the following terms.*

- cell division (appears twice)
- sex cells
- sexual reproduction

A cell division _____

B sex cells produced _____

C sexual reproduction _____

D cell division _____

Life Cycle of Mosses

I found this information on page _____.

SE, pp. 635–636
RE, pp. 277–278

Model *the life cycle of mosses by completing the flowchart below.*

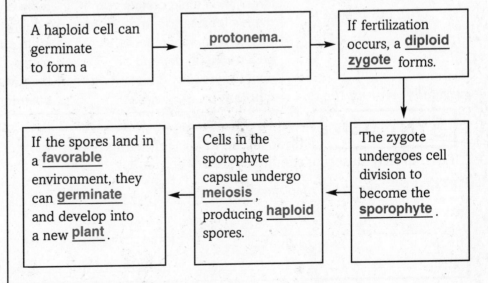

Section 24.1 Life Cycles of Mosses, Ferns, and Conifers (continued)

Main Idea	Details

Life Cycle of Ferns

I found this information on page _____.
SE, pp. 636–637
RE, pp. 278–279

Sequence *the life cycle of ferns by numbering the following steps in the order that they occur. The first and last steps have been done for you.*

__1__ A spore develops to form a prothallus.

__8__ If pieces of the rhizome break off, new fern plants can develop from the pieces by vegetative reproduction.

__4__ If fertilization occurs, the resulting diploid zygote develops into a sporophyte.

__6__ The prothallus dies and decomposes as the sporophyte matures.

__9__ The cycle continues when sporangia develop on the fronds and spores are released.

__7__ The mature fern consists of rhizomes from which roots and fronds grow.

__3__ Sperm released by antheridia swim to eggs in archegonia.

__5__ As soon as the sporophyte produces green fronds, it can carry on photosynthesis and live on its own.

__2__ The prothallus produces archegonia and antheridia on its surface.

Life Cycle of Conifers

I found this information on page _____.
SE, pp. 638–640
RE, pp. 280–281

Compare *female and male conifer cones by completing the table below. List three facts about each type of cone.* Accept all reasonable responses.

Female Cones	Male Cones
larger than male cones; two ovules form at top; megaspores eventually become female gametophyte; depend on sporophyte for protection and nutrition	male cones have sporangia that undergo meiosis to produce; male spores are called microspores; pollen grains have hard, water resistant outer covering

SYNTHESIZE

Choose one of the following plants: mosses, ferns, or conifers. Then briefly describe the life cycle of the plant.

Accept all reasonable responses.

_____

_____

Reproduction in Plants
Section 24.2 Flowers and Flowering

Main Idea	Details
	Assemble *For one week, find images of flowers in magazines and other periodicals. With permission, cut them out and bring them to class. Create a class list of the name of each flower and create a classification system of the flowers.*
	Lists of names will vary as will the classification system. Students might group their flowers by color, size, shape, numbers of flower parts, or whether the reproductive structures are obvious or not.

Review Vocabulary

Use your book to define the following term.

response

an organism's reaction to a change in its internal or external

environment

New Vocabulary

Use your book to define the following term.

photoperiodism

flowering plant response to differences in the length of night and day

Classify each term in the left column as being a type of plant or a part of a plant by filling in the table below. Write a brief definition of each term.

	Type of Flowering Plant (4 terms)	Part of Flowering Plant (6 terms)
anther	day-neutral plants: plants that flower over a range in the number of daylight hours	anther: pollen-producing structure located at the tip of a flower's stamen
day-neutral plants	long-day plants: plants that flower when the number of daylight hours is longer than its critical period	ovary: in plants, the bottom portion of a flower's pistil that contains one or more ovules, each containing one egg
long-day plants	short-day plant: a plant that flowers when the number of daylight hours is shorter than its critical period	petals: leaflike flower organs, usually brightly colored structures at the top of a stem
ovary		pistil: female reproductive organ of a flower
petals		sepals: leaflike, usually green structures that encircle the top of a flower stem below the petals
pistil		stamen: male reproductive organ of a flower consisting of an anther and a filament
sepals		
short-day plant		
stamen		

Section 24.2 Flowers and Flowering (continued)

Main Idea	Details

What is a flower?

I found this information on page _____.
SE, pp. 641–643
RE, pp. 283–284

Compare *the organs of a flower by completing the table below. Give the location and function for each organ.*

Organ	Location	Function
Petal	top of stem	attracts pollinators; provides surface for insect pollinators to rest on
Stamen	inside flower; anther at top of filament	male reproductive organ
Sepals	outermost part of flower	protective covering for flower bud
Pistil	attached to stem inside flower	female reproductive organ

Classify *each of the following as either a complete or an incomplete flower.*

walnut tree incomplete flower

rose complete flower

sweet corn incomplete flower

lily complete flower

Sketch *a flower and label the petals, sepals, stamen, and pistil.*
Sketches should resemble the one on SE p. 642, RE p. 284. The four organs should be labeled appropriately.

Section 24.2 Flowers and Flowering (continued)

Main Idea	Details

Photoperiodism

I found this information on page _____.
SE, pp. 643–645
RE, pp. 284–285

Compare *the four types of plants based on their critical periods.*

	Flowering Season	**Characteristic**	**Example**
Short-Day Plant	late summer, fall, winter or spring	flower when the number of daylight hours is shorter than the critical period	asters, poinsettias, strawberries, ragweed, pansies
Long-Day Plant	summer	flower when the number of daylight hours is longer than the critical period	carnations, petunias, potatoes, lettuce, spinach, wheat
Day-Neutral Plant	any season, as long as proper growing conditions exist	flower over a range in the number of daylight hours	roses, cucumbers, cotton, many tropical plants, dandelions
Intermediate-Day Plant	any season	will not flower if the days are shorter or longer than critical period	sugarcane, some grasses

Explain *why photoperiodism is important to plants.*

Photoperiodism is a physiological adaptation. All the plants of a

particular species flower at the same time, ensuring that there is a

larger population of pollinators. This ensures that the life cycle of a

plant continues.

SYNTHESIZE

Collect a flower from your home or neighborhood. Draw a diagram of the plant and label the major parts.
Accept all reasonable responses.

Reproduction in Plants
Section 24.3 The Life Cycle of a Flowering Plant

(Main Idea) ————

Make sure students use the titles in the section to guide their outlining. Struggling students may be confused by the traditional outline. Ask these students to make a simple numbered list of important concepts under each heading.

(Details) ————————————————

Finding Main Ideas *On a separate sheet of paper, construct an outline about the life cycle of a flowering plant. Use the titles in this section as a guideline. As you read the paragraphs that follow the titles, add important information and vocabulary words to your outline.* Accept all reasonable responses.

New Vocabulary *Use your book to define each term.*

dormancy	period of inactivity in a mature seed prior to germination
double fertilization	anthophyte fertilization in which one sperm fertilizes the egg and the other sperm joins with the central cell; results in the formation of a diploid (2n) zygote and a triploid (3n) endosperm
endosperm	food storage tisue in an anthophyte seed that supports development of the growing embryo
germination	beginning of the development of an embryo into a new plant
hypocotyl	portion of the stem nearest the seed in a young plant
polar nuclei	two nuclei in the center of the egg sac of a flowering plant that become the triploid (3n) endosperm when joined with a sperm during double fertilization
radicle	embryonic root of an anthophyte embryo; the first part of the young sporophyte to emerge during germination

Section 24.3 The Life Cycle of a Flowering Plant (continued)

Main Idea	Details

The Life Cycle of an Anthophyte

I found this information on page _____.
SE, pp. 646–651
RE, pp. 287–290

Summarize *the development of the female gametophyte by completing the flowchart below.*

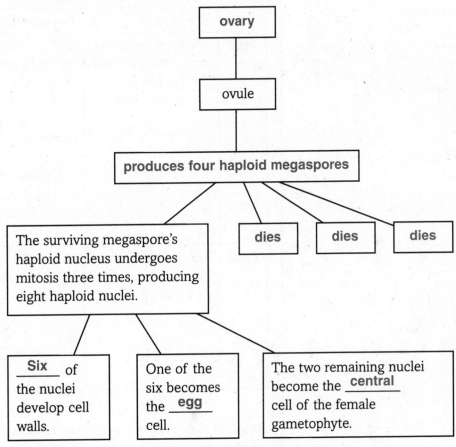

ovary

ovule

produces four haploid megaspores

The surviving megaspore's haploid nucleus undergoes mitosis three times, producing eight haploid nuclei.

dies   dies   dies

__Six__ of the nuclei develop cell walls.

One of the six becomes the __egg__ cell.

The two remaining nuclei become the __central__ cell of the female gametophyte.

Choose *one pollination adaptation and describe it in the space below.*

Accept all reasonable responses. Animal-pollinated plants produce

nectar in order to attract animal pollinators. By doing so, these

plants do not need to produce as much pollen as wind-pollinated

plants.

Describe *how the two haploid nuclei are involved in fertilization.*

Tube Nucleus	Generative Nucleus
directs the growth of the pollen tube down through the pistil to the ovary	divides by mitosis, producing two sperm nuclei, which move down the pollen tube to the microphyle

Section 24.3 The Life Cycle of a Flowering Plant (continued)

Main Idea ———— **Details** ————————————————

Seeds and Fruits

I found this information on page _____.
SE, pp. 651–657
RE, pp. 290–294

Compare *the characteristics of seeds and fruits by completing the table below.*

	Structure	**Formation**	**Benefit to Plant**
Seed	contains embryo and a food supply covered by a protective coat	begins when fertilization occurs; zygote divides and develops into embryo plant; triploid central cell develops into endosperm, wall of ovule becomes seed coat	ensures future generation
Fruit	includes the ripened ovary of a flower	as seed forms, the ovary becomes the fruit	protection of seeds, dispersal of seeds, ensures future generation

Explain *the specific conditions that the following seeds need to germinate.*

some conifer and wildflower seeds: must be exposed to fire

apple seeds: need a period of freezing temperatures

coconut seeds: have to soak in salt water

SYNTHESIZE Describe how seeds are dispersed. Choose one of the methods that is discussed in this section.

Accept all reasonable responses. Animals may eat the fruit and release the seeds as waste;

birds and squirrels may drop seeds; animals may bury seeds; plants produce seeds that float

or get blown by the wind.

Tie-It-All-Together

You have read about the life cycles of mosses, ferns, conifers, and flowering plants. Now create a simple science review manual explaining the life cycles of each type of plant. Your review manual should be easy to read, yet contain basic information on the male and female reproductive cells of each plant. Include specific examples in your review manual. A good review manual will have well-labeled diagrams. When you are finished, share your review manual with the class.

Accept all reasonable responses.

Reproduction in Plants Chapter Wrap-Up

In the "What I Wanted to Find Out" column, copy the questions you listed in the Chapter Preview. In the "What I Learned" column, write down the answers you discovered as you worked through the chapter.

W What I Wanted to Find Out	L What I Learned
1. Accept all reasonable entries. _____ _____	1. _____ _____
2. _____ _____	2. _____ _____
3. _____ _____	3. _____ _____

Use this checklist to help you study.

☐ Study your Science Notebook for this chapter.

☐ Study the definitions of vocabulary words.

☐ Review daily homework assignments.

☐ Reread the chapter and review the tables, graphs, and illustrations.

☐ Review the Section Assessment questions at the end of each section.

☐ Look over the Study Guide at the end of the chapter.

SUMMARIZE
After reading this chapter, list three things you have learned about plant reproduction.

Accept all reasonable responses.

_____

_____

What is an animal?

Before You Read

Use the "What I Know" column to list three things you know about animals. Then list three questions you have about animals in the "What I Want to Find Out" column.

K What I Know	W What I Want to Find Out
1. Accept all reasonable entries. _____	1. _____ _____
2. _____ _____	2. _____ _____
3. _____ _____	3. _____ _____

Science Journal

Describe at least three characteristics that distinguish animals from plants.

Accept all reasonable responses. _____

_____

_____

_____

_____

_____

_____

_____

What is an animal?
Section 25.1 Typical Animal Characteristics

Main Idea ———— **Details** ————————————————————

Scan *the titles, boldfaced words, pictures, figures, and captions in Section 1. Write two facts you discovered about animals as you scanned the section.*

1. Accept all reasonable responses.
_____

2. _____

New Vocabulary *Use your book to define each term.*

blastula cell-covered, fluid-filled ball formed during the early development of an animal embryo

deuterostome animal whose mouth develops from cells other than those at the gastrula opening

ectoderm layer of cells on the outer surface of the gastrula that eventually develops into skin and nervous tissue

endoderm layer of cells on inner surface of the gastrula; develops into digestive tract lining and digestive organs

gastrula embryo development stage; cells on one side of the blastula move inward to form cavity of two or three layers of cells with an opening at one end

mesoderm middle gastrula layer, between ectoderm and endoderm; develops into muscles, circulatory and excretory systems, and in some animals, the respiratory system

protostome animal with a mouth that develops from the gastrula opening

sessile permanently attached to a surface

Section 25.1 Typical Animal Characteristics (continued)

⟨Main Idea⟩———— ⟨Details⟩——————————————————————

Characteristics of Animals

I found this information on page _____ .
SE, pp. 673–675
RE, pp. 296–297

Identify *the following facts about animals.*

six characteristics of animals
they are eukaryotic, multicellular organisms; they move, get food,

reproduce, protect themselves; most have specialized cells that

develop into tissues and organs

one way animals are different from plants
plants make their own food from sunlight, animals have to get food

from other organisms

List *four sessile organisms and analyze the characteristics of their environment that allows them to be sessile.*

1. oysters

2. barnacles

3. corals

4. sponges

environment for sessile organisms: they live in the water and

currents bring food to them, so they do not have to move

Model *the digestive systems of earthworms and flatworms and describe their differences.*

mouth ⊂———————————————⊃ anus
Earthworm

Pharynx
Flatworm

Food enters and wastes exit through the same opening in flatworms.

Earthworms have a mouth and an anus, and food travels in only one

direction. Students may draw an open tube and a closed tube as

simplified diagrams. Accept all reasonable variations.

Section 25.1 Typical Animal Characteristics (continued)

Main Idea ——— **Details** ———————————————

Development of Animals

I found this information on page _____.
SE, pp. 676–679
RE, pp. 297–301

Describe *the sequence for the development of an animal from fertilization to birth by completing the following sentences.*

1. During <u>sexual</u> reproduction, fertilization occurs when an <u>egg cell</u> is penetrated by a <u>sperm cell</u>, forming a <u>zygote</u>.

2. After <u>mitosis</u> and cell division begin, the egg is called an embryo.

3. The cells form a fluid-filled ball called a <u>blastula</u>.

4. Some cells migrate inside, forming a cup-shaped structure called the <u>gastrula</u>, which has two cell layers. The layer on the outside is the <u>ectoderm</u> and will form the <u>nerve tissue and skin</u>. The inner layer is called the <u>endoderm</u>, which will form <u>the animal's digestive tract lining and organs that aid digestion</u>.

5. All animals retain the two embryonic cell layers throughout their lives, but others develop a third cell layer, the <u>mesoderm</u>, between the other layers. This layer forms <u>the muscles and other systems of the body</u>.

Draw *a gastrula. Label the mesoderm, ectoderm, and endoderm. Then in the table below write the tissue types that each layer develops into.*

Cell Layer	Forms These Tissues
Mesoderm	muscle, circulatory, excretory, sometimes respiratory
Ectoderm	skin, nerve
Endoderm	digestive tract lining and organs

Student diagrams should resemble the gastrula on RE p. 299, SE p. 678.

SYNTHESIZE

Compare and contrast protostomes and deuterostomes.

The two groups are differentiated mainly by the origin of their mouths (from the gastrula's opening in protostomes, from other cells in deuterostomes). Biologists hypothesize that protostome animals appeared earlier in evolution than deuterostomes did.

What is an animal?

Section 25.2 Body Plans and Adaptations

Main Idea ——— **Details** ————————————————

Make and Use Tables

After you read about the different types of animal symmetry, make a table to categorize 25 animals according to their symmetry. Include animals that you are familiar with or have read about in this book. Accept all reasonable responses.

Review Vocabulary

Use your book to define the following term.

gastrula | an embryonic structure made up of two layers of cells with an

opening at one end

New Vocabulary

Compare the terms within each table by writing their definitions.

anterior head end of bilateral animals where sensory organs are often located	posterior tail end of bilaterally symmetric animals	dorsal upper surface of bilaterally symmetric animals	ventral lower surface of bilaterally symmetric animals

symmetry a term describing the arrangement of an animal's body structures	
bilateral can be divided down the body's length into two similar right and left halves	radial can be divided along any plane, through a central axis, into roughly equal halves

endoskeleton internal skeleton	exoskeleton hard covering on the outside of some animals

vertebrate an animal with a backbone and endoskeleton	invertebrate an animal without a backbone

coelom fluid-filled body cavity completely surrounded by mesoderm	acoelomate an animal without a coelom	psuedoceolom fluid-filled body cavity partly lined with mesoderm

Section 25.2 Body Plans and Adaptations (continued)

Main Idea ————— **Details** ————————————————————————

What Is Symmetry?

I found this information on page _____.

SE, pp. 680–685
RE, pp. 302–303

Explain *the evolutionary sequence by using the terms below to complete the sentences.*

- anterior
- asymmetrical
- bilateral symmetry
- coelomate
- posterior
- prey
- radial symmetry
- sponges
- three

The earliest animals had __asymmetrical__ body plans, as do their modern descendants, such as __sponges__ .

↓

Later, sea stars, hydras, and other animals appeared with __radial symmetry__ . They were able to detect and capture __prey__ coming from any direction.

↓

The last body plan to develop was __bilateral symmetry__ with a head at the __anterior__ end of the body and a tail at the __posterior__ end of the body.

↓

All of the animals developed from __three__ embryonic cell layers, and many have fluid-filled body cavities. If the cavities are completely lined with mesoderm, the animals are called __coelomates__ .

Model *a bilaterally symmetrical human being. Then create comic book characters, one that is asymmetrical, and one that has radial symmetry. Use your imagination. Explain the number of arms, legs, eyes, etc. that each type of comic book character has.* Students may suggest a variety of fanciful pictures. Accept all answers that show the correct symmetry.

Bilateral Symmetry	Radial Symmetry	Assymetrical
body parts: 2 eyes, 2 legs, 2 arms, 1 nose in center	body parts:	body parts:

Section 25.2 Body Plans and Adaptations (continued)

| Main Idea | Details |

Animal Protection and Support

I found this information on page _____.
SE, pp. 682–684
RE, pp. 304–305

Describe *the types of protection (type of skeleton or shell) each type of animal has and explain characteristics of the skeleton or shell.*

mollusks hard shell protects soft body

beetles exoskeleton is secreted by epidermis and extends into the body where it provides a place for muscle attachment

horses endoskeleton of bone supports the body, protects internal organs, and provides internal brace for muscles to pull against

sharks endoskeleton of cartilage supports the body, protects internal organs, and provides internal brace for muscles to pull against

Origin of Animals

I found this information on page _____.
SE, pp. 682–684
RE, p. 306

Sequence *the organisms with the oldest at the bottom and the most recently evolved at the top.*

acoelomates
coelomates
sponges

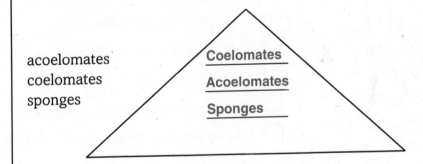

Coelomates
Acoelomates
Sponges

SUMMARIZE

Read each prefix below. Then write what you think is the meaning of the prefix. Afterwards, check the meaning of each prefix in a dictionary and write this definition next to your original one. Accept all reasonable responses. Encourage students to create their own hypotheses before going to the dictionary.

endo- endoskeleton animals have their skeletons inside; inside

exo- exoskeleton animals have their skeletons on the outside; outside

bi- bilateral symmetry is symmetrical in two ways; two parts

in- invertebrates have no vertebrae; without

What is an animal? Chapter Wrap-Up

In the "What I Wanted to Find Out" column, copy the questions you listed in the Chapter Preview. In the "What I Learned" column, write down the answers you discovered as you worked through the chapter.

W What I Wanted to Find Out	L What I Learned
1. Accept all reasonable entries. _____	1. _____ _____
2. _____ _____	2. _____ _____
3. _____ _____	3. _____ _____

Use this checklist to help you study.

☐ Study your Science Notebook for this chapter.

☐ Study the definitions of vocabulary words.

☐ Review daily homework assignments.

☐ Reread the chapter and review the tables, graphs, and illustrations.

☐ Review the Section Assessment questions at the end of each section.

☐ Look over the Study Guide at the end of the chapter.

SUMMARIZE

After reading this chapter, list three things you have learned about animals.

Accept all reasonable responses.

_____

_____

Sponges, Cnidarians, Flatworms, and Roundworms

Before You Read

Use the "What I Know" column to list three things you know about sponges, cnidarians, flatworms, and roundworms. Then list three questions you have about these organisms in the "What I Want to Find Out" column.

K What I Know	W What I Want to Find Out
1. Accept all reasonable entries. 	1. _____ _____
2. _____ _____	2. _____ _____
3. _____ _____	3. _____ _____

Science Journal

Even the simplest organism has a role in the ecological community. Hypothesize the role of sponges and cnidarians in the oceans. Why would people need to know about flatworms and roundworms?

Accept all reasonable responses.

_____

_____

_____

_____

_____

_____

_____

_____

Sponges, Cnidarians, Flatworms, and Roundworms

Section 26.1 Sponges

Main Idea ———— **Details** ————————————

Scan *Section 1 of your book. Use the checklist as a guide.*

☐ Read all section titles.

☐ Read all boldfaced words.

☐ Read all tables and graphs.

☐ Look at all pictures and read the captions.

☐ Think about what you already know about communicating in science.

Write three facts you discovered as you scanned the section.

1. <u>Accept all reasonable responses.</u>

2. _____

3. _____

Review Vocabulary *Use your book to define the following term.*

sessile | an organism that is permanently attached to a surface

New Vocabulary *Use your book to define each term.*

external fertilization | fertilization that occurs outside the animal's body

filter feeding | the filtering of food particles from water as it passes by or through

some part of the organism

hermaphrodite | an animal that can produce both eggs and sperm

internal fertilization | fertilization that occurs inside the female's body

Academic Vocabulary *Define the following term.*

differentiate | to make or become become distinct or different in character

Section 26.1 Sponges (continued)

Main Idea ——

What is a sponge?

I found this information on page _____.

SE, pp. 693–697
RE, p. 309

Details ——

Model *a sponge. Use the figure in your book to help you. Label the six parts that are listed in the table below on your diagram. Then describe the function of each part in the table below.*

Sponges	
Body Part	**Function of Body Part**
osculum	water and wastes are expelled through this large opening at the top of the sponge
epithelial-like cells	thin, flat cells that contract (and close pores) in response to touch or an irritating chemical
collar cells	cells that line the interior of the sponge; their flagella whip back and forth to draw in water
pore cell	cells that surround pores and allow water (with food and oxygen) into the sponge's body
amoebocytes	carry nutrients to other cells, aid in reproduction, and produce spicule chemicals
spicules	small, needlelike structures between cell layers that form the support structure

Section 26.1 Sponges (continued)

Main Idea ———— **Details** ————————————————————

What is a sponge?

I found this information on page _____.

SE, pp. 693–697
RE, pp. 308–311

Summarize *reproduction methods of sponges by completing the following sentences.*

A bud is _____ **an external growth on a sponge** _____.

When a bud drops off, _____ **it floats away, settles, and grows into a** _____ **sponge** _____.

When a bud does not drop off _____ **a single sponge becomes** _____ **a colony of sponges** _____.

If a fragment drops off _____ **it can grow into a whole new sponge** _____.

Gemmules are _____ **seedlike particles** _____ that are produced when **water temperature cools** _____.

In the spring, gemmules _____ **grow into new sponges** _____.

The advantage of hermaphroditism for sessile sponges is that it **increases the chances that fertilization will occur** _____.

Fertilization usually occurs _____ **internally** _____ and results in _____ **free-swimming larvae** that **settle and grow into adult sponges** _____.

SUMMARIZE Create a concept web to connect at least 10–15 facts about sponges from this section. Include all of the terms below.

- evolved
- feeding
- sessile
- reproduction
- species
- shaped
- spicule
- spongin

Accept all reasonable responses. Encourage students to lay out their ideas logically and encourage accuracy and detail. Some students may find it easier to list the facts on paper before connecting them in the web.

Sponges, Cnidarians, Flatworms, and Roundworms

Section 26.2 Cnidarians

Main Idea	Details

Finding Main Ideas *Construct an outline about cnidarian characteristics. Use the titles in this section of your book as a guideline. As you read the paragraphs that follow the titles, add important information and vocabulary words to your outline.*
Accept all reasonable responses.

I. What is a cnidarian?

    A. Body Structure

        1. Radially symmetrical; one opening; two layers of cells

        2. Oxygen and carbon dioxide exchange occurs directly between cells and water

    B. Body Forms

        1. Polyp

        2. Medusa

Review Vocabulary

Use your book to define the following term.

endocytosis
a process where a cell engulfs materials with a portion of the cell's plasma membrane and releases the contents inside the cell

New Vocabulary

Use your book to define each term.

gastrovascular cavity
in cnidarians, a large cavity in which digestion takes place

medusa
a cnidarian body form that is umbrella-shaped with tentacles that hang down

nematocyst
in cnidarians, a capsule that contains a coiled, threadlike tube that may be sticky or barbed or contain poisons; used in capturing prey

nerve net
simple netlike nervous system in cnidarians that conducts nerve impulses from all parts of the cnidarian's body

polyp
tubelike cnidarian body form with a mouth surrounded by tentacles

Section 26.2 Cnidarians (continued)

⟨**Main Idea**⟩——

⟨**Details**⟩————————————————

What is a cnidarian?

I found this information on page _____.

SE, pp. 698–702
RE, pp. 312–314

Compare *a polyp with a medusa by filling in the table.*

	Polyp	**Medusa**
Body shape	tubelike	umbrella (bell)
Position of mouth	top side	underside
Position of tentacles	top side	underside

Model *the complete life cycle of a jellyfish.*

Diagrams should resemble RE p. 313, SE p. 700. Accept all reasonable variations.

Name _____   Date _____

Section 26.2 Cnidarians (continued)

Main Idea ————

Diversity of Cnidarians, Origins of Sponges and Cnidarians

I found this information on page _____.
SE, pp. 702–705
RE, pp. 314–316

Encourage students to make little sketches or notes of each class in the concept map space.

Details ————————————————————

Summarize *the Cnidarian classes and examples of each in the concept map.*

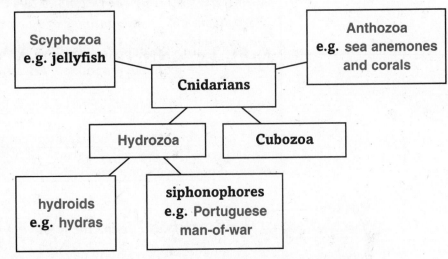

Describe *the symbiotic relationship between corals and zooxanthellae.*

Zooxanthellae photosynthesize and produce food and oxygen for the

corals, while utilizing the carbon dioxide and wastes the corals

produce. Corals get their color from the zooxanthellae and may die

if the zooxanthellae leave.

Identify *two reasons scientists have inferred that sponges and cnidarians evolved from protists.*

1. The flagellated protists resemble collar cells of sponges.

2. The larval form of cnidarians resembles protists.

COMPARE Write a few sentences comparing cnidarians and sponges.

Accept all reasonable responses. Both groups have one body opening and two cell layers.

Gases diffuse directly between the cells and water in both groups. Cnidarians have radial

symmetry, but sponges are asymmetrical. Most cnidarians have polyp and medusa stages in

their life cycle. Most sponges have the same form throughout their life cycle.

Sponges, Cnidarians, Flatworms, and Roundworms

Section 26.3 Flatworms

Main Idea	Details
	Compare and contrast *Compile two lists: Advantages of Parasitism and Disadvantages of Parasitism. Infer what structural adaptations are found in most parasites.*
	Accept all reasonable responses. Advantages of parasitism: easy access to food; no need to move about to escape predators or find food or mates (most are hermaphrodites). Disadvantages: cannot survive outside a host; when host dies, parasite dies.

Review Vocabulary

Use your book to define the following term.

acoelomate | an animal that has no body cavity

New Vocabulary

Use your book to define each term.

pharynx | in planarians, the tubelike, muscular organ that extends from the mouth; aids in feeding and digestion

proglottid | a section of a tapeworm that contains muscles, nerves, flame cells, eggs, and reproductive organs

regeneration | replacement or regrowth of missing body parts

scolex | knob-shaped head of a tapeworm

Academic Vocabulary

Define the following term.

complex | composed of two or more parts; hard to separate, analyze, or solve

Section 26.3 Flatworms (continued)

⟨Main Idea⟩ ————	⟨Details⟩ ————————————————————

What is a flatworm?

I found this information on page _____ .
SE, pp. 706–710
RE, pp. 318–322

Summarize *facts about flatworms in the table.*
Accept all reasonable responses.

Size Range **1mm to several meters**	Number of Species **14 500**
Preferred Environments **freshwater, marine, and even moist land habitats**	Difference Between Flukes and Planarians **flukes are parasitic and cause disease, but planarians can live on their own**
Diet of a Planarian **dead or slow-moving organisms**	Symmetry **bilaterally symmetrical**
What Happens When They Are Damaged **planarians regenerate, or grow new body parts**	Why Parasitic Flatworms are Simpler than Planarians **they are surrounded by nutrients and do not need to move to get food**

Model *a planarian. Include at least nine body parts.*
Diagrams should resemble SE p. 708. RE p. 320. Accept all reasonable variations.

Section 26.3 Flatworms (continued)

Main Idea —— **Details** ———————————————————————

What is a flatworm?

I found this information on page _____.
SE. pp. 708–710
RE, p. 320

Identify *the planarian body part for each function.*

Functions	Body Part
taking in food	pharynx
detecting chemicals and movements in environment	sensory cells
removing excess water	flame cells
sensing and responding to the environment in front of the animal	head, nerve net or central nervous system
sensing light	eyespots
receive messages from eyespots, sensory cells	ganglia
communicates with rest of body	nerve cords
moving	cilia

Model *the life cycle of a fluke.*
Diagrams should resemble RE p. 321, SE p. 710.

CONNECT

Identify a human disorder that tapeworms and flukes may cause.

Group	Human Disorder Caused
Tapeworms	Infestation of intestines
Flukes	Schistosomiasis

Sponges, Cnidarians, Flatworms, and Roundworms

Section 26.4 Roundworms

Main Idea ———— **Details** ——————————————————————————————

Research *Collect information about roundworm life cycles, ways to prevent infection by round worms, and recommended treatments for roundworm infections.*

Accept all reasonable responses. Student research will depend on

geographic area and roundworm pest chosen. Be sure that students

include documentation of facts.

Review Vocabulary *Use your book to define the following term.*

pseudocoelom | fluid-filled body cavity partly lined with mesoderm

New Vocabulary *Use your book to define the following term.*

trichinosis | a disease caused by the roundworm Trichinella that can be ingested

in raw or undercooked pork, pork products, or wild game

Academic Vocabulary *Define the following terms.*

infer | to derive as a conclusion from facts or premises

expose | to lay open to danger or attack; to uncover or bare

Section 26.4 Roundworms (continued)

Main Idea	Details

What is a roundworm?

I found this information on page _____.

SE, p.711
RE, p. 323

Describe *the structure and movement of a roundworm.*

Roundworms are tapered at both ends, with a thick outer covering

that protects them in harsh environments. They have lengthwise

muscles but not circular muscles. They move in a thrashing fashion

as these muscles relax and contract.

Identify *the roundworm that matches each description.*

Description	Animal
most common roundworm parasite in the U.S.	pinworm
enters the human body through bare feet	hookworm
world's most common roundworm infection	Ascaris
carried by infected, undercooked pork	Trichinella
causes plant diseases	nematode

Diversity of Roundworms

I found this information on page _____.

SE, pp. 712–713
RE, p. 324

Identify *a positive and a negative effect of nematodes on plants.*

negative: By attaching themselves to plant roots, nematodes can

cause the plants to sicken.

positive: If added to the soil just after weevil larvae have hatched,

nematodes can protect plants from insects.

CONNECT

Compare the digestive tracts of roundworms with those in sponges, hydras, planarians, and humans. What does the comparison suggest about the probable evolutionary history of roundworms?

Accept all reasonable responses. Unlike sponges, hydras, and planarians, but like humans,

roundworms have digestive tracts with two openings. This type of digestive tract is more

advanced, and so roundworms probably appeared later than sponges, hydras, and planarians.

Tie-It-All-Together

Create a time line to show some important evolutionary advances in the organisms in this chapter. Fill in the diagram to summarize

• the likely order in which major changes occurred;

• what the changes were;

• the groups in which they appeared.

Accept all reasonable responses. Emphasize the fact that this is only a timeline. A group that precedes another in the chart is not necessarily ancestral to the group that follows.

Tell students not to include reproductive structures in the diagram; both asexual and sexual reproduction are found in the protists that preceded these groups, although specific reproductive structures appeared later on.

Group: **Sponges**

Changes: **Change from unicellularity to multicellularity**

Sessile life

Group: **Cnidarians**

Changes: **Two cell layers**

Radial symmetry

Tentacles

Mouth

Group: **Flatworms**

Changes: **Eyespots**

Simple nervous system or nerve net

Group: **Roundworms**

Changes: **Two digestive tract openings**

Three body layers

Pseudocoelom

Sponges, Cnidarians, Flatworms, and Roundworms   Chapter Wrap-Up

In the "What I Wanted to Find Out" column, copy the questions you listed in the Chapter Preview. In the "What I Learned" column, write down the answers you discovered as you worked through the chapter.

W What I Wanted to Find Out	L What I Learned
1. Accept all reasonable entries.	1.
2.	2.
3.	3.

Use this checklist to help you study.

☐ Study your Science Notebook for this chapter.

☐ Study the definitions of vocabulary words.

☐ Review daily homework assignments.

☐ Reread the chapter and review the tables, graphs, and illustrations.

☐ Review the Section Assessment questions at the end of each section.

☐ Look over the Study Guide at the end of the chapter.

SUMMARIZE
After reading this chapter, list three things you have learned about sponges, cnidarians, flatworms, and roundworms.

Accept all reasonable responses.

_____

_____

_____

Mollusks and Segmented Worms

Before You Read

Before you read the chapter, use the "What I Know" column to list three things you know about mollusks and segmented worms. Then list three questions you have about these animals in the "What I Want to Find Out" column.

K What I Know	W What I Want to Find Out
1. Accept all reasonable entries.	1.
2.	2.
3.	3.

Science Journal

What is the purpose of the mucus layer on snails, slugs, and other mollusks? Write about experiences you have had with snails and slugs.

Accept all reasonable responses.

Mollusks and Segmented Worms
Section 27.1 Mollusks

Main Idea	Details
	Skim *Section 1 of your book. Write three questions that come to mind from reading the headings and the illustration captions.*
	1. Accept all reasonable responses.
	2. _____
	3. _____
Review Vocabulary	*Use your book to define the following term.*
coelom	a fluid-filled body cavity completely surrounded by mesoderm
New Vocabulary	*Use your book to define each term.*
closed circulatory system	system in which blood moves through the body enclosed entirely in a series of blood vessels
mantle	a membrane that surrounds the internal organs of a mollusk; in mollusks with shells, it secretes the shell
nephridia	organs that remove metabolic wastes from an animal's body
open circulatory system	system where blood moves through vessels into open spaces around the body organs
radula	in some snails and mollusks, the rasping, tonguelike organ used to drill, scrape, grate, or cut food
Academic Vocabulary	*Define the following term.*
coordinate	to bring into a common action, movement, or condition; harmonize

Section 27.1 Mollusks (continued)

Main Idea	Details

What is a mollusk?

I found this information on page _____.
SE, pp. 721–725
RE, pp. 326–328

Draw *a snail and a squid. Label the parts of each. Identify the structures that make the organism different.*

> Diagrams should resemble RE p. 327, SE p. 722. Accept all reasonable responses.

The structures that make them different are the snail's foot and the squid's tentacles

Describe *two ways mollusks feed.*

Radula: a tonguelike organ with rows of teeth used to scrape, cut, and grate food

Filter feeders: mollusks that draw in food from the water and strain it

Compare *the way mollusks reproduce in water and on land.*

in water: eggs and sperm are released at the same time and fertilization is external	on land: many land mollusks are hermaphrodites and produce both sperm and eggs, and fertilization takes place within the animal

Section 27.1 Mollusks (continued)

Main Idea ——— **Details** ———————————————————

Diversity of Mollusks

I found this information on page _____.
SE, pp. 725–727
RE, pp. 329–330

Identify *the three classes of mollusks and the meaning of each class name. Provide at least three examples of each class.*

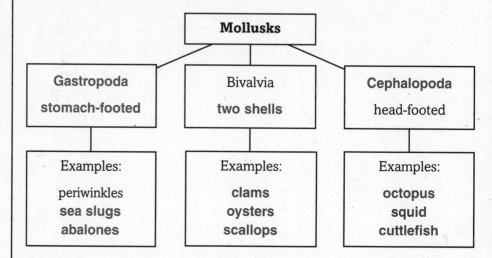

Classify *each mollusk in the left column of the table. Place it in the proper class (such as Bivalvia).*

Mollusk	Class
has a beautiful shell that is often collected on beaches and a large foot under the body	Gastropoda
has no radula; has two shells connected with a ligament, and a large, muscular foot for digging in the sand	Bivalvia
is brightly colored and has a layer of mucus covering its body; has a large foot under the body and no shell	Gastropoda
has a radula and tentacles; has no shell; squirts ink at predators	Cephalopoda

CONNECT Write a few lines comparing mollusks' excretory structures with those of two or more groups that evolved earlier.

Accept all reasonable responses. Mollusks have nephridia, excretory structures that filter

metabolic wastes from the coelom and remove the wastes from the body. Planarias have

simpler structures called flame cells that move fluid along and eliminate water. A jellyfish has

no excretory structures; water and salts move in and out of the body by osmosis.

Mollusks and Segmented Worms

Section 27.2 Segmented Worms

Main Idea ——— **Details** ————————————————

Finding Main Ideas *As you read through Section 2, answer the following questions.*

1. What is the basic body plan of a segmented worm?

a tube within a tube

2. Describe the digestive process of an earthworm.

Food and soil are taken in by the mouth, passed to the gizzard, and

then to the intestine. Undigested material and solid waste pass out

of the body through the anus.

3. Why are some leeches considered parasites?

Most leeches suck blood or body fluid from the bodies of their

hosts.

Review Vocabulary

Use your book to define the following term.

parasitism

symbiotic relationship in which one organism benefits at the

expense of the other species

New Vocabulary

Model a segmented worm. Write captions to define the gizzard, setae, and other parts. Diagrams should resemble RE p. 334, SE p. 731.

gizzard

part of the worm's digestive tract with a muscular sac and hard particles that help grind soil and food before they pass into the worm's intestine

setae

tiny bristles on each segment of a segmented worm that help it move

Academic Vocabulary

Define the following terms.

to discover or determine the existence or presence of

detect

distinguishable to the eye or mind as discrete

distinct

Name _____ Date _____

Section 27.2 Segmented Worms (continued)

(Main Idea) ——

(Details) ————————————————————————————

What is a segmented worm?/Why is segmentation important?

I found this information on page _____.

SE, pp. 728–730
RE, pp. 332–334

Define *segmentation and state its two main advantages.*

Segmented animals have corresponding inner and outer segments.

(1) Because each segment has its own muscles, a worm can move

by shortening and lengthening its body. (2) Segmentation allows

for specialization of body tissues, with different segments being

adapted for different purposes.

Sequence *the process of digestion in segmented worms.*

Food enters through the mouth.	Food passes through the digestive tract to the gizzard, which grinds the food.
Undigested food and solid wastes leave the body through the anus.	Food is digested in the intestine.

Create *a diagram of the process of reproduction in earthworms, based on the word description in your book.*

Accept all reasonable responses. Artwork is unimportant; the important item that should be included is the mutual exchange of sperm by these hermaphroditic animals.

Section 27.2 Segmented Worms (continued)

Main Idea ——— **Details** ————————————————————————

Diversity of Segmented Worms

I found this information on page _____ .
SE, pp. 730–732
RE, pp. 335–336

Describe *two characteristics of each group of animals. Then write the class and the phylum to which they belong.* Accept all reasonable responses.

fanworms sea mice bristleworms	leeches	earthworms
they have many bristles; have heads and eyes	segmented worms with flattened bodies and front and rear suckers to attach to host body	have anterior and posterior sections but no heads; fertlize the soil
Class: **Polychaeta**	Class: **Hirudinea**	Class: **Oligochaeta**

Phylum: **Annelida**

Origins of Mollusks and Segmented Worms

I found this information on page _____ .
SE, p. 733
RE, pp. 336–337

Summarize *the fossilization of segmented worms and mollusks by completing the sentences.*

Because ____annelids____ have nearly no hard body parts, the fossil record for segmented worms is limited. The most common fossils they left were tubes formed by the __polychaetes__ . They appear in the fossil record __540 million years ago__ . The phylum may have originated from the larvae of ancestral ____flatworms____ . ____Mollusks____ are seen later in the fossil record. Precambrian deposits include shells of __gastropods__ , __bivalves__ , and __cephalopods__ .

CONNECT

Compare the kind of circulatory system found in annelids with that found in some mollusks. State the advantage of the annelid type.

Accept all reasonable responses. Annelids have closed circulatory systems, with the blood

entirely enclosed in blood vessels. Some mollusks have open circulatory systems, in which

the blood flows through vessels and in open spaces, as well. A closed system provides a

more efficient means for gas exchanges (oxygen and carbon dioxide) in the animal.

Mollusks and Segmented Worms Chapter Wrap-Up

In the "What I Wanted to Find Out" column, copy the questions you listed in the Chapter Preview. In the "What I Learned" column, write down the answers you discovered as you worked through the chapter.

W What I Wanted to Find Out	L What I Learned
1. Accept all reasonable entries. _____	1. _____ _____
2. _____ _____	2. _____ _____
3. _____ _____	3. _____ _____

Use this checklist to help you study.

☐ Study your Science Notebook for this chapter.

☐ Study the definitions of vocabulary words.

☐ Review daily homework assignments.

☐ Reread the chapter and review the tables, graphs, and illustrations.

☐ Review the Section Assessment questions at the end of each section.

☐ Look over the Study Guide at the end of the chapter.

SUMMARIZE

After reading this chapter, list three things you have learned about mollusks and segmented worms.

Accept all reasonable responses.

_____

_____

_____

Arthropods

Before You Read

Use the "What I Know" column to list three things you know about arthropods. Then list three questions you have about them in the "What I Want to Find Out" column.

K What I Know	W What I Want to Find Out
1. Accept all reasonable entries. _____ _____	1. _____ _____
2. _____ _____	2. _____ _____
3. _____ _____	3. _____ _____

Science Journal

Speculate about what would happen if cockroaches and other insects were to disappear.

Accept all reasonable responses. Because of their importance in food webs, the impact of

extinguishing insect species might be disastrous.

_____

_____

_____

_____

_____

Arthropods

Section 28.1 Characteristics of Arthropods

Main Idea ———— **Details** ————————————————————————

Skim *Section 1 of your book. Write three questions that come to mind from reading the headings and the illustration captions.*

1. Accept all reasonable responses._____

2. _____

3. _____

Review Vocabulary *Use your book to define the following term.*

exoskeleton | a hard coating that provides support and protection in some animals

New Vocabulary

appendage

book lungs

cephalothorax

compound eye

Malpighian tubule

mandibles

molting

parthenogenesis

pheromones

simple eye

spiracles

tracheal tubes

Use your book to help you place the vocabulary terms where they belong in the following table. The number in brackets shows the number of terms in each column. Write one or two words to help you remember what each term means. Accept all reasonable responses.

Body Parts (8)	Chemicals (1)	Processes (2)
appendage: arm, leg	pheromones:	parthenogenesis:
book lungs: spiders	odor signals	asexual reproduction
cephalothorax: fused		molting: shedding
compound eye:		
multiple lenses		
Malpighian tubule:		
wastes		
mandibles:		
mouth parts		
simple eye: light		
spiracles: openings		
tracheal tubes: air		

Section 28.1 Characteristics of Arthropods (continued)

Main Idea ———— **Details** ————————————————

What is an arthropod?

I found this information on page _____.

SE, pp. 741–746
RE, pp. 338–342

Identify *six characteristics of arthropods.*

> invertebrate,
> bilateral symmetry,
> segmentation, jointed appendages,
> coelom, external skeleton

List *the advantages and disadvantages of an exoskeleton.* Accept all reasonable responses.

Advantages	Disadvantages
slows water loss	has extra weight
protects the body	limits body size
supports internal organs	must be molted
provides points of attachment for muscles	

Discuss *the different body sections and amount of fusion in various types of arthropods.*

Accept all reasonable responses. Arthropods have fewer segments

than worms. Most have a head, thorax, and abdomen, though some

have a cephalothorax which is a fused head and thorax. Other

arthropods have a fused thorax and abdomen with a separate head.

With more fusion, there is more protection, but less flexible

movement.

Section 28.1 Characteristics of Arthropods (continued)

Main Idea	Details
What is an arthropod? *I found this information on page* _____ *.* SE, pp. 741–746 RE, pp. 338–342	**Model** *the respiratory structures for a grasshopper, a crab, and a spider.* Diagrams should resemble SE p. 744, RE p. 340. Accept all reasonable variations.

Create *a concept map with at least four facts about arthropod reproduction.*

Accept all reasonable responses. Encourage detail. Facts student may include: arthropods may be hermaphrodites (such as barnacles)—which means they have male and female sex organs, or they may have separate sexes (most species do). They may reproduce sexually, then fertilization is usually external. Bees, ant, aphids, and wasps reproduce by parthenogenesis.

ANALOGY   Describe at least three kinds of arthropod mandibles, and name an animal in which each kind of mandible is found. For each one, state a human tool that performs a similar function.

Accept all reasonable responses. (1) piercing, sand flies, knife or spear (2) sucking tube,

moths, drinking straw (3) sponging tongue, housefly, spoon or sponge

_____

Arthropods

Section 28.2 Diversity of Arthropods

Main Idea	Details
	Infer *What structures enable arthropods to eat varied diets? Explain.*
	Mouth parts are modified to chew or take in a variety of foods. Legs are modified to capture prey or take in other materials. Digestive systems are modified to digest specific foods.
Review Vocabulary	*Use your book to define the following term.*
habitat	A place where an organism lives out its life
New Vocabulary	*Use your book to define each term.*
chelicerae	appendages located near the mouth; they are often modified into pincers or fangs
larva	in insects, the free-living, wormlike stage of metamorphosis, such as a caterpillar
metamorphosis	in insects, a series of chemically-controlled changes in body structure from juvenile to adult; may be complete or incomplete
nymph	stage of incomplete metamorphosis where an insect hatching from an egg has the same general appearance as the adult but is smaller and sexually immature
pedipalps	arachnid appendages that are often adapted for handling food and sensing
pupa	stage of insect metamorphosis where tissues and organs are broken down and replaced by adult tissues; larva emerges from pupa as mature
spinnerets	glands that spin silk into thread, located at the rear end of a spider

Section 28.2 Diversity of Arthropods (continued)

Main Idea — **Details**

Arachnids

I found this information on page _____.
SE, pp. 747–749
RE, pp. 344–345

Identify *the body part for each function.*

Function	Spider Body Part or Product
spinning silk	spinnerets
protection of eggs	cocoon
imageless, light-sensitive sight	simple eyes
holding and moving food or sperm	pedipalps
poisoning prey	chelicerae
gas exchange	book lungs
making silk	silk glands

Draw *a spider. Label at least six parts.*
Drawings should resemble SE p. 749, RE p. 345. Accept all reasonable variations. Encourage students to make brief notes to help them remember and understand.

Describe *the type of food eaten by each group of arachnids.*

Arachnid Group	Food
scorpions	insects, spiders
mites	fungi, plants, animals
ticks	blood from reptiles, birds, and mammals

Section 28.2 Diversity of Arthropods (continued)

Main Idea ——— **Details** ————————————————————

Crustaceans, Centipedes and Millipedes, Horseshoe Crabs: Living Fossils, and Insects

I found this information on page _____.

SE, pp. 748–754
RE, pp. 346–348

Organize *arthropod classifications and examples by completing the map.*

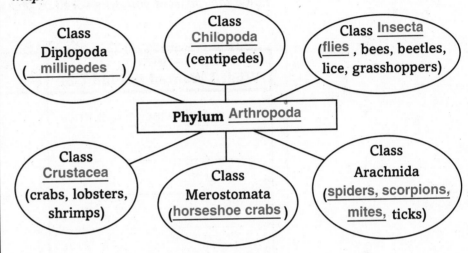

Class Diplopoda (<u>millipedes</u>)

Class <u>Chilopoda</u> (centipedes)

Class <u>Insecta</u> (<u>flies</u> , bees, beetles, lice, grasshoppers)

Phylum <u>Arthropoda</u>

Class <u>Crustacea</u> (crabs, lobsters, shrimps)

Class Merostomata (<u>horseshoe crabs</u>)

Class Arachnida (<u>spiders, scorpions, mites,</u> ticks)

Identify *four stages in metamorphosis.*

<u>Fertilized eggs hatch into larvae, which eat huge amounts of food to</u>

<u>grow and become pupae. Pupae reorganize into a new body form</u>

<u>and sexually mature adult insects emerge.</u>

Origins of Arthropods

I found this information on page _____.

SE, pp. 754–755
RE, pp. 348–349

Write *the missing words in the sentences about arthropod evolution.*

The success of arthropods is due in part to their <u>varied life cycles</u>, <u>high reproductive output</u>, and <u>structural adaptations</u>.
They evolved from the same ancestors as <u>annelids</u>, but arthropods have more developed <u>nerve tissue</u> and <u>sensory organs</u> and their <u>exoskeletons</u> provide protection and support. Muscles in arthropods are arranged in <u>bands</u>.

COMPARE AND CONTRAST

Compare and contrast insects and arachnids.

<u>Accept all reasonable responses. Both groups are small arthropods with a head, thorax, and</u>

<u>abdomen. Arachnids have a cephalothorax (a fused head and thorax); insects have all three</u>

<u>sections. Insects have six legs; arachnids have eight. Insects have mandibles for chewing, but</u>

<u>arachnids liquefy their prey by poisoning them.</u>

Arthropods Chapter Wrap-Up

In the "What I Wanted to Find Out" column, copy the questions you listed in the Chapter Preview. In the "What I Learned' column, write down the answers you discovered as you worked through the chapter.

W What I Wanted to Find Out	L What I Learned
1. Accept all reasonable entries. _____	1. _____ _____
2. _____ _____	2. _____ _____
3. _____ _____	3. _____ _____

Use this checklist to help you study.

☐ Study your Science Notebook for this chapter.

☐ Study the definitions of vocabulary words.

☐ Review daily homework assignments.

☐ Reread the chapter and review the tables, graphs, and illustrations.

☐ Review the Section Assessment questions at the end of each section.

☐ Look over the Study Guide at the end of the chapter.

SUMMARIZE After reading this chapter, list three things you have learned about arthropods.

Accept all reasonable responses. _____

_____

_____

Echinoderms and Invertebrate Chordates

Before You Read

Use the "What I Know" column to list three things you know about echinoderms and invertebrate chordates. Then list three questions you have about them in the "What I Want to Find Out" column.

K What I Know	W What I Want to Find Out
1. Accept all reasonable entries. _____	1. _____ _____
2. _____ _____	2. _____ _____
3. _____ _____	3. _____ _____

Science Journal

Write what you know or stories you have heard about starfish, sea urchins, and other spiny sea creatures.

Accept all reasonable responses.
_____
_____
_____
_____
_____
_____
_____
_____

Echinoderms and Invertebrate Chordates

Section 29.1 Echinoderms

Main Idea ——— **Details** ——————————————————————

Skim *Section 1 of your book. Read the headings and the illustration captions. Write three questions that come to mind.*

1. Accept all reasonable responses._____

2. _____

3. _____

Review Vocabulary *Use your book to define the following term.*

endoskeleton | internal skeleton of vertebrates and some invertebrates

New Vocabulary *Use your book to define each term.*

ampulla | the round, muscular structure on a tube foot

madreporite | a disk-shaped opening, on the upper surface of an echinoderm's body through which water flows in and out; operates like a sieve or strainer to keep large particles out of the animal

pedicellariae | pincerlike appendages found on sea stars and sea urchins; used for protection and for cleaning the body

rays | the long tapering arms of an echinoderm, especially a sea star

tube foot | a hollow, thin-walled tube that ends in a suction cup

water vascular system | the system that allows water to enter and leave the system of a sea star; works as a hydraulic system that operates under water pressure

Academic Vocabulary *Define the following terms.*

flexible | capable of being flexed; pliant

rigid | deficient in or devoid of flexibility

Section 29.1 Echinoderms (continued)

Main Idea

What is an echinoderm?

I found this information on page _____.
SE, pp. 763–766
RE, pp. 351–354

Details

Describe *the water vascular system. In your description, include the terms* ampulla, excrete, gases, madreporite, *and* tube feet.

Accept all reasonable responses. A disk-shaped opening, called a

madreporite, on the animal's upper surface strains out large bits of

material and allows water to pass into the body. The tube feet are

hollow tubes extending outward from the animal's surface. An

ampulla on the inner end of each tube foot contracts and relaxes to

create suction. That makes it possible for the animal to move and

even open clam shells. Gases can be exchanged, and the animal can

excrete wastes into the water by diffusion through the walls of

the tube feet.

Diversity of Echinoderms

I found this information on page _____.
SE, pp. 767–768
RE, pp. 354–356

Identify *each echinoderm class that is described below.*

Echinoderm Class	Characteristics
Holothuroidea	long, oblong shape; leathery surface
Asteroidea	five to 40 rays; calcium carbonate skeleton
Concentricycloidea	very small; disk-shaped; feet along edge
Crinoidea	feathery rays catch food; only sessile echinoderms; resemble plants
Ophiuroidea	fragile; can regenerate broken rays; don't use their tube feet for movement
Echinoidea	shaped like globes or disks; may be covered with long, pointed spines

Describe *echinoderm methods for coping with encounters with predators.*

brittle stars can regenerate broken-off rays

sea urchins are protected by their pointed spines or by burrowing

into rocks

sea cucumbers confuse their predators by expelling a tangled,

stick mass of tubes, or by releasing internal organs

Section 29.1 Echinoderms (continued)

Main Idea	Details

Diversity of Echinoderms

I found this information on page _____.

SE, pp. 767–768
RE, pp. 354–356

Draw *a sea star. Label 15 parts. Use the figure in your book to help you.* Illustrations should resemble RE p. 355, SE p. 766. Accept all reasonable variations.

Origins of Echinoderms

I found this information on page _____.

SE, p. 769
RE, p. 357

Write *words to fill in the blanks in the following discussion of the origins of echinoderms.*

Echinoderms are the only invertebrates that are __deuterostomes__.

That characteristic makes biologists think echinoderms may be the

closest invertebrate relatives of the ____chordates____. Though

echinoderms are now ___radially___ symmetrical, the earliest

members of the group may have had ___bilateral___ symmetry.

Because of their ___endoskeletons___, made of calcium carbonate,

we have a lot of ___fossil evidence___ of echinoderms, beginning in

the ___Paleozoic___ Era.

CONNECT Identify a major clue that suggests a link between echinoderms and chordates. Suggest one characteristic that links echinoderms to annelids and mollusks.

Accept all reasonable responses. (1) They are both deuterostomes.

(2) They have no vertebrae.

Echinoderms and Invertebrate Chordates

Section 29.2 Invertebrate Chordates

Main Idea	Details
	Finding Main Ideas *Construct an outline about invertebrate chordates. Use the titles in this section of your book as a guideline. As you read the paragraphs that follow the titles, add important information and vocabulary words to your outline.* Accept all reasonable responses.

I. What is an invertebrate chordate?

    A. What is a dorsal hollow nerve cord?

    B. What is a pharyngeal pouch?

    C. What is a postanal tail?

    D. How do homeotic genes control development?

II. Diversity of invertebrate chordates

    A. What are tunicates?

    B. What are lancelets?

III. Origins of invertebrate chordates

Review Vocabulary

Use your book to define the following term.

mesoderm   middle cell layer in the gastrula, between the ectoderm and endoderm

New Vocabulary

Use your book to define each term.

dorsal hollow nerve cord   develops from a plate of ectoderm that rolls into a hollow tube; in most adult chordates, this develops into the spinal cord

notochord   a long, semi-rigid rodlike structure located between the dorsal hollow nerve cord and the digestive system

pharyngeal pouches   paired openings located in the pharynx, behind the mouth

Academic Vocabulary

Define the following term.

structure   arrangement of parts

Section 29.2 Invertebrate Chordates (continued)

(Main Idea)	(Details)

What is an invertebrate chordate?

I found this information on page _____.

SE, pp. 770–772
RE, pp. 359–361

Identify *the phylum and subphyla described below.*

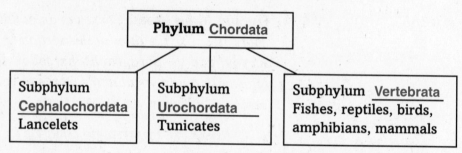

Describe *four characteristics of chordates. For each one, state where it is on the animal and describe what it does.* Accept all reasonable responses.

Characteristic	Location	Function
notochord	between the digestive system and the dorsal hollow nerve cord	holds internal muscles in place; may be replaced by backbone
dorsal hollow nerve cord	above notochord	usually develops into a spinal cord
pharyngeal pouches	pharynx	develop into gill slits or other structures
postanal tail	posterior to anus	becomes a tail in some chordates

Diversity of Invertebrate Chordates

I found this information on page _____.

SE, pp. 772–775
RE, pp. 361–363

Draw *a tunicate. Use the figure in your book to help you. Label eight parts.* Responses should resemble SE p. 774, RE p. 361.

Section 29.2 Invertebrate Chordates (continued)

Main Idea ——— **Details** ————————————————————————

Diversity of Invertebrate Chordates, Origins of Invertebrate Chordates

I found this information on page _____.
SE, pp. 772–775
RE, pp. 361–363

Draw *a lancelet (longitudinal view). Use the figure in your book to help you. Label nine parts.*

Responses should resemble SE p. 773, RE p. 362.

Compare and contrast *tunicates and lancelets by completing the table.*

Characteristic	Tunicates	Lancelets
Are all chordate features present in adults?	no	yes
What kind of body covering do they have?	heavy tunic	one layer of skin
Do they sometimes live in colonies?	yes	no
Do they have gill slits?	yes	yes
How are their bodies shaped?	tadpole-like in larval stage	fishlike

CONNECT

Explain why scientists think modern vertebrates may have arisen from free-swimming larval stages of ancestral invertebrate chordates.

Accept all reasonable responses. The larvae of tunicates, as well as adult lancelets, have a

fishlike appearance that includes a tail. The larvae of invertebrate chordates have the

characteristics of all chordates, even if they are lost when the larvae become adults.

Echinoderms and Invertebrate Chordates Chapter Wrap-Up

In the "What I Wanted to Find Out" column, copy the questions you listed in the Chapter Preview. In the "What I Learned" column, write down the answers you discovered as you worked through the chapter.

W What I Wanted to Find Out	L What I Learned
1. Accept all reasonable entries.	1.
2.	2.
3.	3.

Use this checklist to help you study.

☐ Study your Science Notebook for this chapter.

☐ Study the definitions of vocabulary words.

☐ Review daily homework assignments.

☐ Reread the chapter and review the tables, graphs, and illustrations.

☐ Review the Section Assessment questions at the end of each section.

☐ Look over the Study Guide at the end of the chapter.

SUMMARIZE After reading this chapter, list three things you have learned about echinoderms and invertebrate chordates.

Accept all reasonable responses.

Fishes and Amphibians

Before You Read

Use the "What I Know" column to list three things you know about fishes and amphibians. Then list three questions you have about them in the "What I Want to Find Out" column.

K What I Know	W What I Want to Find Out
1. Accept all reasonable entries. _____	1. _____ _____
2. _____ _____	2. _____ _____
3. _____ _____	3. _____ _____

Science Journal

Hypothesize what factors might be responsible for amphibian species becoming extinct.

Accept all reasonable responses. Most biologists think amphibians are disappearing because

their habitats are becoming smaller or unusable; but pollution, temperature variations, and

other factors have been suspected as well.

_____

_____

_____

_____

_____

Fishes and Amphibians

Section 30.1 Fishes

Main Idea	Details
	Skim *Section 1 of your book. Write two questions that come to mind from reading the headings and the illustration captions.*

1. Accept all reasonable responses._____

2. _____

Review Vocabulary

Use your book to define the following term.

vertebrate | an animal with a backbone

New Vocabulary

Use your book to define each term.

cartilage | a tough, flexible material that forms the skeletons of two classes of

fishes

fin | fan-shaped membrane used for balance, swimming, and steering

lateral line system | a line of fluid-filled canals that run along the sides of a fish and

enable the fish to detect movement and vibrations in the water

scale | thin, bony plate formed from the skin of fishes

spawning | external reproduction in some species of fishes; fishes that spawn

may produce as many as 9 million eggs, and provide no care for

their young after spawning

swim bladder | thin-walled internal sac located just below the backbone in most

bony fishes; can be filled with mostly oxygen or nitrogenous gases

that diffuse out of a fish's blood

Section 30.1 Fishes (continued)

| Main Idea | Details |

What is a fish?

I found this information on page _____ .

SE, pp. 793–799
RE, pp. 364–368

Identify *the classes of fishes, what the class names mean, and some examples.*

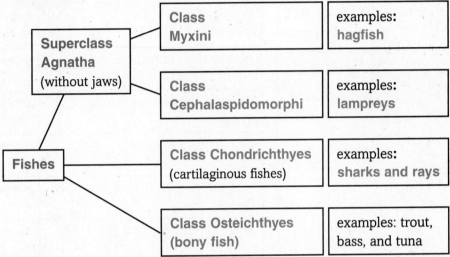

Model *how oxygen moves from water into a fish's blood. Use the figure in your book to help you. Write brief captions about the gills, the heart, and blood flow.*

Diagrams may resemble SE p. 795, RE p. 365. Accept all reasonable variations.

Gills are made of filaments, which are feathery and thread-like.

Oxygen is received by capillaries in the gills from the water which passes over them.

heart: 2-chambered

blood flow is slow

Section 30.1 Fishes (continued)

Main Idea	Details

What Is a Fish, Diversity of Fishes, Origins of Fishes

I found this information on page _____.
SE, pp. 793–802
RE, pp. 364–369

Identify *a term or phrase for each fact about fishes.* Accept all reasonable responses.

Where fishes live	nearly every kind of water environment
how fishes reproduce	sexually
purpose of the lateral line system	detecting movement and vibrations
egg laying in fishes	spawning
first developed in ancestral fishes	jaws
way that sharks find prey	sense of smell
vision in fishes	can see objects and contrast; some see little or not at all
when coelacanths appear in fossils	395 million years ago
two types of bony fishes	ray-finned and lobe-finned fishes
early jawless fishes	ostracoderms
type of skeleton that is not bone	cartilage
number of chambers in a fish heart	two
purpose of swim bladder	controlling depth by regulating gases
purpose of fins	balance, swimming, and steering

COMPARE

Identify characteristics of fishes that are similar to lancelets and characteristics that are more advanced.

Accept all reasonable responses. They share the chordate characteristics of a notochord,

dorsal hollow nerve cord, pharyngeal pouches, and postanal tail. Fishes have a

two-chambered heart, gills, scales, and eyes.

Fishes and Amphibians
Section 30.2 Amphibians

(Main Idea) ——   **(Details)** ———————————————————

Infer *Make a list of characteristics that are necessary for an animal to live successfully on land.*

Accept all reasonable responses. lungs for breathing air, protection

to keep skin from drying out, skeleton and appendages that will

support a body on land, ways to control internal temperature when

temperatures on land vary more than in water

(Review Vocabulary) *Use your book to define the following term.*

metamorphosis   a series of changes in an organism that are controlled by chemical

substances

(New Vocabulary) *Use your book to define each term.*

ectotherm   an animal whose body temperature changes; an ectotherm gets its

heat from external sources

vocal cord   band of tissue located in the throat; as air passes over the cord, it

vibrates and the molecules around the vocal cord tissues vibrate,

making sounds

(Academic Vocabulary) *Define the following terms.*

external   on or having to do with the outside; exterior

range   a sequence, series, or scale between limits; the limits of a series, or

the distance or extent between possible extremes

Section 30.2 Amphibians (continued)

Main Idea	Details

What is an amphibian?

I found this information on page _____.
SE, pp. 803–806
RE, pp. 371–373

Summarize *how ectotherms cope with changes in environmental temperature.*

Accept all reasonable responses. Amphibians cannot regulate their body temperature, so it is the same as the environment. Many of their body processes can occur only within a certain range of temperature, so these animals tend to live where the surroundings are warm year-round. If the temperature becomes too hot or cold, amphibians become dormant. They may burrow into mud and stay buried until the temperature changes.

Compare *the stages in metamorphosis for a frog and a salamander.* Accept all reasonable responses.

Frog	Salamander
Young: Fertilized frog eggs hatch into tadpoles, which are totally aquatic and have fins, gills, and a two-chambered heart like fishes.	Young: aquatic larvae with gills and a tail fin
Adult: have legs, lungs, and a three-chambered heart	Adult: do not have gills or fins, and breathe through their skin or with lungs, if they have them

Create *a concept map to show characteristics and examples of each order of the class Amphibia.*

Class Amphibia

Order Caudata	Order Anura	Order Apoda
salamanders	frogs, toads	caecilians
smooth, moist skin; tails; long, slender bodies; hatchlings look like small adults	no tails; jaws and teeth; vocal cords	limbless; tails short or absent

Section 30.2 Amphibians (continued)

Main Idea	Details

Amphibian Diversity

I found this information on page _____.
SE, pp. 806–807
RE, pp. 373–374

Describe *each chamber of the amphibian heart and gas exchange in amphibians.*

Accept all reasonable responses. Amphibians have a three-chambered heart. One chamber receives oxygen-rich blood from the lungs and skin. Another chamber receives oxygen-poor blood from the body tissues. Both of these pour into the third chamber, which pumps oxygen-rich blood to the tissues and oxygen-poor blood to the heart, but the two types mix in the third chamber and in blood vessels. Amphibians also receive gases through their moist skin.

Origins of Amphibians

I found this information on page _____.
SE, pp. 807–809
RE, p. 374

State *three adaptations that helped amphibians leave water.*
Accept all reasonable responses.

1. lungs for breathing air

2. three-chambered hearts

3. four limbs that lifted their bodies off the ground

Summarize *the advantages and difficulties for amphibians emerging onto land from life in water.* Accept all reasonable responses.

Advantages	Difficulties
large food supply; good shelter; no predators at the time; more oxygen	variations in air temperature; animal is heavier and more clumsy; movement is more difficult

COMPARE

Compare amphibians with fishes. List some important evolutionary advances seen in amphibians.

Accept all reasonable responses. Amphibians have a three-chambered heart, and fishes have two chambers. Amphibians have lungs during part of their life cycle; fish breathe by using gills. Most amphibians have limbs.

Fishes and Amphibians Chapter Wrap-Up

In the "What I Wanted to Find Out" column, copy the questions you listed in the Chapter Preview. In the "What I Learned" column, write down the answers you discovered as you worked through the chapter.

W What I Wanted to Find Out	L What I Learned
1. Accept all reasonable entries. _____ _____	1. _____ _____
2. _____ _____	2. _____ _____
3. _____ _____	3. _____ _____

Use this checklist to help you study.

☐ Study your Science Notebook for this chapter.

☐ Study the definitions of vocabulary words.

☐ Review daily homework assignments.

☐ Reread the chapter and review the tables, graphs, and illustrations.

☐ Review the Section Assessment questions at the end of each section.

☐ Look over the Study Guide at the end of the chapter.

SUMMARIZE

After reading this chapter, list three things you have learned about fishes and amphibians.

Accept all reasonable responses.

_____

_____

_____

Reptiles and Birds

Before You Read

Use the "What I Know" column to list three things you know about reptiles and birds. Then list three questions you have about them in the "What I Want to Find Out" column.

K What I Know	W What I Want to Find Out
1. Accept all reasonable entries. _____	1. _____ _____
2. _____ _____	2. _____ _____
3. _____ _____	3. _____ _____

Science Journal

Think about the life of fishes compared to the lives of reptiles and the lives of birds. What adaptations do birds and reptiles have to suit them to life on land and in the air?

Accept all reasonable responses._____

_____

_____

_____

_____

_____

_____

_____

Reptiles and Birds

Section 31.1 Reptiles

⌐Main Idea⌐ ———	⌐Details⌐ ———————————————————————————

Skim *Section 1 of your book. Read the headings and the illustration captions. Write three questions that come to mind.*

1. Accept all reasonable responses. _____

2. _____

3. _____

Review Vocabulary   *Use your book to define the following term.*

embryo   the earliest stage of growth and development of both plants and

animals

New Vocabulary   *Use your book to define each term.*

amniotic egg   provides nourishment for the embryo; contains membranes that

protect the egg while it develops on land

Jacobson's organ   a pitlike structure located in the roof of the mouth in both snakes

and lizards; special cells in the organ help identify and differentiate

smells

Draw *a cross-section of the head of a reptile and label the Jacobson's organ. Use the figure in your book to help you.*
Diagrams should resemble SE p. 821, RE p. 379.

Section 31.1 Reptiles (continued)

| Main Idea | Details |

What is a reptile?

I found this information on page _____.
SE, pp. 817–821
RE, pp. 376–379

Identify *how reptiles adapted to deal with each factor needed for life on land.*

Needed for Life on Land	Adaptation
running and walking without support from water	sturdy limbs beneath body
protection of embryo from drying out	amniotic egg
slowing of moisture loss from body	scaly, thick skin
gas exchange other than through skin	lungs
protection from predators	claws, scales
delivering more oxygen to tissues that require more energy	four-chambered heart

Draw *a reptilian egg. Label the amnion, embryo, allantois, albumen, yolk, shell, and chorion.*
Diagrams should resemble SE p. 819, RE p. 377. Accept reasonable variations.

Section 31.1 Reptiles (continued)

Main Idea —————— **Details** ———————————————————————

Diversity of Reptiles

I found this information on page _____.
SE, pp. 822–824
RE, pp. 379–381

Summarize *characteristics about each order in class Reptilia.*
Accept all reasonable responses.

Squamata	Chelonia
includes: snakes, lizards	includes: turtles
adapted to hot, dry climates; may burrow, live on ground, live in trees, or live in water; snakes may climb trees or move quickly over land or swim	shells with two parts–carapace and plastron; do not have teeth; crush food with jaws; can draw inside shell for protection; may be aquatic or live on land
Crocodilia	**Rhynochocephalia**
includes: alligators, crocodiles	includes: tuataras
excellent, fast hunters; do not migrate to reproduce; lay eggs in ground nests and protect them; live in fresh or salt water; can breathe with mouths full of food and water	only two living species in New Zealand; have teeth fused to jaws; rest of order died out 100 million years ago

Origins of Reptiles

I found this information on page _____.
SE, pp. 824–825
RE, p. 381

Create *a map to identify three groups that evolved from stem reptiles. Use dashed lines to show two places on this evolutionary map where birds have been thought to fit.*

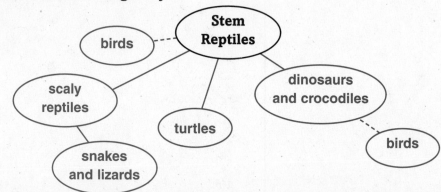

CONNECT

Hypothesize what clues might have led scientists to believe that birds belong in each of the two places in the evolutionary map you created above.

Accept all reasonable responses. Differences in fossil features from the other three groups

would have led scientists to classify birds as a fourth group. Fossil evidence has led to the

reclassification of birds as descendants of dinosaurs.

Reptiles and Birds

Section 31.2 Birds

Main Idea —— **Details** ————————————————————————————

Infer *the characteristics that birds have that make them different from reptiles.*

Accept all reasonable responses. Modern birds have feathers, wings,

lungs with air sacs, hollow bones, and beaks. They also are

endotherms.

Review Vocabulary *Use your book to define the following term.*

phylogeny evolutionary history of a species based on comparative relationships

of structures and comparisons of modern life forms with fossils

New Vocabulary *Use your book to define each term.*

endotherm animal that maintains a nearly constant body temperature; it is not

dependent upon the environmental temperature

feather lightweight, modified scales found only on birds; provide insulation

and enable flight

incubate keeping eggs laid outside of the body warm

sternum breastbone

Academic Vocabulary *Define the following terms.*

factor something that actively contributes to the production of a result; a

substance that functions in or promotes the function of a particular

physiological process or bodily system

retain to keep in possession or use; to hold secure or intact

Section 31.2 Birds (continued)

Main Idea —— | ## Details ——

What is a bird?

I found this information on page _____.
SE, pp. 826–830
RE, pp. 383–385

Create *a concept web about the structure and function of feathers.*
Accept all reasonable responses. Encourage detail and logical layout of facts.

Describe *the role of the sternum in flight.*

Strong muscles that are used to fly are attached to the sternum and

the upper bone of each wing. The sternum supports the thrust and

power that the muscles produce.

Sequence *the organs air passes through as a bird breathes.*

trachea—lungs—posterior air sacs—lungs—anterior air sacs—trachea

Contrast *how birds stay warm and how they cool off. List factors or make sketches to explain.*

To stay warm: feathers are fluffed up; a layer of air is trapped around the bird's body as insulation against cold; eating large amounts of food to make heat	Cooling off: feathers can be flattened against the body and wings held outstretched; panting

Section 31.2 Birds (continued)

┌──────────────────┐   ┌──────────┐
Main Idea   **Details**

Diversity of Birds

*I found this information
on page _____ .*
SE, pp. 830–831
RE, p. 386

Compare *bird adaptations to various habitats and food sources.*
Accept all reasonable responses.

Kind of Bird	Adaptations
Ptarmigans	feathered legs and feet making it easier to walk in snow
Penguins	flightless; wings and feet modified for swimming, thick layer of fat to keep them warm
Owls	large eyes, keen hearing, sharp claws making them successful hunters at night
Hummingbirds	long beaks for obtaining nectar from flowers
Hawks	curved beaks for tearing apart prey
Pelicans	large, pouched bills used as nets for capturing fish
Cardinals	short, stout beaks for cracking seeds

Origins of Birds

*I found this information
on page _____ .*
SE, pp. 832–833
RE, p. 386

Identify *features shared by birds and therapods.*

sternum, wishbone, shoulder blades, flexible wrists, three fingers on

each hand, clawed front toes, long tail, teeth, feathers

┌─────────────┐
COMPARE Compare ectothermy and endothermy. In what animal groups are
they found? What are the advantages and disadvantages of each?

Accept all reasonable responses. Ectothermy is found in the more primitive animal groups,

such as invertebrates, fish, amphibians, and reptiles. Birds and mammals are endothermic.

Ectotherms do not have to obtain large quantities of energy, but endotherms can carry on life

processes more efficiently and do not need to become dormant. They can live in a greater

range of climates.

Reptiles and Birds Chapter Wrap-Up

In the "What I Wanted to Find Out" column, copy the questions you listed in the Chapter Preview. In the "What I Learned" column, write down the answers you discovered as you worked through the chapter.

W What I Wanted to Find Out	L What I Learned
1. Accept all reasonable entries. _____ _____	1. _____ _____
2. _____ _____	2. _____ _____
3. _____ _____	3. _____ _____

Use this checklist to help you study.

☐ Study your Science Notebook for this chapter.

☐ Study the definitions of vocabulary words.

☐ Review daily homework assignments.

☐ Reread the chapter and review the tables, graphs, and illustrations.

☐ Review the Section Assessment questions at the end of each section.

☐ Look over the Study Guide at the end of the chapter.

SUMMARIZE

After reading this chapter, list three things you have learned about reptiles and birds.

Accept all reasonable responses._____

_____

_____

Mammals

Before You Read

Use the "What I Know" column to list three things you know about mammals. Then list three questions you have about mammals in the "What I Want to Find Out" column.

K What I Know	W What I Want to Find Out
1. **Accept all reasonable entries.** 	1. _____
2. _____ 	2. _____
3. _____ 	3. _____

Science Journal

Mammals are one of the most successful groups of animals on Earth. Think about a specific mammal and some of its characteristics. Write about how you think some of these characteristics help the mammal to survive and be successful.

Accept all reasonable responses. _____

_____

_____

_____

_____

_____

_____

Mammals

Section 32.1 Mammal Characteristics

Main Idea	Details

Skim *Section 1 of your book. Write three questions that come to mind from reading the headings and the illustration captions.*

1. Accept all reasonable responses._____

2. _____

3. _____

Review Vocabulary

Use your book to define the following term.

metabolism   all of the chemical reactions that occur within an organism

New Vocabulary

Use your book to define each term. Then label each term on the sketch of the fox below.

diaphragm   in mammals, the sheet of muscles located beneath the lungs that

separates the chest from the abdominal cavity; expands the chest

cavity, which increases the amount of oxygen entering the body

gland   in mammals, a cell or a group of cells that secretes fluids

mammary gland   modified sweat gland in female mammals, which produces and

secretes milk to feed their young

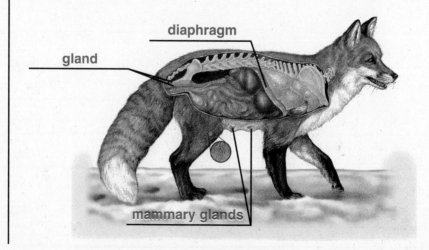

Section 32.1 Mammal Characteristics (continued)

Main Idea ——   **Details** ————————————————————————

What is a mammal?

I found this information on page _____.
SE, pp. 841–843
RE, pp. 388–390

Organize *the concept map about the characteristics of mammals.*
Accept all reasonable responses.

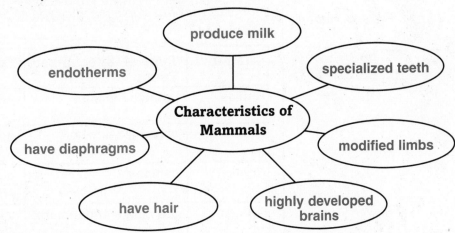

Describe *how mammals feed their young by completing the statements.*

Mammals feed their young from _____ mammary glands _____, which produce ___ milk ___ and may be _____ modified sweat glands _____. Milk is rich in ___ fats ___, ___ sugars ___, ___ proteins ___, ___ minerals ___, and ___ vitamins ___. Mammals stop feeding their young when _____ the young can digest and absorb nutrients from solid food _____.

Sequence *the steps that occur during respiration and circulation to help mammals maintain a high metabolism. Write the steps in the correct order in the boxes on the left.*

The diaphragm helps expand the chest cavity to allow oxygen into the lungs.	The heart delivers blood with nutrients and oxygen to the cells.
↓	
In the lungs, oxygen diffuses into the blood.	The diaphragm helps expand the chest cavity to allow oxygen into the lungs.
↓	
The heart delivers blood with nutrients and oxygen to the cells.	Oxygen in the cells helps maintain an endothermic metabolism.
↓	
Oxygen in the cells helps maintain an endothermic metabolism.	In the lungs, oxygen diffuses into the blood.

Section 32.1 Mammal Characteristics (continued)

Main Idea ——— **Details** ————————————————

What is a mammal?

I found this information on page _____.

SE, pp. 843–847
RE, pp. 390–391

Organize *information about different types of specialized adaptations and how they help mammals. Give an example of a mammal that has each specific type of teeth or limb adaptation if possible.*

Mammal	Type of Specialized Teeth	Function
moles	pointed incisors	grasp and hold small prey
beavers	chisel-like incisors	gnawing
lions	canines	puncture and tear flesh of prey
humans	premolars and molars	slicing or shearing, crushing, and grinding

Mammal	Type of Specialized Limb	Function
primates	opposable thumbs	grasp objects
moles	short powerful limbs with large claws	help to dig
bats	long finger bones	support the flight membrane of their wings

Analyze *why mammals are able to learn. Explain the characteristics mammals have that enable them to learn and remember.*

Accept all reasonable responses. Mammals have highly developed

brains and a complex nervous system. The outer layer of a mammal's

brain is often folded and forms ridges and grooves. This arrangement

gives their brains more surface area for them to be active and to

learn and remember things.

SYNTHESIZE Evaluate how a mammal's ability to learn and remember can help it to adapt and survive in its habitat. Give a specific example.

Accept all reasonable responses. Since mammals can learn and remember, they can remember

ways they did things that were helpful to their survival and use them over and over. For example,

chimpanzees can use tools to help them get things they need in their habitat, such as food.

Mammals

Section 32.2 Diversity of Mammals

Main Idea ———   **Details** —————————————————————

Finding Main Ideas *As you read Section 2, complete the outline about mammal classification.*

I. Mammal Classification

    A. __Placental__ mammals

       1. give birth to young that have developed inside mother's uterus

    B. __Pouched__ mammals

       1. __young develop in mother for a short period and then develop inside a pouch__

    C. Monotremes

       1. lay __eggs__

New Vocabulary 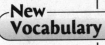   *Read the definitions below. Then write the correct term in the left margin.*

__therapsids__	reptilian ancestors of mammals that had features of both reptiles and mammals
__placenta__	organ that provides food and oxygen to and removes wastes from young inside the uterus of placental mammals
__monotreme__	subclass of mammals that have hair and mammary glands but reproduce by laying eggs
__uterus__	in females, the hollow, muscular organ in which offspring of placental mammals develop
__placental mammal__	mammals that give birth to young that have developed inside the mother's uterus until their body systems are fully functional and they can live independently of their mother's body
__marsupial__	subclass of mammals in which young develop for a short period in the uterus and complete their development outside of the mother's body in a pouch made of skin and hair
__gestation__	time during which placental animals develop inside the uterus

Section 32.2 Diversity of Mammals (continued)

<Main Idea> —— <Details>_____

Mammal Classification

I found this information on page _____.
SE, pp. 848–851
RE, pp. 392–394

Describe *the three subclasses of mammals by completing the concept map below.*

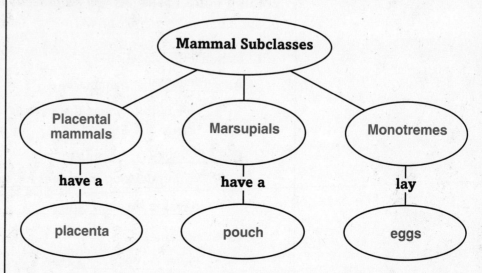

Compare and contrast *the development of young in a placental mammal with the development of young in a marsupial.* Accept all reasonable responses.

Placental Mammal	Marsupial
The young develop inside the mother's uterus. There they are nourished through the placenta. When their body systems are fully functional and they can live outside their mother's body, they are born.	The young develop for a short time within the mother's body. Then they are born. They finish developing in a pouch outside the mother's body.

Describe *the rise of marsupials in Australia and the effect of the introduction of placental mammals there.*

Accept all reasonable responses. Marsupials evolved in the absence

of placental mammals. Since the introduction of placental mammals

such as sheep and rabbits to Australia, marsupials have experienced

a decline. Because they have to compete with other successful

mammals.

Section 32.2 Diversity of Mammals (continued)

Main Idea	Details

Mammal Classification

I found this information on page _____.
SE, pp. 848–851
RE, pp. 392–394

Organize *information about the characteristics of the platypus using the table.*

Characteristics
mostly aquatic
flat tail similar to a beaver
webbed front feet
sharp claws on its feet for digging and burrowing
mammary glands

Classify *animals discussed in this section as placental mammals, marsupials, or monotremes.* Accept all reasonable responses.

Placental Mammals	Marsupials	Monotremes
monkeys, humans, cats, zebras, bats, camels, elephants	opossum, giant anteater, numbat, kangaroo	platypus, spiny anteater

Origins of Mammals

I found this information on page _____.
SE, p. 851
RE, pp. 394–395

Summarize *four past causes of the increase in the number of mammals on Earth.*

1. mass extinction of dinosaurs   2. breaking apart of Pangaea

3. changes in climate   4. appearance of flowering plants as a

source of food, living areas, and shelter

ANALYZE Examine the diagram showing the orders of mammals in your book. Describe how the connection between therapsids, placental mammals, and marsupials is different from the connection between therapsids and monotremes.

Accept all reasonable responses. The placental mammals and marsupials are connected to

therapsids by the same line. The monotremes are connected to therapsids by their own line.

This suggests that marsupials and placental mammals are more closely related than they are

to monotremes and that the monotremes developed more directly from the therapsids and the

placental mammals and marsupials may have developed together for a time from therapsids.

Mammals Chapter Wrap-Up

In the "What I Wanted to Find Out" column, copy the questions you listed in the Chapter Preview. In the "What I Learned" column, write down the answers you discovered as you worked through the chapter.

W What I Wanted to Find Out	L What I Learned
1. Accept all reasonable entries. _____	1. _____ _____
2. _____ _____	2. _____ _____
3. _____ _____	3. _____ _____

Use this checklist to help you study.

☐ Study your Science Notebook for this chapter.

☐ Study the definitions of vocabulary words.

☐ Review daily homework assignments.

☐ Reread the chapter and review the tables, graphs, and illustrations.

☐ Review the Section Assessment questions at the end of each section.

☐ Look over the Study Guide at the end of the chapter.

SUMMARIZE After reading this chapter, list three things you have learned about mammals.

Accept all reasonable responses.

_____

_____

_____

Animal Behavior

Before You Read

Use the "What I Know" column to list three things you know about animal behavior. Then list three questions you have about animal behavior in the "What I Want to Find Out" column.

K What I Know	W What I Want to Find Out
1. Accept all reasonable entries. _____	1. _____ _____
2. _____ _____	2. _____ _____
3. _____ _____	3. _____ _____

Science Journal

Describe two behavior patterns in humans.

Accept all reasonable responses.

_____

_____

_____

_____

_____

_____

_____

Animal Behavior

Section 33.1 Innate Behavior

Main Idea ———— **Details** ————————————

Finding Main Ideas *Use the headings in your book to make an outline of the main ideas of the section.*

Accept all reasonable responses.

_____

_____

_____

Review Vocabulary   *Use your book to define the following term.*

population   a group of organisms of one species that interbreed and live in the

same place at the same time

New Vocabulary   *Use the new vocabulary words to complete the paragraph below.*

aggressive behavior   Anything an animal does in response to something is a __behavior__.

There are different kinds of behavior. Some behaviors, like

behavior   __innate behaviors__, are inherited. With this type of behavior, animals

circadian rhythm   often respond automatically to a stimulus. Examples of automatic

courtship behavior   responses include __reflex__ and __fight-or-flight response__.

Animals also may show an __instinct__, which is a complex pattern

dominance hierarchy   of innate behavior. For example, __courtship behavior__

estivation   is instinctive. Animals also show instinctive behavior when they are

fight-or-flight response   defending their __territory__. They may use __aggressive behavior__

hibernation   to intimidate another animal of the same species. Sometimes this kind

of behavior leads to social ranking within a group, called a

innate behavior   __dominance hierarchy__. Behavior can be a response to internal

instinct   biological rhythms. For example, a sleep/wake cycle of behavior is

migration   called a __circadian rhythm__. __Migration__ is an instinctive

reflex   behavior that happens on a seasonal cycle. Animals that do not

migrate may go into __hibernation__. Animals in hot climates

territory   may go into __estivation__.

Name _____   Date _____

Section 33.1 Innate Behavior (continued)

Main Idea	Details

Main Idea

What is behavior?

I found this information on page _____.

SE, p. 859
RE, p. 397

Identify *a behavior that you did in response to a stimulus today.*

Accept all reasonable responses. The water in the shower this morning

got too hot. I moved out of the shower and turned on more cold water.

Inherited Behavior

I found this information on page _____.

SE, pp. 860–861
RE, pp. 397–398

Analyze *the relationship of behavior and natural selection. Fill in the blanks.*

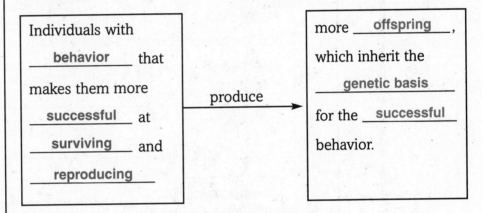

Individuals with ____behavior____ that makes them more ____successful____ at ____surviving____ and ____reproducing____ **produce** more ____offspring____, which inherit the ____genetic basis____ for the ____successful____ behavior.

Define *fixed-action response and give an example.*

A fixed-action response is a behavior that, once begun, continues until

completed. An example is a bird or toad eating bugs.

Automatic Responses and Instinctive Behavior

I found this information on page _____.

SE, pp. 861–867
RE, pp. 398–402

Compare *automatic responses and instinctive behavior by placing each characteristic or response in the correct place in the diagram.*

- complex behavior pattern
- has adaptive value
- has survival value
- innate behavior
- no conscious control
- simple behavior

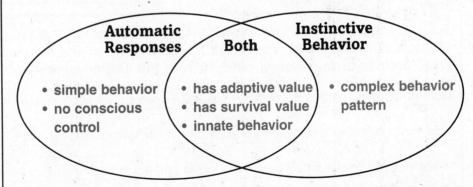

Automatic Responses
- simple behavior
- no conscious control

Both
- has adaptive value
- has survival value
- innate behavior

Instinctive Behavior
- complex behavior pattern

Section 33.1 Innate Behavior (continued)

(Main Idea)———— **(Details)**————————————————

Instinctive Behavior

I found this information on page _____ .
SE, pp. 861–867
RE, pp. 398–402

Evaluate *instinctive behaviors. Choose one type and describe its benefit to an animal.*

1. <u>Accept all reasonable responses. Courtship behavior ensures that</u>

<u>members of the same species can find each other and mate.</u>

Summarize *the different kinds of innate behavior. Use the word bank to fill in the graphic organizer.*

- aggressive behavior
- dominance hierarchy
- hibernation
- reflexes
- automatic response
- fight-or-flight
- instinctive behavior
- territoriality
- courtship behavior
- migration
- fixed-action response

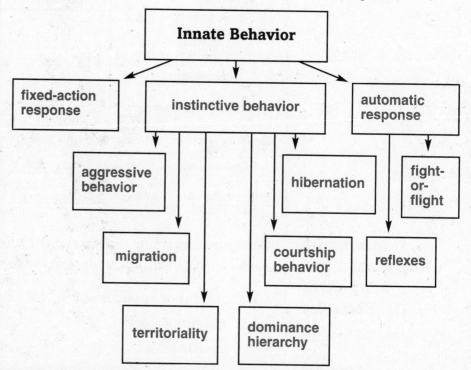

CONNECT You have dominance hierarchies in your life similar to some animals. Although they function differently, some of the benefits are the same. Describe one of these hierarchies in your life and its advantages.

Accept all reasonable responses. There is a dominance hierarchy in my classroom. My

teacher is dominant. She or he makes the classroom rules and leads the class in discussions.

This makes the class flow more smoothly and be more organized so we can learn more.

Animal Behavior

Section 33.2 Learned Behavior

Main Idea —————— **Details** ———————————————————

Skim *Section 2 of your book. Write three questions that come to mind from reading the headings and the illustration captions.*

1. <u>Accept all reasonable responses.</u> _____

2. _____

3. _____

New Vocabulary   *Use your book to define each term.*

classical conditioning   <u>learning by association</u> _____

communication   <u>exchange of information that results in a change of behavior</u>

habituation   <u>learned behavior that occurs when an animal is repeatedly given a</u>

<u>stimulus not associated with any punishment or reward</u>

imprinting   <u>learned behavior in which an animal, at a specific critical time of its</u>

<u>life, forms a social attachment to another object; usually occurs</u>

<u>early in life and allows an animal to recognize its mother and others</u>

<u>of its species</u>

insight   <u>type of learning in which an animal uses previous experiences to</u>

<u>respond to a new situation</u>

language   <u>use of symbols to represent ideas; usually present in animals with</u>

<u>complex nervous systems, memory, and insight</u>

motivation   <u>internal need that causes an animal to act and that is necessary for</u>

<u>learning to take place; often involves hunger or thirst</u>

trial-and-error learning   <u>type of learning in which an animal receives a reward for making a</u>

<u>particular response</u>

Section 33.2 Learned Behavior (continued)

Main Idea ———— **Details** ————————————————

What is Learned Behavior?

I found this information on page _____ .

SE, p. 868
RE, p. 404

Analyze *why learned behaviors are more common in vertebrates than in invertebrates and give a benefit of learned behavior.*

Sample response: The brains of invertebrates and vertebrates are

different. Vertebrates are able to learn more detailed behaviors

because their brains are more complex. Learning allows an animal

to adapt to change and survive longer.

Kinds of Learned Behavior

I found this information on page _____ .

SE, pp. 860–861
RE, pp. 397–398

Organize *information about the different kinds of learned behavior in the table.*

Kind of Learned Behavior	Description	Example
Habituation	a lack of response after repeated exposure to a stimulus	a horse ignoring noisy cars that pass by their pasture
Imprinting	a form of learning in which an animal forms a social attachment to another object at a specific critical time in its life	a duck imprinting on its mother
Trial and Error	an animal receives a reward for making a particular response and learns which solutions to a problem work best	a bird learning which materials work best for building a nest
Classical Conditioning	learning by association	a cat responding to the sound of a can opener because its food is opened with a can opener
Insight	learning in which an animal uses previous experience to respond to a new situation	a chimpanzee connecting two short bamboo poles to make a longer one to reach fruit outside its cage

Section 33.2 Learned Behavior (continued)

Main Idea ——

Details ————————————————————

Kinds of Learned Behavior

I found this information on page _____.
SE, p. 871
RE, p. 406

The Role of Communication

I found this information on page _____.
SE, pp. 872–873
RE, pp. 407–408

Evaluate *Describe why insight is the most complex type of learning.*

Sample response: Animals need to recall and build on previous

experiences. With insight, animals are using what they already know

to solve new problems.

Summarize *the different ways animals communicate. Include an example of each method.*

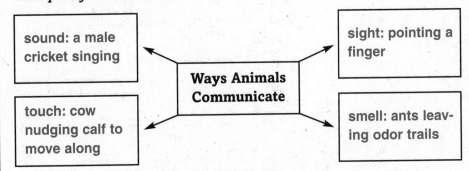

sound: a male cricket singing

touch: cow nudging calf to move along

Ways Animals Communicate

sight: pointing a finger

smell: ants leaving odor trails

Contrast *how language is different from communication. Give an example of communication and an example of language.*

Communication is very simple. With sounds, sights, touches, or

smells, animals can send each other signals. For example, a dog

communicates by growling. Language is more complex. Symbols

are used to represent ideas. Language is understood by animals

with complex nervous systems, memory, and insight.

COMPARE Compare the types of motivation involved with trial-and-error learning, classical conditioning, and insight.

Accept all reasonable responses. Motivation is necessary for all three types

of learning. In trial-and-error learning, an animal is rewarded for making a particular response.

The reward is the motivation. In classical conditioning, an animal learns to associate the

reward with something else, like the opening of a can opener. In insight, the reward varies with

the problem. Often the reward is in finding a solution to the problem.

Animal Behavior Chapter Wrap-Up

In the "What I Wanted to Find Out" column, copy the questions you listed in the Chapter Preview. In the "What I Learned" column, write down the answers you discovered as you worked through the chapter.

W What I Wanted to Find Out	L What I Learned
1. Accept all reasonable entries. _____	1. _____ _____
2. _____ _____	2. _____ _____
3. _____ _____	3. _____ _____

Use this checklist to help you study.

☐ Study your Science Notebook for this chapter.

☐ Study the definitions of vocabulary words.

☐ Review daily homework assignments.

☐ Reread the chapter and review the tables, graphs, and illustrations.

☐ Review the Section Assessment questions at the end of each section.

☐ Look over the Study Guide at the end of the chapter.

SUMMARIZE

After reading this chapter, list three things you have learned about animal behavior.

Accept all reasonable responses.

_____

_____

Protection, Support, and Locomotion

Before You Read

Use the "What I Know" column to list three things you know about how the body protects itself, supports itself, and moves. Then list three questions you have about these ideas in the "What I Want to Find Out" column.

K What I Know	W What I Want to Find Out
1. Accept all reasonable entries. _____	1. _____ _____
2. _____ _____	2. _____ _____
3. _____ _____	3. _____ _____

Science Journal

Think about a sport you or someone you know plays. Describe how your skin, skeleton, and muscles help you play that sport.

Accept all reasonable responses. _____

_____

_____

_____

_____

_____

_____

_____

Protection, Support, and Locomotion
Section 34.1 Skin: The Body's Protection

Main Idea	Details

Scan *Use the checklist below to preview Section 1 of your book.*

☐ Read all section titles.

☐ Read all bold words.

☐ Read all tables and graphs.

☐ Look at all pictures and read the captions.

☐ Think about what you already know about skin.

Write two facts you discovered about skin as you scanned the section.

1. Accept all reasonable responses.

2. _____

Review Vocabulary

Use your book to define the following term.

homeostasis | regulation of an organism's internal environment to maintain
conditions suitable for its survival

New Vocabulary

Read the definitions below, then write the correct term in the left column.

epidermis | the outermost layer of the skin

melanin | a pigment that colors the skin

dermis | the inner, thicker portion of the skin

hair follicle | narrow opening in the dermis from which hair grows

keratin | a protein found in the exterior portion of the epidermis that helps protect the interior layer of the epidermis from exposure to bacteria, heat, and chemicals

Academic Vocabulary

Define the following term.

role | proper or customary function, especially as part of a whole or a group

Section 34.1 Skin: The Body's Protection (continued)

Main Idea	Details

Structure and Functions of the Integumentary System

I found this information on page _____.
SE, pp. 893–896
RE, pp. 409–410

Identify *the four types of body tissues in the integumentary system. Then give the function of each one.*

1. epithelial tissue; covers surfaces of the body

2. connective tissue; holds your body together

3. muscle tissue; interact with hairs on the skin to respond to stimuli

4. nervous tissue; helps sense external stimuli

Compare and contrast *the structures and functions of the epidermis with the dermis. Place each phrase below in the correct place in the Venn diagram.*

- can be covered in hair
- has exterior and interior portions
- helps the body maintain homeostasis
- consists of dead, flattened cells

- contains keratin
- contains melanin
- contains blood vessels, nerves, sweat glands, and oil glands
- outer layer of skin
- inner, thicker portion of the skin

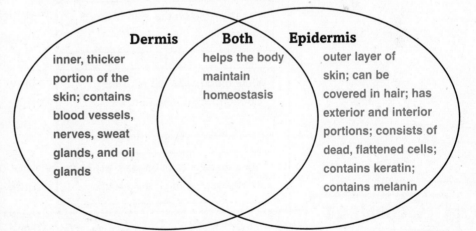

Dermis
inner, thicker portion of the skin; contains blood vessels, nerves, sweat glands, and oil glands

Both
helps the body maintain homeostasis

Epidermis
outer layer of skin; can be covered in hair; has exterior and interior portions; consists of dead, flattened cells; contains keratin; contains melanin

Describe *the diagram of the integumentary system in your book.*

Accept all reasonable responses. Encourage students to describe how

each part looks and the arrangement of the parts around each other.

Section 34.1 Skin: The Body's Protection (continued)

| ⟨Main Idea⟩ | ⟨Details⟩ |

Structure and Functions of the Integumentary System

I found this information on page _____.

SE, pp. 896–897
RE, pp. 410–412

Describe *the five functions of skin in the graphic organizer below.*

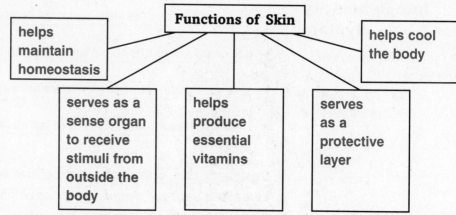

| helps maintain homeostasis | | Functions of Skin | | helps cool the body |

| serves as a sense organ to receive stimuli from outside the body | helps produce essential vitamins | serves as a protective layer |

Skin Injury and Healing

I found this information on page _____.

SE, p. 898
RE, pp. 412–413

Sequence *the steps that occur during skin healing. Write the steps in the correct order.*

| The skin receives a scrape that bleeds. | A scab forms on the skin to close the wound. |

↓

| Blood flows out onto the skin until a clot forms. | The skin receives a scrape that bleeds. |

↓

| A scab forms on the skin to close the wound. | White blood cells move to the wound to fight infection. |

↓

| White blood cells move to the wound to fight infection. | New skin cells form beneath the scab eventually pushing the scab off. |

↓

| New skin cells form beneath the scab eventually pushing the scab off. | Blood flows out onto the skin until a clot forms. |

CONNECT Your skin changes as you age. **Describe some things you can do to protect your skin so that it can better protect your body.**

Accept all reasonable responses. I can wear sunscreen when I am out in the sun or just not go out in the sun to protect my skin from ultraviolet rays. I can also use lotion to help my skin stay moisturized.

Protection, Support, and Locomotion
Section 34.2 Bones: The Body's Support

Main Idea ——————   **Details** ——————————————————————————

Organize *As you read Section 2, complete the outline about bones.*

I. ____Skeletal____ system ____structure____

   A. ____Joints____

      1. Ligaments, bursae, and ____tendons____

   B. Two types of ____bone tissue____

      1. ____Compact____ bone

      2. ____Spongy____ bone

New Vocabulary

Identify each vocabulary word as indicated below. Make a short note or definition about each term.

appendicular skeleton

axial skeleton

bursa

compact bone

joint

ligament

osteoblast

osteocyte

red marrow

spongy bone

tendon

yellow marrow

Skeletal System Structure (9 terms)	Bone Formation (1 term)	Skeletal System Functions (2 terms)
axial skeleton—skull and the bones that support it	osteoblasts—potential bone-forming cells	red marrow—production site for red blood cells, white blood cells, and fragments involved in clotting
appendicular skeleton—bones of arms and legs, shoulders, hip bones cell		
joint—where two bones meet		yellow marrow—consists of stored fat, found in many bones
ligament—attaches one bone to another		
compact bone—outer layer of hard protective bone		
osteocytes—new bone cells		
spongy bone—less dense bone with holes and spaces		
tendon—attaches muscle to bone		
bursa—fluid-filled sac that prevents bones from rubbing against each other		

Section 34.2 Bones: The Body's Support (continued)

Main Idea — **Details**

Skeletal System Structure

I found this information on page _____.
SE, pp. 899–902
RE, pp. 414–416

Classify *List the two main parts of the human adult skeleton and the bones each includes.*

1. Axial skeleton includes the skull and the bones that support it, the vertebral column, the ribs, and the sternum.

2. Appendicular skeleton includes the bones of the arms and legs, shoulder and hip bones, wrists, ankles, fingers, and toes.

Identify *five characteristics of joints.*

1. held together by ligaments

2. connected to muscle by tendons

3. ends of bones covered in cartilage in movable joints

4. help bones move in relation to each other

5. bursae on outside of some joints

Classify *each movable joint as a hinge joint or a ball-and-socket joint.*

hip joints ___ball-and-socket___   elbow joints ___hinge___

finger joints ___hinge___   shoulder joints ___ball-and-socket___

Create *a sketch of a bone. Show compact bone, spongy bone, and the location of osteocytes. Use the figure in your book to help you.* Students should sketch a simple bone showing compact bone, spongy bone, and osteocytes in the area along the length of compact bone. Sketches may resemble those in the book. Accept reasonable variations.

Section 34.2 Bones: The Body's Support (continued)

Main Idea —— **Details** ——————————————————————

Formation of Bone

I found this information on page _____.
SE, pp. 902–903
RE, pp. 416–417

Sequence *the steps in the formation of bone from osteoblasts. The first step has been completed for you.* Accept all reasonable responses.

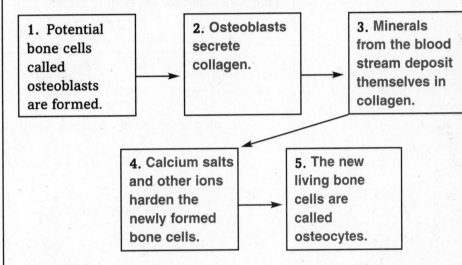

1. Potential bone cells called osteoblasts are formed.

2. Osteoblasts secrete collagen.

3. Minerals from the blood stream deposit themselves in collagen.

4. Calcium salts and other ions harden the newly formed bone cells.

5. The new living bone cells are called osteocytes.

Skeletal System Functions

I found this information on page _____.
SE, pp. 903–904
RE, pp. 417–418

Complete *the concept map about the skeletal system functions.* Accept all reasonable responses.

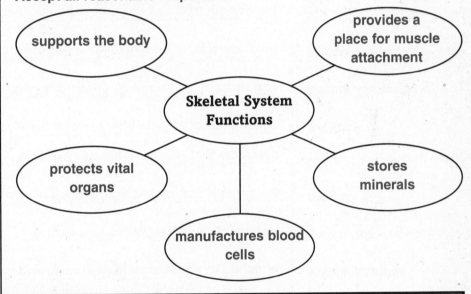

supports the body

provides a place for muscle attachment

Skeletal System Functions

protects vital organs

stores minerals

manufactures blood cells

COMPARE

Compare yellow marrow and red marrow.

Red marrow is found in the femur, humerus, sternum, ribs, vertebrae, and pelvis. This marrow

makes red blood cells, white blood cells, and cell fragments needed for clotting. Yellow marrow

does not produce any blood cells. It is stored fat that can be used at times when the body

needs it.

Protection, Support, and Locomotion
Section 34.3 Muscles for Locomotion

Main Idea ———— **Details** ———————————————————————

Organize Information *As you read, complete the concept map to compare different types of muscles.*

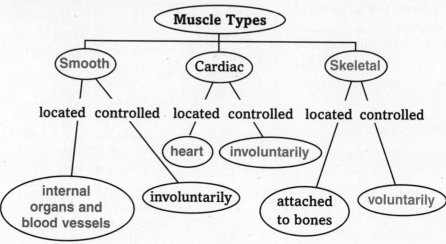

New Vocabulary *Use your book to define each term.*

actin	the protein that makes up the thin filaments of myofibrils
cardiac muscle	heart muscle; it is an involuntary muscle
involuntary muscle	contracts by itself, not by conscious control
myofibril	small units of muscle fiber; myofibrils are made up of small protein filaments that can be either thick or thin
myosin	the protein that makes up the thick filaments of myofibrils
sarcomere	each section of a myofibril in a muscle
skeletal muscle	attached to and moves bones; contracts under conscious control
sliding filament theory	actin filaments slide toward each other during muscle contraction, but myosin filaments do not move
smooth muscle	involuntary muscle found in walls of internal organs and blood vessels; common job is to squeeze to exert pressure inside a tube or organ
voluntary muscle	a muscle that contracts under conscious control

Section 34.3 Muscles for Locomotion (continued)

Main Idea ———— **Details** ——————————————————

Three Types of Muscles

I found this information on page _____ .
SE, pp. 905–906
RE, pp. 420–421

List *the three types of muscles. Classify each as voluntary or involuntary.*

1. smooth muscle—involuntary

2. cardiac muscle—involuntary

3. skeletal muscle—voluntary

Distinguish *between voluntary muscles and involuntary muscles.*

Voluntary muscles are muscles you have to think about moving.

They contract under conscious control. Involuntary muscles are

muscles that contract by themselves. You do not consciously

control involuntary muscles.

Model *the structure and appearance of each type of muscle fiber. Label the fiber, the nucleus, and striation if the muscle fiber is striated. Next to each muscle fiber, write its function.*

smooth muscle fiber Sketches may resemble Figure 34.11 on page 905 of the SE/ pages 420–421 of the RE. The muscle fiber and nucleus should be labeled.	squeezes
cardiac muscle fiber The muscle fiber, nucleus, and striation should be labeled.	contracts regularly to keep your heart beating
skeletal muscle fiber The muscle fiber, nucleus, and striation should be labeled.	moves your bones

Section 34.3 Muscles for Locomotion (continued)

Main Idea ———— **Details** ——————————————————

Skeletal Muscle Contraction

I found this information on page _____.
SE, pp. 906–907
RE, p. 421

Analyze *muscle tissue by completing the graphic organizer.*

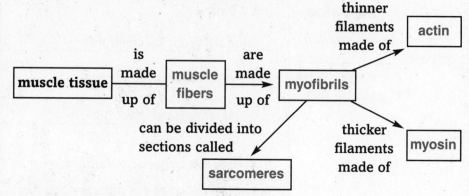

Explain *the sliding filament theory.*

Accept all reasonable responses. A muscle contracts when it is

signaled. When the actin filaments in a muscle get a signal, they

slide toward each other. They are part of sarcomeres in the muscle

so when they slide toward each other, the sarcomeres get shorter.

This makes the whole sarcomere get shorter which makes the

muscle contract. The myosin filaments do not move.

Muscle Strength and Exercise

I found this information on page _____.
SE, pp. 907–909
RE, pp. 421–422

Contrast *the effects on your body of moderate and vigorous exercise.*

Accept all reasonable responses. Moderate exercise increases

muscle fibers through aerobic respiration. During vigorous exercise,

muscles can't get enough oxygen so lactic acid builds up and you

may get cramps.

CONNECT Contract your biceps muscle. Describe what you did to contract the muscle and which muscle is relaxed. Try the opposite and contract the muscle that was relaxed and describe what happens.

Accept all reasonable responses. I contracted my biceps by bending my arm. The triceps was

relaxed. Then I contracted my triceps by straightening my arm and the biceps muscle was

relaxed.

Tie-It-All-Together

CONNECT

Recall what you have learned about the different types of burns. In third degree burns, both the epidermis and dermis are destroyed. Skin grafts are often necessary to replace this lost skin. Think about the functions of skin and predict what problems people with third degree burns might face if skin grafts are not possible.

Accept all reasonable responses. People with third degree burns have lost the skin that protects the body. Their body may be at greater risk for infections because bacteria can get into the body more easily at the burned areas. They may also have problems with their body temperature. They won't have skin to help them sweat in that area. They also will likely not be able to sense anything in the area where the skin has been burned.

Some people suffer from a disease called osteogenesis imperfecta. It is commonly called brittle bone disease. The disease is caused by a mutation in the gene that produces collagen. Think about the formation of bones. Describe how this weaker form of collagen may lead to weaker bones.

Accept all reasonable responses. If the collagen that is produced is weaker, minerals from the bloodstream may have a more difficult time depositing themselves in this collagen. Calcium salts and other ions would be less likely to be able to deposit themselves and harden in the defective collagen. Fewer or weaker bone cells would be formed in this process. This makes the bones weaker and more likely to break.

Protection, Support, and Locomotion Chapter Wrap-Up

In the "What I Wanted to Find Out" column, copy the questions you listed in the Chapter Preview. In the "What I Learned" column, write down the answers you discovered as you worked through the chapter.

W What I Wanted to Find Out	L What I Learned
1. Accept all reasonable entries.	1.
2.	2.
3.	3.

Use this checklist to help you study.

☐ Study your Science Notebook for this chapter.

☐ Study the definitions of vocabulary words.

☐ Review daily homework assignments.

☐ Reread the chapter and review the tables, graphs, and illustrations.

☐ Review the Section Assessment questions at the end of each section.

☐ Look over the Study Guide at the end of the chapter.

SUMMARIZE

After reading this chapter, list three things you have learned about protection, support, and locomotion.

Accept all reasonable responses.

The Digestive and Endocrine Systems
Before You Read

Use the "What I Know" column to list three things you know about the digestive and endocrine systems. Then list three questions you have about these systems in the "What I Want to Find Out" column.

K What I Know	W What I Want to Find Out
1. Accept all reasonable entries. _____ _____	1. _____ _____
2. _____ _____	2. _____ _____
3. _____ _____	3. _____ _____

Science Journal

What can go wrong with your digestive and endocrine systems? Describe your own experience, that of someone you know, or items you have heard about in the media.

Accept all reasonable responses. _____

_____

_____

_____

_____

_____

_____

_____

The Digestive and Endocrine Systems

Section 35.1 Following Digestion of a Meal

(Main Idea) ——— **(Details)** ————————————

Skim *Section 1 of your text. Write three questions that come to mind from reading the headings and the illustration captions.*

1. Accept all reasonable responses._____

2. _____

3. _____

(New Vocabulary) *Read the definitions below, then write the correct term in the left column.*

_____amylase_____   breaks down the starches in food into smaller molecules

_____pepsin_____   an enzyme that begins the chemical digestion of protein in food; works best in an acidic environment

_____bile_____   a chemical that helps break down large drops of fats into smaller droplets

_____villus_____   a tiny, fingerlike structure that is a projection on the lining of the small intestine; works in absorption of digested food

_____peristalsis_____   a series of smooth muscle contractions along the walls of the digestive tract

epiglottis
esophagus
gallbladder
large intestine
liver
pancreas
rectum
small intestine
stomach

Use the vocabulary words in the left column to label the parts of the digestive system in the diagram to the right.

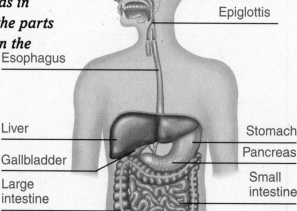

Epiglottis

Esophagus

Liver

Gallbladder

Large intestine

Stomach

Pancreas

Small intestine

Rectum

Section 35.1 Following Digestion of a Meal (continued)

⟨Main Idea⟩ ——— **⟨Details⟩** ——————————————————————

Functions of the Digestive System

I found this information on page _____ .

SE, p. 917
RE, p. 424

Sequence *the functions of the digestive system. Some of the steps have been completed for you. (Hint: focus on the functions, not the organs.)* Accept all reasonable responses.

1. Ingestion—You put food into your mouth.

⬇

2. System takes ingested food and begins moving it through the digestive tract.

⬇

3. Complex food molecules are broken down mechanically and chemically.

⬇

4. Digestive system absorbs the digested food and sends it to your cells.

⬇

5. Materials that cannot be digested are eliminated from your body.

The Mouth

I found this information on page _____ .

SE, pp. 917–920
RE, pp. 424–425

Describe *how each type of digestion takes place in the mouth.*

Mechanical digestion breaks down the food into smaller pieces. This

happens as you chew your food. Chemical digestion changes the

food on a molecular level. This happens as the enzymes in your

mouth, such as amylase, begin to work on the food molecules.

Sequence *how food moves from the mouth to the stomach by adding arrows between the boxes. Then describe the function of each organ or process.*

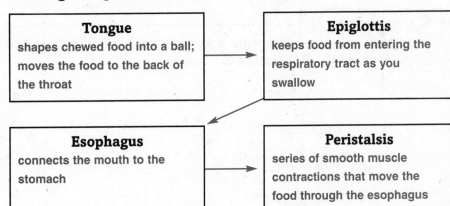

Tongue
shapes chewed food into a ball; moves the food to the back of the throat

Epiglottis
keeps food from entering the respiratory tract as you swallow

Esophagus
connects the mouth to the stomach

Peristalsis
series of smooth muscle contractions that move the food through the esophagus

Section 35.1 Following Digestion of a Meal (continued)

(Main Idea)——— (Details)———————————————————

The Stomach and Small Intestine

I found this information on page _____.

SE, pp. 920–922
RE, pp. 426–428

Summarize *how each organ below mechanically and chemically digests food.*

Organ	Mechanical Digestion	Chemical Digestion
Stomach	stomach muscles contract and physically break down swallowed food into smaller pieces	glands in the stomach secrete gastric juice that contains pepsin and hydrochloric acid; pepsin digests the proteins in food
Small intestine	muscle contractions help break down the food	enzymes break down the food chemically
Pancreas	does not apply	secretes enzymes that break down carbohydrates, proteins, and fats; alkaline pancreatic juices neutralize acidity of liquid food in small intestine stopping any further action of pepsin
Liver	does not apply	produces bile that breaks down fats

The Large Intestine

I found this information on page _____.

SE, p. 923
RE, p. 428

Contrast *what happens in the small intestine with what happens in the large intestine.*

In the small intestine, food digestion is completed. The digested food

is absorbed through the villi and diffuses into the bloodstream. In

the large intestine, no food is absorbed, only water and salts. The

large intestine moves indigestible material into the rectum.

SYNTHESIZE Describe how your body's ability to absorb nutrients would change if your small intestine did not have villi.

Accept all reasonable responses. If the small intestine did not have villi, less food could be

absorbed into the bloodstream. This is because there would be less surface area in the small

intestine for the food to be absorbed through. The villi provide more surface area to absorb

more food.

The Digestive and Endocrine Systems
Section 35.2 Nutrition

Main Idea _____

Details _____

Using Prior Knowledge *List the foods you eat in a day. Then use the food pyramid in your book as a guide to categorize the foods into different groups according to food type.*

_____

_____

_____

Fats and Sugars	Dairy	Meat, Fish, and Eggs
Vegetables	Fruits	Grains

Review Vocabulary *Use your book to define the following term.*

carbohydrate | organic compound used by cells to store and release energy

New Vocabulary *Use your book to define each term.*

Calorie | unit of heat used to measure energy content of food; each Calorie

represents a kilocalorie, or 1000 calories; a calorie is the amount of

heat that is needed to raise the temperature of 1 mL of water by 1°C

mineral | an inorganic substance found mainly in the skeleton that serves as a

building material for your body

vitamin | organic nutrients required in small amounts to maintain growth and

metabolism

Section 35.2 Nutrition (continued)

Main Idea —

Details _____

The Vital Nutrients

I found this information on page _____.
SE, pp. 924–927
RE, pp. 430–432

Name *the six basic kinds of nutrients that can be found in foods.*

1. ____carbohydrates____   4. ____minerals____

2. _____fats_____   5. ____vitamins____

3. _____proteins_____   6. _____water_____

Summerize *how your body uses each kind of nutrient by completing the graphic organizer.* Accept all reasonable responses.

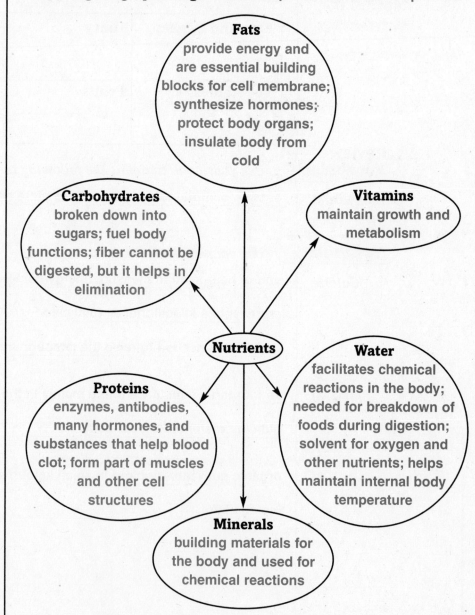

Fats
provide energy and are essential building blocks for cell membrane; synthesize hormones; protect body organs; insulate body from cold

Carbohydrates
broken down into sugars; fuel body functions; fiber cannot be digested, but it helps in elimination

Vitamins
maintain growth and metabolism

Nutrients

Proteins
enzymes, antibodies, many hormones, and substances that help blood clot; form part of muscles and other cell structures

Water
facilitates chemical reactions in the body; needed for breakdown of foods during digestion; solvent for oxygen and other nutrients; helps maintain internal body temperature

Minerals
building materials for the body and used for chemical reactions

Section 35.2 Nutrition (continued)

Main Idea	Details

The Vital Nutrients

I found this information on page _____.
SE, pp. 924–927
RE, pp. 430–432

Describe *what the liver does with each of the following nutrients.*

1. Carbohydrates— It stores the sugars from carbohydrates as glycogen.

2. Fats — It converts fatty acids to glycogen.

3. Proteins— It converts amino acids to fats or glucose.

Calories and Metabolism

I found this information on page _____.
SE, pp. 927–928
RE, pp. 432–433

Identify *four factors that affect a person's metabolic rate.*

1. _____body mass_____   3. _____gender_____

2. _____age_____   4. level of physical activity

Explain *the relationship between calories and health by completing the cause and effect diagram.*

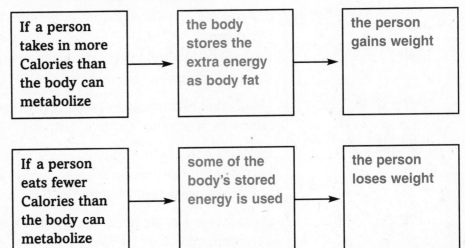

If a person takes in more Calories than the body can metabolize	→	the body stores the extra energy as body fat	→	the person gains weight

If a person eats fewer Calories than the body can metabolize	→	some of the body's stored energy is used	→	the person loses weight

ANALYZE Analyze why men usually need more Calories per day than females, why teenagers use more Calories than adults, and why active people use more Calories than inactive people.

Accept all reasonable responses. Males are usually larger than females. They need more

Calories because of this larger body mass. Teenagers are younger than adults and still

growing. This is why they need more Calories. Active people need more Calories than inactive

people because their level of physical activity is greater.

The Digestive and Endocrine Systems
Section 35.3 The Endocrine System

Main Idea _____

Details _____

Organize Information *As you read this section, complete the concept map about internal feedback in the endocrine system.*

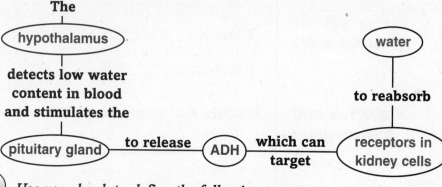

Review Vocabulary _____

Use your book to define the following term.

gland | in mammals, a cell or group of cells that secretes fluid

New Vocabulary _____

Read the definitions below, then write the correct term in the left column.

__hypothalamus__ | the part of the brain that connects the endocrine system and the nervous system

__endocrine glands__ | glands that release chemicals directly into the bloodstream; relay information to other parts of the body

__adrenal gland__ | located on top of the kidneys; outer portion secretes steroid hormones; inner portion secretes amino acid hormones; amino acid hormones are responsible for the fight-or-flight response

__thyroid gland__ | gland located in the neck that regulates metabolism, growth, and development

__parathyroid gland__ | gland attached to the thyroid gland involved in mineral regulation in the body

__pituitary gland__ | the main gland of the endocrine system; controlled by the hypothalamus

__receptors__ | the binding sites on target cells

__target cells__ | cells to which hormones attach themselves; contain specific binding sites either on the plasma membranes, or in the nuclei

__negative feedback system__ | type of internal feedback mechanism that generally controls adjustments to the endocrine system

Section 35.3 The Endocrine System (continued)

Main Idea ————— **Details** ————————————————————————

Control of the Body

I found this information on page _____ .
SE, pp. 929–930
RE, pp. 435–436

Identify *the two systems that direct internal control of the body.*

1. endocrine system _____

2. nervous system _____

Describe *how the nervous and endocrine systems interact by completing the graphic organizer.*

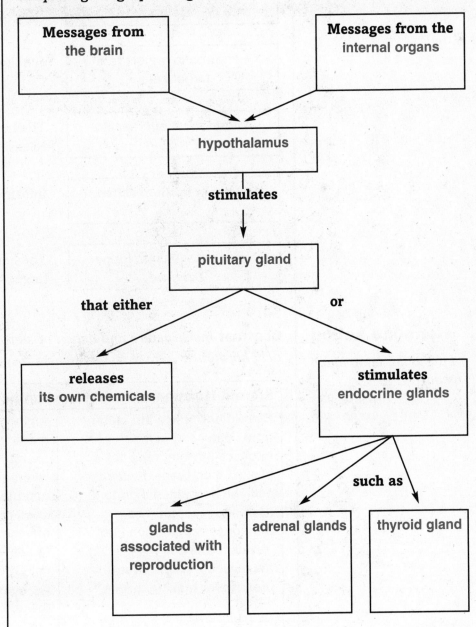

| Messages from the brain | Messages from the internal organs |

hypothalamus

stimulates

pituitary gland

that either   **or**

releases its own chemicals   stimulates endocrine glands

such as

glands associated with reproduction   adrenal glands   thyroid gland

Section 35.3 The Endocrine System (continued)

Main Idea —— **Details** ———————————————

Negative Feedback Control

I found this information on page _____.
SE, pp. 930–932
RE, pp. 437–438

Sequence *the steps that occur in a negative feedback system. They are written in scrambled order at right. Write the steps in the correct order in the boxes.*

Homeostasis is disrupted.
↓
| Endocrine glands are stimulated to secrete hormone. |
↓
| The hormone travels to the target cells. |
↓
| Information is fed back. |
↓
| Homeostasis is reached. |
↓
| The hormone is no longer released. |

Endocrine glands are stimulated to secrete hormone.

Homeostasis is reached.

Homeostasis is disrupted.

The hormone is no longer released.

Information is fed back.

The hormone travels to the target cells.

Hormone Action

I found this information on page _____.
SE, pp. 932–933
RE, pp. 438–439

Contrast *the structure and action of steroid hormones and amino acid hormones.* **Accept all reasonable responses.**

Steroid Hormones	Amino Acid Hormones
Steroid hormones are made from lipids, and can diffuse into a cell through the cell's plasma membrane. Inside the cell, the hormones bind to a hormone receptor. The hormone-receptor complex travels to the cell nucleus. In the nucleus, it starts the process for making mRNA.	Amino acid hormones are made from amino acids and secreted into bloodstream where they bind with embedded receptors of the target cell. They open ion channels in the membrane, which route signals to activate enzymes within the cell. The enzymes change the behavior of other molecules in the cell.

Section 35.3 The Endocrine System (continued)

Main Idea ——— **Details** ————————————————

Adrenal Hormones and Stress

I found this information on page _____.
SE, pp. 933–934
RE, p. 439

Compare *four adrenal hormones in the table below.*

Amino Acid or Steroid Hormone	Adrenal Hormone	What do they do?
steroid	glucocorticoids	cause an increase in available glucose, raise blood pressure, help the body combat fear, very hot or very cold temperatures, bleeding, infection, disease, and other anxieties
	aldosterone	
amino acid	epinephrine (adrenaline)	stimulate heart rate, blood pressure, and the rate of breathing; increase the efficiency of muscle contractions and increase blood sugar levels
	norepinephrine	

Thyroid and Parathyroid Hormones

I found this information on page _____.
SE, pp. 934–935
RE, pp. 439–440

Summarize *thyroid and parathyroid hormones in the organizer.*

Thyroid gland		Parathyroid gland
Hormone: thyroxine **Function:** affects rate at which your body uses energy; determines how much food you need	**Hormone:** calcitonin **Function:** regulates calcium levels in blood; increases calcium absorption to make bone	**Hormone:** parathryroid hormone **Function:** involved in mineral regulation (calcium, phosphate, and magnesium)

SYNTHESIZE

Predict how an underactive pituitary gland (one that does not produce enough human growth hormone) would affect a person's blood glucose levels. Explain.

Accept all reasonable responses. If a person has an underactive pituitary gland, their blood glucose levels would be too low. When the hypothalamus stimulates the pituitary gland to release hGH, the pituitary gland would not release enough. It would stimulate the liver to release some glucose, but not enough. The person's blood sugar levels would remain low.

The Digestive and Endocrine Systems Chapter Wrap-Up

In the "What I Wanted to Find Out" column, copy the questions you listed in the Chapter Preview. In the "What I Learned" column, write down the answers you discovered as you worked through the chapter.

W What I Wanted to Find Out	L What I Learned
1. Accept all reasonable entries.	1.
2.	2.
3.	3.

Use this checklist to help you study.

☐ Study your Science Notebook for this chapter.

☐ Study the definitions of vocabulary words.

☐ Review daily homework assignments.

☐ Reread the chapter and review the tables, graphs, and illustrations.

☐ Review the Section Assessment questions at the end of each section.

☐ Look over the Study Guide at the end of the chapter.

SUMMARIZE

After reading this chapter, list three things you have learned about the digestive and endocrine systems.

Accept all reasonable responses.

_____

_____

The Nervous System

Before You Read

Use the "What I Know" column to list three things you know about the nervous system. Then list three questions you have about this system in the "What I Want to Find Out" column.

K What I Know	W What I Want to Find Out
1. Accept all reasonable entries. _____	1. _____ _____
2. _____ _____	2. _____ _____
3. _____ _____	3. _____ _____

Science Journal

Think about a time you have been very frightened. Describe how you felt and how your body responded.

Accept all reasonable responses.

_____

_____

_____

_____

_____

_____

_____

The Nervous System
Section 36.1 The Nervous System

Main Idea ————

Details —————————————————————

Sequence *As you read through this section, record the sequence of changes that occurs in a neuron when it is excited by a stimulus.* Accept all reasonable responses.

At rest, a neuron is polarized—the inside of the cell is more negative

than the outside. As an impulse moves down a neuron, sodium

channels open, sodium ions enter the cell, and the inside becomes

more positively charged than the outside of the cell (depolarization).

After the impulse passes, the sdium/potassium pump returns ions to

normal concentrations and the neuron is repolarized.

New Vocabulary

autonomic nervous
system
axon
central nervous system
cerebellum
cerebrum
dendrite
medulla oblongata
neuron
neurotransmitters
parasympathetic
nervous system
peripheral nervous
system
reflex
somatic nervous system
sympathetic nervous
system
synapse

Classify each vocabulary word as a nervous system, or part of the brain, or neurons. The number of terms in each column is given to you. One term will not fit into any of the three categories. Define that term on the lines below the chart.

Nervous System (6 terms)	Brain (3 terms)	Neurons (5 terms)
autonomic nervous system central nervous system parasympathetic nervous system peripheral nervous system somatic nervous system sympathetic nervous system	cerebellum cerebrum medulla oblongata	neuron axon dendrite neurotransmitters synapse

reflex—simple, automatic response in an animal that involves no

conscious control; usually acts to protect an animal from serious injury

Section 36.1 The Nervous System (continued)

Main Idea ————

Details ————————————————————————

Neurons: Basic Units of the Nervous System

I found this information on page _____ .
SE, pp. 943–946
RE, pp. 442–444

Label *the neuron. Include the axon, axon endings, cell body dendrites, nucleus, and myelin sheath. Draw arrows to show the direction that impulses move through the neuron.*

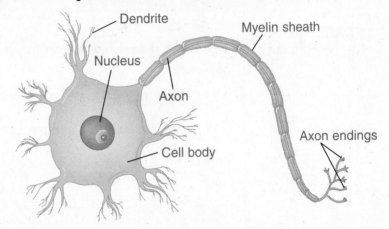

Dendrite

Myelin sheath

Nucleus

Axon

Cell body

Axon endings

Arrows should point from the dendrite to the cell body and away from the cell body through the axon.

Analyze *how the myelin sheath increases the speed at which impulses move.*

The myelin sheath keeps the ions from moving across the plasma

membrane of the axon. This makes the ions move quickly down the

axon until they find a gap in the sheath where they can pass

through. This makes the impulses jump from gap to gap so they

move faster.

Evaluate *the diagram of how neurotransmitters move across synapses. Write one question and answer about the diagram.*

Question: Accept all reasonable responses.

_____

Answer: _____

_____

Section 36.1 The Nervous System (continued)

| Main Idea | Details |

The Central Nervous System

I found this information on page _____.
SE, pp. 946–947
RE, pp. 445–446

Identify *two parts of the body that make up the central nervous system.*

1. _____ the brain _____   2. _____ the spinal cord _____

Contrast *the central nervous system and the peripheral nervous system.*

The central nervous system coordinates all of your body's activities.

The peripheral nervous system carries messages to and from the

central nervous system.

_____

_____

_____

_____

_____

Describe *the three main sections of the brain in the table below.*

Section:	Cerebrum	Cerebellum	Medulla Oblongata
Description	divided into two halves that are connected by bundles of nerves, sections are called hemispheres	located at the back of the brain	part of the brain stem
Function	controls all conscious activity, intelligence, memory, language, skeletal muscle movements, and senses	controls balance, posture, and coordination	controls involuntary activities such as breathing and heart rate

Section 36.1 The Nervous System (continued)

⊂Main Idea⊃ ——— **⊂Details⊃** ————————————————————

The Peripheral Nervous System

I found this information on page _____.

SE, pp. 948–950
RE, pp. 446–448

Describe *each division of the nervous system and its function in the graphic organizer below.*

- Autonomic
- Peripheral
- Central
- Somatic
- Parasympathetic
- Sympathetic

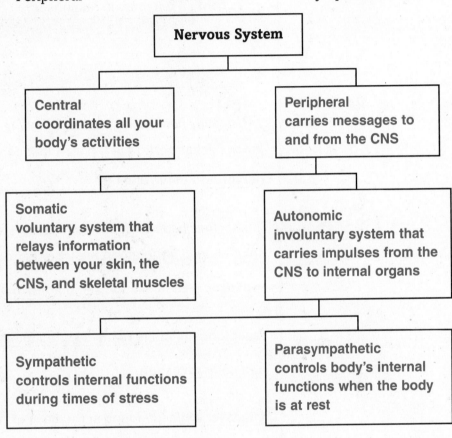

Nervous System

Central
coordinates all your body's activities

Peripheral
carries messages to and from the CNS

Somatic
voluntary system that relays information between your skin, the CNS, and skeletal muscles

Autonomic
involuntary system that carries impulses from the CNS to internal organs

Sympathetic
controls internal functions during times of stress

Parasympathetic
controls body's internal functions when the body is at rest

CONNECT Describe a voluntary response that would happen under the control of the somatic nervous system. Then describe a reflex and compare it to the voluntary response you chose.

Accept all reasonable responses. A voluntary response would be my deciding to take a drink

of hot cocoa. I would voluntarily control the muscles that moved my hand and arm to grasp

and lift the cup and bring it to my mouth. If the cup of hot cocoa were too hot to grasp, I would

pull my hand away as a reflex. It would happen without my brain even thinking about it.

The Nervous System
Section 36.2 The Senses

Main Idea ———— **Details** —————————————————————

Skim *Section 2 of your book. Write three questions that come to mind from reading the headings and the illustration captions.*

1. Accept all reasonable responses.

2. _____

3. _____

Review Vocabulary *Use your book to define the following term.*

dermis
inner, thicker portion of the skin that contains structures, such as

nerves and nerve endings

New Vocabulary *Use your book to define each term.*

cochlea
snail-shaped structure in the inner ear containing fluid and hairs;

produces electrical impulses that the brain interprets as sound

cones
receptor cells in the retina adapted for sharp vision in bright light

and color detection

retina
thin layer of tissue found at the back of the eye made up of light

receptors and sensory neurons

rods
receptor cells in the retina that are adapted for vision in dim light;

also help detect shape and movement

semicircular canals
structures in the inner ear containing fluid and hairs that help the

body maintain balance

taste buds
sensory receptors located on the tongue that result in taste

perception

Section 36.2 The Senses (continued)

Main Idea —— **Details** ————————————————————————

Sensing Chemicals

I found this information on page _____ .
SE, pp. 951–952
RE, p. 450

List *the two senses that are involved in sensing chemicals.*

1. _____smell_____   2. _____taste_____

Compare *the steps in smelling and tasting. Write the steps for smelling on the left. Write the steps for tasting on the right. Some steps have been completed for you.*

Chemical molecules touch receptors in your nose.

↓

Chemicals acting on the receptors initiate impulses in the olfactory nerve.

↓

The olfactory nerve sends the impulses to the brain.

Chemicals dissolved in saliva contact your taste buds.

↓

The cells of taste buds are depolarized.

↓

Signals from your taste buds are sent to the cerebrum.

↘   ↙

Your brain interprets the signal as a particular taste or odor.

Sensing Light

I found this information on page _____ .
SE, p. 952
RE, p. 451

Compare *how the rods and cones in your eyes help you to sense light.*

Rods and cones are both receptor cells in the eye. Rods are adapted for vision in dim light and cones are adapted for sharp vision in bright light. Rods help you detect shape and movement. Cones help you detect color.

(Main Idea)_____ (Details)_____

Sensing Mechanical Stimulation

I found this information on page _____.
SE, pp. 952–955
RE, pp. 451–453

Sequence *the steps in how your sense of hearing works. The steps are in scrambled order at right. Write them in the correct order in the boxes.*

| 1. Sound waves enter your ear and travel down to the end of the ear canal. |

The hairs produce electric impulses that travel to the cerebrum where they are interpreted as sound.

↓

| 2. Sound waves strike the eardrum and cause it to vibrate. The vibrations pass to the bones in the middle ear. |

The stapes causes the membrane of the oval window to move back and forth.

↓

| 3. The stapes causes the membrane of the oval window to move back and forth. |

Sound waves enter your ear and travel down to the end of the ear canal.

↓

| 4. Fluid in the cochlea moves, causing the hair cells to bend. |

Sound waves strike the eardrum and cause it to vibrate. The vibrations pass to the bones in the middle ear.

↓

| 5. The hairs produce electric impulses that travel to the cerebrum where they are interpreted as sound. |

Fluid in the cochlea moves, causing the hair cells to bend.

Identify three changes that receptors in the dermis of the skin respond to.

1. ___temperature___   2. ___pressure___   3. ___pain___

SYNTHESIZE Predict how damage to your semicircular canals in the ears would affect balance. Explain.

Accept all reasonable responses. If your semicircular canals were damaged, you would not be

able to balance as well. The hairs in the semicircular canals are responsible for telling the

brain if you are balanced or not. If they were not working properly, your brain would not

receive these signals.

The Nervous System

Section 36.3 The Effects of Drugs

⟨Main Idea⟩ ———   **⟨Details⟩** —————————————————

Finding Main Ideas *As you read Section 3, complete the outline below about the effects of drugs on the nervous system.*

    I. Drugs act on the ___body___ :

        A. __Drugs__ affect body __functions__

    II. __Medicinal__ Uses of Drugs

        A. Relieving ___pain___ :

           1. __Narcotics__

⟨Review Vocabulary⟩ *Use your book to define the following term.*

receptors | **specific binding sites found on the surface of or within a cell**

⟨New Vocabulary⟩ *Read the definitions below, then write the correct term in the left column.*

drug	chemical substance that affects body functions
tolerance	the body becomes less responsive to a drug and an individual needs larger or more frequent doses of the drug to achieve the same effect
depressant	type of drug that lowers or depresses the activity of the nervous system
narcotic	type of pain relief drug that affects the central nervous system
withdrawal	psychological response or physiological illness that occurs when a person stops taking a drug
addiction	psychological and/or physiological drug dependence
stimulant	drug that increases the activity of the central and sympathetic nervous systems
hallucinogen	drug that stimulates the central nervous system so that the user becomes disoriented and sees, hears, feels, tastes, or smells things that are not there

Section 36.3 The Effects of Drugs (continued)

Main Idea	Details

Drugs Act on the Body

I found this information on page _____.

SE, p. 956
RE, p. 455

Summarize *three ways drugs can act on the body in the graphic organizer.*

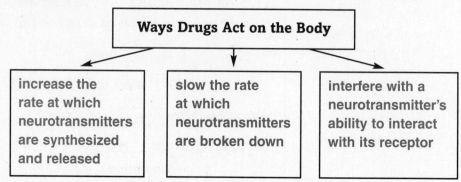

Ways Drugs Act on the Body

increase the rate at which neurotransmitters are synthesized and released	slow the rate at which neurotransmitters are broken down	interfere with a neurotransmitter's ability to interact with its receptor

Medicinal Uses of Drugs

I found this information on page _____.

SE, pp. 957–958
RE, pp. 455–456

Compare *the different medicinal uses of drugs in the graphic organizer. Identify each type of drug and give examples of what it is used for. Some have been completed for you.*

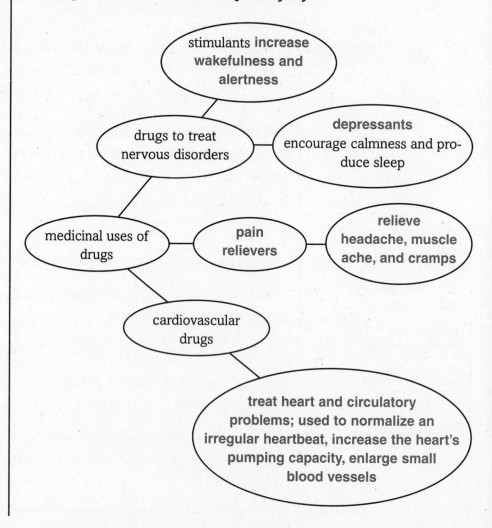

stimulants increase wakefulness and alertness

drugs to treat nervous disorders

depressants encourage calmness and produce sleep

medicinal uses of drugs

pain relievers

relieve headache, muscle ache, and cramps

cardiovascular drugs

treat heart and circulatory problems; used to normalize an irregular heartbeat, increase the heart's pumping capacity, enlarge small blood vessels

Section 36.3 The Effects of Drugs (continued)

<Main Idea> ——— <Details> ————————————————————

The Misuse and Abuse of Drugs, Classes of Commonly Abused Drugs

I found this information on page _____.

SE, pp. 958–963
RE, pp. 456–459

Compare *the effects of each class of drugs by completing the table.*
Accept all reasonable responses.

Class	Effect on Body	Side Effects	Example
Stimulants	increase the activity of the central and sympathetic nervous systems	paranoia nervousness, anxiety, and convulsions	cocaine
Depressants	slow down the activities of the central nervous system	cirrhosis, drowsiness	alcohol
Narcotics	act directly on the brain, depressing the central nervous system	lowers heart rate	opiates
Hallucinogens	stimulate the central nervous system altering moods, thoughts, and sensory perceptions	convulsions, increase blood pressure, heart rate, respiratory rate	LSD
Anabolic Steroids	stimulate muscles to increase size	infertility in men, high blood pressure and mood swings	none given

Identify *the two types of therapy people may need to break a drug addiction.*

Breaking the Habit

I found this information on page _____.

SE, p. 963
RE, pp. 459–460

1. ____medical therapy____ 2. __psychological therapy__

ANALYZE Hypothesize why some stimulants are illegal and others are not.

Accept all reasonable responses. Stimulants like amphetamines have a much greater effect on

the nervous system than stimulants like caffeine. For example, amphetamines cause irregular

heartbeat, chest pain, and paranoia. Coffee causes increased alertness and mood swings. Its

adverse affects are much less severe than amphetamines.

The Nervous System Chapter Wrap-Up

In the "What I Wanted to Find Out" column, copy the questions you listed in the Chapter Preview. In the "What I Learned" column, write down the answers you discovered as you worked through the chapter.

W What I Wanted to Find Out	L What I Learned
1. Accept all reasonable entries. _____ 2. _____ _____ 3. _____ _____	1. _____ _____ 2. _____ _____ 3. _____ _____

Use this checklist to help you study.

☐ Study your Science Notebook for this chapter.

☐ Study the definitions of vocabulary words.

☐ Review daily homework assignments.

☐ Reread the chapter and review the tables, graphs, and illustrations.

☐ Review the Section Assessment questions at the end of each section.

☐ Look over the Study Guide at the end of the chapter.

SUMMARIZE

After reading this chapter, list three things you have learned about the nervous system.

Accept all reasonable responses.

_____

_____

_____

Respiration, Circulation, and Excretion

Before You Read

Use the "What I Know" column to list three things you know about respiration, circulation, and excretion. Then list three questions you have about these topics in the "What I Want to Find Out" column.

K What I Know	W What I Want to Find Out
1. Accept all reasonable entries.	1.
2.	2.
3.	3.

Science Journal

When you breathe in, oxygen enters your lungs. Describe what you understand about how oxygen from the air reaches the cells in your body.

Accept all reasonable responses.

Respiration, Circulation, and Excretion
Section 37.1 The Respiratory System

Main Idea ———

Details ————————————————

Skim *Section 1 of your book. Read the headings and illustration captions. Write three questions that come to mind.*

1. <u>Accept all reasonable responses.</u>

_____

2. _____

_____

3. _____

_____

Review Vocabulary) *Use your book to define the following term.*

diaphragm sheet of muscles beneath the lungs that separates the chest cavity

from the abdominal cavity

New Vocabulary) *Use your book to define the each term.*

alveoli sacs in the lungs where oxygen diffuses into the blood and carbon

dioxide diffuses into the air

trachea tubelike passageway for air flow that connects with two bronchi

tubes that lead into the lungs

Academic Vocabulary) *Define the following term.*

create to produce something or make something happen

Section 37.1 The Respiratory System (continued)

Main Idea	Details

Passageways and Lungs

I found this information on page _____ .
SE, pp. 971–973
RE, pp. 462–464

Identify *the role of the cilia in respiration.*

Cilia move foreign matter that is taken in from the air to where it can

be swallowed or expelled by coughing or sneezing. They prevent

most of the foreign matter from reaching the lungs.

Analyze *the process of gas exchange by completing the sentences in the flow chart below.*

When you breathe:

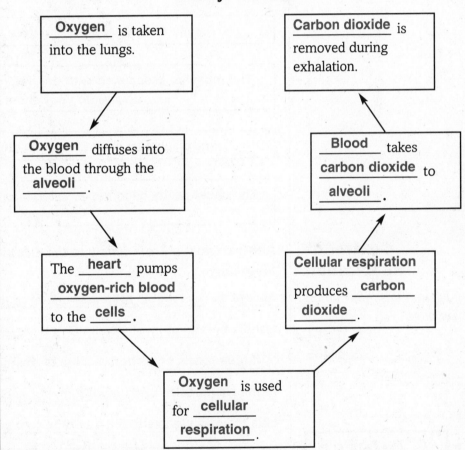

__Oxygen__ is taken into the lungs.

__Oxygen__ diffuses into the blood through the __alveoli__ .

The __heart__ pumps __oxygen-rich blood__ to the __cells__ .

__Oxygen__ is used for __cellular__ __respiration__ .

Cellular respiration produces __carbon__ __dioxide__ .

__Blood__ takes __carbon dioxide__ to __alveoli__ .

__Carbon dioxide__ is removed during exhalation.

Contrast *external and cellular respiration.*

External respiration involves breathing, or taking oxygen to the cells

of your body and exhaling carbon dioxide. Cellular respiration uses

oxygen to break down glucose and release energy as ATP. Carbon

dioxide is a waste product of this process.

Section 37.1 The Respiratory System (continued)

(Main Idea) ———— **(Details)** ————————————————————

The Mechanics of Breathing

I found this information on page _____.

SE, pp. 973–974
RE, p. 464

Sequence *what happens when you inhale and exhale. Some of the steps have been completed for you.*

> You inhale, the muscles in your ribs contract and your rib cage rises.
>
> ↓
>
> At the same time, the diaphragm muscle contracts. It becomes flattened and moves lower in the chest cavity.
>
> ↓
>
> More space in the chest cavity creates a slight vacuum.
>
> ↓
>
> Air rushes into your lungs.
>
> ↓
>
> The muscles associated with the ribs relax, and your ribs drop down into your chest cavity.
>
> ↓
>
> The diaphragm relaxes, returning to its resting position.
>
> ↓
>
> The chest cavity becomes smaller, forcing most of the air out of the alveoli.

Control of Respiration

I found this information on page _____.

SE, p. 974
RE, p. 465

Analyze *how a brain injury to the medulla oblongata may affect breathing.*

Accept all reasonable responses. That person would probably have

trouble breathing involuntarily. Since the medulla oblongata responds

to higher levels of carbon dioxide in the blood by sending signals

to the rib muscles and diaphragm, if it is damaged, it may not be

able to send signals to tell a person to breathe.

CONNECT Think of an example of when breathing is not an involuntary process. Describe how breathing is controlled in the example you give.

Accept all reasonable responses. When you hold your breath, breathing is a voluntary process.

You control how long you hold your breath by contracting your muscles. Other examples include

thoughtful breathing while playing a musical instrument, singing, or during meditation.

Respiration, Circulation, and Excretion
Section 37.2 The Circulatory System

(Main Idea) —————— **(Details)** ——————————————————————————

Infer *Think about the functions of your blood such as forming clots, carrying oxygen, and taking away cellular wastes. Infer how the other cells in your body would be affected if blood could not carry out its functions.*

Accept all reasonable responses. Blood delivers oxygen and nutrients

to the cells and removes waste products from cellular respiration.

Without this transportation system, cells of the body would die.

(New Vocabulary) *Use terms from the left column to complete the paragraphs below.*

antibodies

antigens

aorta

arteries

atria

blood pressure

capillaries

hemoglobin

plasma

platelets

pulse

red blood cells

veins

venae cavae

ventricles

white blood cells

The fluid portion of your blood is called ____plasma____. Suspended in fluid are ____red blood cells____ and ____white blood cells____. Red blood cells have ____hemoglobin____, which is an iron-containing protein molecule that helps carry oxygen to cells. White blood cells help protect us from diseases. Blood also contains small cell fragments called ____platelets____, which help blood to clot.

Different blood types are caused by proteins on the membranes of red blood cells, called ____antigens____. Blood plasma contains proteins called ____antibodies____, which are shaped to match the antigens.

The three main types of vessels that carry blood are ____arteries____, ____capillaries____, and ____veins____. The heart pumps the blood throughout the body. The two upper chambers of the heart are the ____atria____. The two lower chambers are the ____ventricles____. The right atrium of the heart gets blood through the ____venae cavae____. The left ventricle of the heart pushes blood out through the ____aorta____. Each time the heart beats, a ____pulse____ can be felt in arteries close to the surface of the body. ____Blood pressure____ is the force that the blood exerts on the vessels as the heart pumps it through the body.

Section 37.2 The Circulatory System (continued)

Main Idea ——— **Details** ——————————————

Your Blood: Fluid Transport

I found this information on page _____.
SE, pp. 975–976
RE, pp. 466–467

Compare *the different parts of blood in the table below.*

Part of Blood	Description	Function
red blood cells	round, disk-shaped cells, produced in red bone marrow, have nuclei in early development, then lose it; active in blood stream about 120 days, break down and are removed as waste; have hemoglobin	carry oxygen to body cells
white blood cells	make up one percent of the total volume of blood	play a role in protecting the body from foreign substances and microscopic organisms that cause disease
platelets	small cell fragments	help blood to clot
plasma	fluid portion of the blood	suspends red and white blood cells and platelets

ABO Blood Groups

I found this information on page _____.
SE, pp. 977–979
RE, p. 467–469

Distinguish *each blood type by putting checks in the correct boxes to show which antigens and antibodies it contains.*

Blood Type	Antigen A	Antigen B	Anti-A Antibody	Anti-B Antibody
A	√			√
B		√	√	
AB	√	√		
O			√	√

Analyze *why the Rh factor does not cause complications in some pregnancies until the mother is pregnant a second time.*

Accept all reasonable responses. If a Rh⁻ mother is exposed to the

blood of her Rh⁺ baby during birth, the mother will make anti-Rh⁺

antibodies. If the mother becomes pregnant again, the antibodies can

cross the placenta and enter the fetus. If the fetus is Rh⁺, the anti-Rh⁺

antibodies will destroy red blood cells of the fetus.

Section 37.2 The Circulatory System (continued)

Main Idea	Details

Your Blood Vessels: Pathways of Circulation and Your Heart: The Vital Pump

I found this information on page _____.
SE, pp. 979–984
RE, pp. 469–472

Describe *each type of blood vessel.*

1. Arteries   Large, thick-walled, muscular, elastic blood vessels that carry blood away from the heart. Their walls expand slightly. Blood surges through the arteries in pulses that correspond with the heartbeat.

2. Capillaries   These microscopic blood vessels are so small that red blood cells must go through in single file. They go to almost every cell in the body and allow nutrients and gases to diffuse easily between blood cells and tissue cells.

3. Veins   Large blood vessels that carry blood from tissues back to the heart. Blood is not under great pressure like in the arteries. Some veins have valves to keep blood from flowing backward.

Summarize *information about the pacemaker by completing the table below.*

what it looks like	how it works
a bundle of nerve cells	It makes an electrical impulse that spreads over both atria. This signals the two atria to contract at almost the same time. It also triggers a second set of cells at the base of the right atrium to send the same impulse over the ventricles. This causes the ventricles to contract.
where it is found	
at the top of the right atrium	
its function	
to set the heart rate	

Section 37.2 The Circulatory System (continued)

Main Idea ——

Details ——

Your Blood Vessels: Pathways of Circulation and Your Heart: The Vital Pump

I found this information on page _____ .
SE, pp. 979–984
RE, pp. 469–472

Identify the path blood takes through the human body by completing the flowchart below.

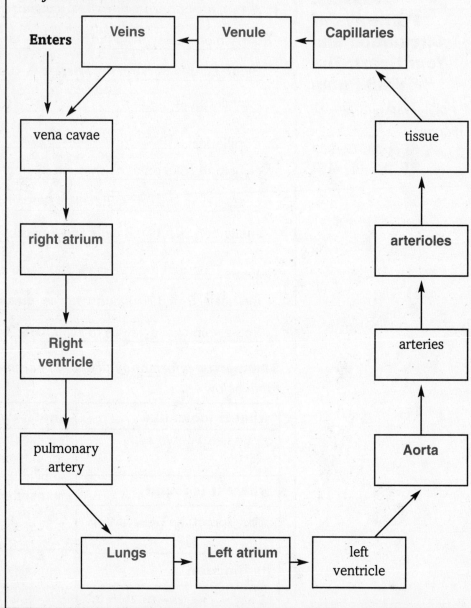

Enters

| Veins | ← | Venule | ← | Capillaries |

↓

| vena cavae |

↓

| right atrium |

↓

| Right ventricle |

↓

| pulmonary artery |

| Lungs | → | Left atrium | → | left ventricle |

| tissue |
| arterioles |
| arteries |
| Aorta |

SYNTHESIZE Explain why some people need artificial pacemakers, which are battery-operated devices that send electrical signals to stimulate your heart to contract. Explain how an artificial pacemaker is different from your body's natural pacemaker.

Accept all reasonable responses. Someone would need an artificial pacemaker if their natural

pacemaker is not regulating their heartbeat correctly. Artificial pacemakers are different in that

they are not regulated by the medulla oblongata. They are machines.

Respiration, Circulation, and Excretion

Section 37.3 The Urinary System

Main Idea	Details
	Explain *Your urinary system filters your blood and removes wastes. Why is it important that waste material be excreted from the body?*
	Accept all reasonable responses. Waste material from digestive
	processes in the cells is toxic. If these molecules build up in the
	body, cells will die.

Review Vocabulary

Use your book to define the following term.

amino acids	basic building blocks of proteins

New Vocabulary

Read the definitions below, then write the correct term in the left column.

urinary bladder	smooth muscle bag that stores urine until it is expelled from the body
urethra	tube through which urine is passed from the urinary bladder to the outside of the body
nephron	individual filtering unit of the kidneys
urine	liquid composed of wastes that is filtered from the blood by the kidneys, stored in the urinary bladder, and eliminated through the urethra
kidneys	organs of the vertebrate urinary system; remove wastes, control sodium levels of the blood, and regulate blood pH levels
ureter	tube that transports urine from each kidney to the urinary bladder

Academic Vocabulary

Define the following term.

process	a series of natural occurrences that produce change or development

Section 37.3 The Urinary System (continued)

Main Idea	Details

Kidneys: Structure and Function

I found this information on page _____.
SE, pp. 985–986
RE, pp. 474–475

Model *the urinary system. Draw a kidney, ureter, urinary bladder, and the urethra. Write a brief caption about the function of each one.*

Drawings should include kidneys, ureters, urinary bladder, and urethra, and should be properly labeled:
kidneys—filter blood to remove wastes and control pH and sodium levels;
ureter—carry urine from kidneys to urinary bladder;
urinary bladder—stores urine until it is expelled from the body;
urethra—carries urine from bladder to outside the body

Sequence *how the kidneys remove waste from the body by completing the flow chart below. The first and last steps have been completed for you.* Accept all reasonable responses.

Blood enters a nephron in the kidney and flows into the glomerulus.	Water, glucose, vitamins, amino acids, urea, salt and ions from the blood pass out of the capillaries of the glomerulus into the Bowman's capsule.
Liquid in the Bowman's capsule passes through a narrow, U-shaped tubule.	Most of the ions and water and all of the glucose and amino acids are reabsorbed into the bloodstream.
Urine flows out of the kidneys through the ureter into the urinary bladder.	Urine passes out of the body through the urethra.

Section 37.3 The Urinary System (continued)

Main Idea ———— **Details** ——————————————

The Urinary System and Homeostasis

I found this information on page _____.

SE, p. 987
RE, p. 475

Identify *the major waste products of cells in the graphic organizer below.*

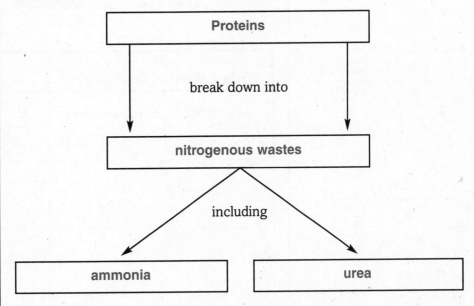

Describe *three ways the kidney helps maintain homeostasis of the body.*

1. It removes wastes from the blood regularly.
_____

2. It controls the level of sodium in the blood by removing and reabsorbing sodium ions.

3. It regulates pH of the blood by filtering out hydrogen ions and allowing bicarbonate to be reabsorbed into the blood.

COMPARE AND CONTRAST Distinguish between the ureter and the urethra by describing their differences and similarities.

The ureter and the urethra both transport urine. The ureter transports it from the kidneys to

the urinary bladder and the urethra transports it from the bladder to outside the body. The

ureter is connected to two body organs while the urethra is only connected to the bladder.

Respiration, Circulation, and Excretion   Chapter Wrap-Up

In the "What I Wanted to Find Out" column, copy the questions you listed in the Chapter Preview. In the "What I Learned" column, write down the answers you discovered as you worked through the chapter.

W What I Wanted to Find Out	L What I Learned
1. Accept all reasonable entries.	1.
2.	2.
3.	3.

Use this checklist to help you study.

☐ Study your Science Notebook for this chapter.

☐ Study the definitions of vocabulary words.

☐ Review daily homework assignments.

☐ Reread the chapter and review the tables, graphs, and illustrations.

☐ Review the Section Assessment questions at the end of each section.

☐ Look over the Study Guide at the end of the chapter.

SUMMARIZE After reading this chapter, list three things you have learned about respiration, circulation, and excretion.

Accept all reasonable responses.

_____

_____

Reproduction and Development

Before You Read

Use the "What I Know" column to list three things you know about reproduction and development. Then list three questions you have about these topics in the "What I Want to Find Out" column.

K What I Know	W What I Want to Find Out
1. Accept all reasonable entries. 	1.
2. 	2.
3. 	3.

Science Journal

As you have grown and developed since birth, you have gone through many changes. Write about some of the physical changes you have experienced since you were born.

Accept all reasonable responses.

Reproduction and Development
Section 38.1 Human Reproductive Systems

◖Main Idea◗ ——— **◖Details◗** ——————————————

Skim *Section 1 of your book. Read the headings and the illustration captions. Write three questions that come to mind.*

1. Accept all reasonable responses. _____

_____

2. _____

_____

_____

3. _____

_____

New ———
◖Vocabulary◗   *Classify each vocabulary term. Give a brief description of each. One term fits in both categories.*

Male Reproductive System	Female Reproductive System
bulbourethral gland: secretes a clear, sticky alkaline fluid	cervix: lower end of the uterus
epididymis: single coiled tube where sperm mature	corpus luteum: secretes estrogen and progesterone
prostate gland: secretes an alkaline fluid that helps sperm move	follicle: cells that surround a developing egg
puberty: time when secondary sex characteristics develop	menstrual cycle: changes in the female reproductive cycle each month
scrotum: sac that contains the testes	oviduct: tube that carries egg from ovary to uterus
semen: combination of sperm and fluids	ovulation: egg rupturing the ovary wall and moving through it to oviduct
seminal vesicle: secretes a fructose-rich fluid into the vas deferens	puberty: time when secondary sex characteristics develop
vas deferens: duct that carries sperm from the epididymis toward the ducts that will force the sperm out of the body	

bulbourethral gland

cervix

corpus luteum

epididymis

follicle

menstrual cycle

oviduct

ovulation

prostate gland

puberty

scrotum

semen

seminal vesicle

vas deferens

Section 38.1 Human Reproductive Systems (continued)

Main Idea —————— **Details** —————————————————————————

Human Male Anatomy

I found this information on page _____.
SE, pp. 995–997
RE, pp. 477–479

Sequence *the path sperm take from their production to when they leave the male body. List the organs on the left, and their function on the right.*

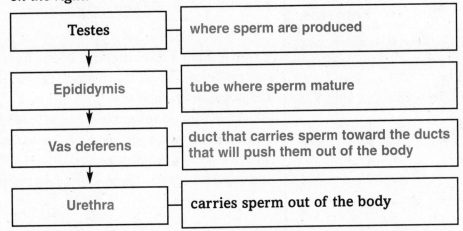

Testes	where sperm are produced
Epididymis	tube where sperm mature
Vas deferens	duct that carries sperm toward the ducts that will push them out of the body
Urethra	carries sperm out of the body

Organize *List the glands that produce fluids to help transport sperm and describe the fluids they secrete.*

1. seminal vesicles: secrete a thick, mucus-like fluid rich in fructose that provides energy for the sperm cells

2. prostate gland: secretes an alkaline fluid that helps the sperm move

3. bulbourethral glands: secrete a clear, sticky alkaline fluid that helps protect sperm because it neutralizes the acidic environment of the urethra and vagina

Puberty in Males

I found this information on page _____.
SE, pp. 997–998
RE, pp. 479–480

Create *a diagram to show how the negative feedback system works to control FSH and LH in the male body.*
Accept all reasonable diagrams that show that as the levels of testosterone in the blood increase, the body decreases the production of FSH and LH. Increased sperm production also decreases the production of these. When the levels of testosterone drop, the body increases production of FSH and LH.

Section 38.1 Human Reproductive Systems (continued)

Main Idea ———— **Details** —————————————————————————————

Human Female Anatomy, Puberty in Females

I found this information on page _____.
SE, pp. 999–1001
RE, pp. 480–482

Identify *the three main functions of the female reproductive system.*

to produce eggs, to receive sperm, and to provide an environment

in which a fertilized egg can develop

Create *Sketch the structures of the human female reproductive system below. Label the oviduct, cervix, ovary, and uterus. Describe the function of each.*

Sketches should resemble SE p. 999, RE p. 480.

ovary—produces eggs, oviduct—moves eggs to the uterus, uterus—
where a fetus develops, cervix—lower end of the uterus that leads to
the vagina, vagina—leads to outside the female body

Describe *eggs in the female body at each stage of development.*

Before Birth	Birth to Puberty	Beginning at Puberty
Eggs develop before birth; cells divide until they reach prophase I, then they rest. At birth, there are about two million potential eggs.	Oocytes break down so that at puberty there are about 40,000 primary oocytes.	Meiosis starts again in several of the prophase I cells. This happens about once a month; each cell completes meiosis I and begins meiosis II; ovulation occurs.

Section 38.1 Human Reproductive Systems (continued)

⟨**Main Idea**⟩ —— ⟨**Details**⟩ ——————————————

The Menstrual Cycle

I found this information on page _____ .
SE, pp. 1002–1004
RE, pp. 482–484

Sequence *the steps in the menstrual cycle. Describe the changes in hormones, the uterus, and the ovary at each stage.*

1. The Flow Phase		
Changes in Hormones	**Changes in the Uterus**	**Changes in the Ovary**
Level of FSH in blood begins to rise.	Endometrium is shed; uterine muscle contracts to help expel endometrium.	A follicle in one of the ovaries begins to mature as the meiosis of the prophase I cells goes on.

2. The Follicular Phase		
Changes in Hormones	**Changes in the Uterus**	**Changes in the Ovary**
Estrogen is secreted to stimulate the repair of the endometrial lining; pituitary slows production of FSH and LH. Estrogen peaks causing sharp increase in release of LH.	Endometrial cells undergo mitosis and uterine lining thickens.	Follicle ruptures and egg is released into oviduct.

3. The Luteal Phase		
Changes in Hormones	**Changes in the Uterus**	**Changes in the Ovary**
Progesterone and estrogen are produced and production of LH is prevented. If egg not fertilized, release of FSH and LH blocked, hormone levels drop.	Endometrium accumulates lipids and tissue fluid. If egg is not fertilized, lining sheds. If egg is fertilized, endometrium secretes fluid rich in nutrients.	Corpus luteum develops from ruptured follicle. If egg is not fertilized, corpus luteum breaks up.

SYNTHESIZE Hypothesize what piece of information in this section could help a female predict when she is ovulating.

Since the body temperature of a female increases about 0.5° during ovulation, a woman may

be able to predict when she is ovulating by an increase in body temperature.

Name _____ Date _____

Reproduction and Development
Section 38.2 Development Before Birth

(Main Idea) ———— **(Details)** ——————————————

Organize Information *As you read the section, identify which structures are involved in the exchange of materials between the fetus and the mother.*

Accept all reasonable responses. The placenta and the umbilical

cord are involved in the exchange of materials between the fetus

and mother.

(Review Vocabulary) *Use your book to define the following term.*

zygote | a diploid cell formed when a sperm fertilizes an egg

(New Vocabulary) *Use your book to define each term. Then make a sketch of each to help you remember.*

implantation | name given to the attachment of

the blastocyst, or hollow ball of

cells, to the uterine lining, which

occurs six days after fertilization

umbilical cord | a ropelike structure made up of

blood vessels of the allantois

that attaches the embryo to the

wall of the uterus

(Academic Vocabulary) *Define the following term.*

attach | to secure one thing to another

372   *Development Before Birth*

Section 38.2 Development Before Birth (continued)

Main Idea —— **Details** _____

Fertilization and Implantation

I found this information on page _____.
SE, pp. 1005–1006
RE, pp. 486–487

Sequence *the steps of fertilization of an egg and implantation of a blastocyst. The steps are written in scrambled form at right. Write the steps in the correct order in the boxes.*

300 to 500 million sperm are released in the female's vagina.

↓

The sperm that survive the acidic vagina swim through the vagina into the uterus.

↓

A few hundred sperm make it into the two oviducts.

↓

One sperm penetrates the egg, which changes the electrical charge of the egg's membrane so other sperm cannot enter.

↓

The nucleus of the sperm and the nucleus of the egg unite, forming a zygote.

↓

The zygote moves down the oviduct and begins to divide by mitosis.

↓

The zygote moves into the uterus and becomes a blastocyst.

↓

The blastocyst attaches to the uterine lining.

One sperm penetrates the egg, which changes the electrical charge of the egg's membrane so other sperm cannot enter.

300 to 500 million sperm are released in the female's vagina.

The zygote moves into the uterus and becomes a blastocyst.

The nucleus of the sperm and the nucleus of the egg unite, forming a zygote.

A few hundred sperm make it into the two oviducts.

The zygote moves down the oviduct and begins to divide by mitosis.

The blastocyst attaches to the uterine lining.

The sperm that survive the acidic vagina swim through the vagina into the uterus.

Section 38.2 Development Before Birth (continued)

Main Idea ———— **Details** ——————————————————

Embryonic Membranes and the Placenta

I found this information on page _____.
SE, pp. 1007–1008
RE, pp. 487–489

Create *a diagram of a placenta and umbilical cord attached to an embryo. Draw arrows to show the route oxygen and nutrients take from the mother's blood to the embryo and how wastes are removed.*
Accept all reasonable diagrams. Arrows on the diagram should show that nutrients and oxygen diffuse into the placenta from the mother's blood and travel to the fetus through the umbilical cord. Arrows should show the reverse for waste removal.

Fetal Development

I found this information on page _____.
SE, pp. 1008–1011
RE, pp. 489–491

Compare *development of an embryo into a fetus during each trimester. Describe the changes that occur.*

First Trimester	Second Trimester	Third Trimester
Organs like the heart and lungs form; arms and legs form; bones begin to harden; nearly all muscles appear. Eye tissue develops. Fetus weighs about 28 g and is about 7.5 cm long.	Body growth increases; eyes open and eyelashes form; movement of fetus is felt; metabolism cannot maintain a constant body temperature and lungs are not mature.	Mass of the fetus more than triples; lungs are completely developed; fat is deposited beneath the skin. Fetus weighs about 3300 g and is about 51 cm long.

ANALOGY Think of an analogy to explain to younger students the growth and development of a fetus over nine months.

Accept all reasonable responses. A developing plant is similar to a fetus growing. The seed

sprouts and the young plant begins to grow. This is similar to the first trimester growth of a

fetus. The plant is developing new parts. In the second trimester, the plant makes its way

above the surface of the soil. In the third trimester, the plant continues to grow and grow.

Reproduction and Development

Section 38.3 Birth, Growth, and Aging

Main Idea ———— **Details** ——————————————————

Infer *which organ systems are involved in growth of the human body.*
Accept all reasonable responses. All organ systems are involved in
growth of the human body. As the body grows, each of the organ
systems enlarges. The growth is controlled primarily by human growth
hormone, which acts mainly on the skeleton and skeletal muscles.

Review Vocabulary

Use your book to define the following term.

growth

increase in the amount of living material and formation of new
structures in an organism

New Vocabulary

*Use your book to define the following term. Then create a
concept map with facts about it.* Accept all reasonable responses.

labor

the physiological and physical changes that a female goes through
to give birth

Academic Vocabulary

Define the following term.

physical

pertaining to the body or the concrete world

Section 38.3 Birth, Growth, and Aging (continued)

| Main Idea | Details |

Birth

I found this information on page _____.
SE, pp. 1012–1013
RE, pp. 493–494

Compare *Describe the three stages of birth in the graphic organizer below.*

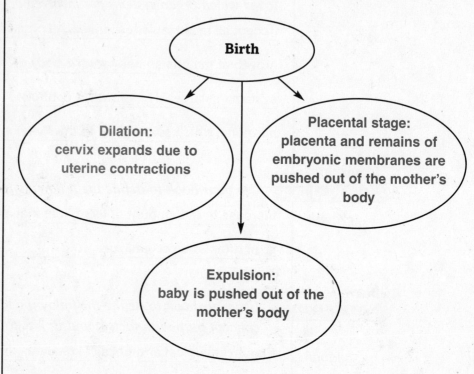

Growth and Aging

I found this information on page _____.
SE, pp. 1013–1015
RE, pp. 494–496

Identify *the cells the human growth factor (hGH) acts on and describe how it works by completing the graphic organizer below.*

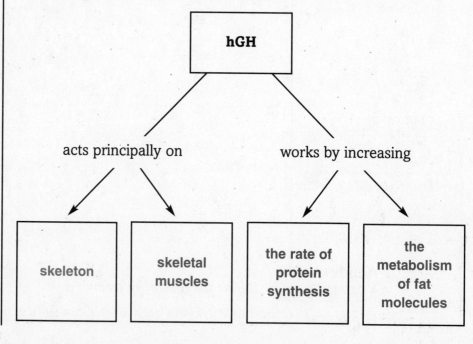

Section 38.3 Birth, Growth, and Aging (continued)

Main Idea	Details

Growth and Aging

I found this information on page _____.
SE, pp. 1013–1015
RE, pp. 494–496

Describe *the changes that occur at each stage of growth and development.*

---

1. Infancy

Infancy describes the first two years of life. The child grows tremendously, increasing physical coordination and mental development. The infant's birth weight triples in the first year. When the child is two years old, it weighs four times more than it did at birth. Infants learn to control their legs and arms, roll over, sit, crawl, and walk. Child may begin to talk toward end of stage.

---

2. Childhood

Childhood lasts from the end of infancy to adolescence.
Most children grow steadily.
The child develops ability to reason and solve problems.

---

3. Adolescence

Adolescence follows childhood and begins at puberty. Teenagers have growth spurts that can be surprisingly large. Adolescents gain their maximum height. By the time adulthood is reached, the organs have reached maximum mass and physical growth is complete.

---

4. Adulthood

During adulthood, metabolism slows down, the skin begins to lose its elasticity, wrinkles appear, and hair begins to turn white. Bones can become thinner and more brittle and may break or fracture more easily. Disks between vertebrae compress so people become shorter. Vision and hearing may diminish.

CONNECT

Identify the stage of growth and development that you are currently in. Describe some of the changes your body has undergone in the last few years.

Accept all reasonable responses. I am in the adolescence stage. In the last few years I have had several growth spurts. I am close to my maximum height.

Reproduction and Development Chapter Wrap-Up

In the "What I Wanted to Find Out" column, copy the questions you listed in the Chapter Preview. In the "What I Learned" column, write down the answers you discovered as you worked through the chapter.

W What I Wanted to Find Out	L What I Learned
1. Accept all reasonable entries.	1.
2.	2.
3.	3.

Use this checklist to help you study.

- ☐ Study your Science Notebook for this chapter.
- ☐ Study the definitions of vocabulary words.
- ☐ Review daily homework assignments.
- ☐ Reread the chapter and review the tables, graphs, and illustrations.
- ☐ Review the Section Assessment questions at the end of each section.
- ☐ Look over the Study Guide at the end of the chapter.

SUMMARIZE

After reading this chapter, list three things you have learned about reproduction and development.

Accept all reasonable responses.

_____

_____

Immunity from Disease

Before You Read

Use the "What I Know" column to list three things you know about disease and immunity. Then list three questions you have about disease and immunity in the "What I Want to Find Out" column.

K What I Know	W What I Want to Find Out
1. Accept all reasonable entries. _____ _____	1. _____ _____
2. _____ _____	2. _____ _____
3. _____ _____	3. _____ _____

Science Journal

When you get a cold, your immune system fights it and you eventually feel better. Hypothesize how people with weakened immune systems may need to live their lives differently to stay healthy.

Accept all reasonable responses. _____

_____

_____

_____

_____

_____

_____

_____

Immunity from Disease

Section 39.1 The Nature of Disease

Main Idea ———— **Details** ————————————————

Scan *Use the checklist below to preview Section 1 of your book.*

☐ Read all section titles.

☐ Read all boldfaced words.

☐ Read all tables and graphs.

☐ Look at all pictures and read the captions.

☐ Think about what you already know about disease.

Write two facts you discovered about the nature of disease as you scanned the section.

1. Accept all reasonable responses._____

2. _____

Review Vocabulary *Use your book to define the following term.*

virus | a disease-causing, nonliving particle composed of an inner core of

nucleic acids surrounded by a capsid; replicates inside a living cell

New Vocabulary *Read the definitions below, then write the correct term in the left column.*

epidemic | occurs when many people in a given area are afflicted with the same disease at about the same time

pathogens | disease-producing agents such as bacteria, protozoans, fungi, viruses, and other parasites

Koch's postulates | experimental steps relating a specific pathogen to a specific disease

endemic disease | disease that is constantly present in a population

infectious disease | any disease caused by pathogens in the body

antibiotics | substances produced by a microorganism that, in small amounts, will kill or inhibit growth and reproduction of other microorganisms

Section 39.1 The Nature of Disease (continued)

Main Idea ———— **Details** ————————————————————

What is an infectious disease? Determining What Causes a Disease, The Spread of Infectious Diseases

I found this information on page _____.
SE, pp. 1023–1027
RE, pp. 497–501

Identify *the facts about disease.*

Five types of pathogens that cause disease:	Five places that helpful microorganisms live in your body:
1. bacteria	1. skin
2. protozoans	2. upper respiratory system
3. fungi	3. urinary tract
4. parasites	4. reproductive tract
5. viruses	5. lower intestinal tract

Four diseases not caused by pathogens, and their causes	Four main ways pathogens can be transmitted
1. osteoarthritis - wear of aging	1. by direct contact
2. cirrhosis - chemicals or toxins	2. by an object
3. scurvy - malnutrition	3. through the air
4. hemophilia - inherited	4. by a vector

Three main sources of pathogens

1. soil

2. contaminated water

3. infected animals

Write *the four experimental steps of Koch's postulates.*

1. The pathogen must be found in the host in every case of the
   disease.

2. The pathogen must be isolated from the host and grown in a pure
   culture containing no other organisms.

3. When the pathogen from the pure culture is placed in a healthy
   host, it must cause the disease.

4. The pathogen must be isolated from the new host and be shown to
   be the original pathogen.

Section 39.1 The Nature of Disease (continued)

Main Idea	Details

What causes the symptoms of a disease?

I found this information on page _____.
SE, pp. 1028–1029
RE, p. 501

Contrast *two causes of symptoms of a disease and the effects of each.*

Toxins produced by pathogens are transported by the blood. Toxins may cause serious effects and sometimes death.

Causes of Disease Symptoms

Viruses directly damage the cell by taking over its genetic and metabolic machinery. Many cause the death of the cells they invade.

Patterns of Diseases, Treating Diseases

I found this information on page _____.
SE, pp. 1029–1030
RE, pp. 502

Compare *diseases that occur periodically, endemic diseases, and an epidemic. Describe each and give examples.*

Periodic	Endemic	Epidemic
a disease that occurs only occasionally in the United States; usually happens because someone traveling brought it back with them Example: typhoid fever	a disease which is constantly present in the population Example: chicken pox	happens when many people have the same disease at about the same time Example: polio

CONNECT

Hypothesize what people can do to help make antibiotics effective for a longer period of time.

Accept all reasonable responses. People should try to use antibiotics only when they are

absolutely necessary. This will keep them from being overused, which can lead to bacteria

becoming resistant.

_____

_____

_____

Immunity from Disease
Section 39.2 Defense Against Infectious Diseases

Main Idea ————— **Details** ——————————————————————

Infer *how your body saves you from microscopic foes that cause infectious diseases and how the body's defenses protect you.*

Accept all reasonable responses. The body saves you from the

microscopic foes by activating the immune system, which involves the

innate, non-specific immunity and the acquired, specific immunity.

New Vocabulary

Use vocabulary terms (in singular or plural form) to complete the paragraphs below about the body's defenses.

Your body's immune system works to protect you from diseases.

Its _____innate immunity_____ is always present and defends the body

against all pathogens. _____Interferons_____ protect cells from viruses.

_____Phagocytes_____ are white blood cells that destroy pathogens by

surrounding and engulfing them. _____Macrophages_____ attack anything

they recognize as foreign. After a few days of immune response,

infected tissue develops _____pus_____, which contains dead and live

white blood cells, multiplying and dead pathogens, and body fluids.

    Your immune system may gradually build up a resistance to a

pathogen. This is called _____acquired immunity_____. Acquired

immunity involves antibody immunity and cellular immunity. Both

_____T cells_____ and _____B cells_____ are involved in antibody immunity.

Your body can gain active immunity naturally or artificially by

injecting a _____vaccine_____. Your lymphatic system helps your body

defend against diseases and keep fluids at a constant level. It contains

_____lymph nodes_____, which are small masses of tissue that contain

lymphocytes. _____Lymphocytes_____ are white blood cells that defend the

body against foreign substances. _____Tissue fluid_____ constantly bathes

cells and collects in open-ended lymph capillaries. When it enters the

lymph vessels, it is called _____lymph_____.

acquired immunity

B cell

innate immunity

interferon

lymph

lymph node

lymphocyte

macrophage

phagocyte

pus

T cell

tissue fluid

vaccine

Section 39.2 Defense Against Infectious Diseases (continued)

Main Idea ———— **Details** —————————————————————

Innate Immunity

I found this information on page _____.
SE, pp. 1031–1034
RE, pp. 504–506

Summarize *the functions of innate immunity by completing the table.*

Function	How it works
skin	keeps microorganisms from entering the body
mucus	prevents various areas of the body from drying out; traps microorganisms and other foreign substances; mucus is swallowed and sent to the stomach where gastric juice destroys most bacteria
sweat, tears, and saliva	contain lysozyme, which breaks down the cell walls of some bacteria
inflammation response	mast cells and white blood cells release histamine, causing blood vessels in the injured area to dilate; fluid from the vessels helps the body destroy toxic agents and restore homeostasis
phagocytosis	phagocytes engulf and destroy pathogens
interferons	protect cells from viruses

Acquired Immunity

I found this information on page _____.
SE, pp. 1035–1036
RE, pp. 506–508

Compare *the functions of these organs of the lymphatic system.*

Tonsils	Spleen	Lymph Nodes	Thymus Gland
form a protective ring around nasal and oral cavities to protect against bacteria and other pathogens that enter the nose and throat	stores certain types of lymphocytes; filters and destroys bacteria and worn-out red blood cells	filter pathogens from the lymph	stores immature lymphocytes until they mature and are released into the body's defense system

Section 39.2 Defense Against Infectious Diseases (continued)

Main Idea	Details

Antibody Immunity, Cellular Immunity

I found this information on page _____.
SE, pp. 1037–1038
RE, pp. 508–509

Compare *antibody and cellular immunity in the Venn diagram.*

- forms antibodies
- involves B cells
- involves cytotoxic T cells
- involves helper T cells
- involves T cells
- T cells produce clones

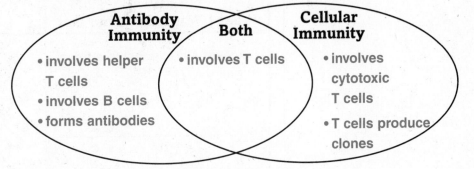

Antibody Immunity
- involves helper T cells
- involves B cells
- forms antibodies

Both
- involves T cells

Cellular Immunity
- involves cytotoxic T cells
- T cells produce clones

Passive and Active Immunity

I found this information on page _____.
SE, pp. 1038–1040
RE, pp. 509–510

Distinguish *between passive immunity and active immunity.*

Passive immunity develops by acquiring antibodies that are generated

in another host. Active immunity develops when your body produces

antibodies in response to being directly exposed to antigens.

AIDS and the Immune System

I found this information on page _____.
SE, pp. 1040–1041
RE, pp. 510–511

Identify *the facts about HIV and AIDS.*

Two Ways HIV Can Be Spread	Seven Early Symptoms of AIDS
direct contact with infected blood or body fluids; contact with objects that have been contaminated by infected blood or body fluids	swollen lymph nodes, loss of appetite, weight loss, fever, rashes, night sweats, fatigue

ANALYZE Analyze how vaccines have affected the health of people around the world in the last 100 years. Explain.

Accept all reasonable responses. Vaccines have improved the health of people around the

world in the last 100 years. There are now fewer epidemics than there were 100 years ago.

Some diseases have completely disappeared.

Immunity from Disease Chapter Wrap-Up

In the "What I Wanted to Find Out" column, copy the questions you listed in the Chapter Preview. In the "What I Learned" column, write down the answers you discovered as you worked through the chapter.

W What I Wanted to Find Out	L What I Learned
1. Accept all reasonable entries. _____	1. _____ _____
2. _____ _____	2. _____ _____
3. _____ _____	3. _____ _____

Use this checklist to help you study.

☐ Study your Science Notebook for this chapter.

☐ Study the definitions of vocabulary words.

☐ Review daily homework assignments.

☐ Reread the chapter and review the tables, graphs, and illustrations.

☐ Review the Section Assessment questions at the end of each section.

☐ Look over the Study Guide at the end of the chapter.

SUMMARIZE

After reading this chapter, list three things you have learned about immunity and disease.

Accept all reasonable responses.

_____

_____

_____